JOHN CATT'S

Preparatory Schools 2017

20th Edition
Editor: Meena Ameen

JOHN
CATT®
EDUCATIONAL
LIMITED

Published in 2017 by
John Catt Educational Ltd,
12 Deben Mill Business Centre,
Woodbridge, Suffolk IP12 1BL UK
Tel: 01394 389850   Fax: 01394 386893
Email: enquiries@johncatt.com
Website: www.johncatt.com
© 2017 John Catt Educational Ltd

**A CIP catalogue record for this book is available from the
British Library.**

ISBN: 978 1 911382 11 9

Contacts
Editor
Meena Ameen

Advertising & School Profiles
Tel: +44 (0) 1394 389850
Email: sales@johncatt.com

Distribution/Book Sales
Tel: +44 (0) 1394 389863
Email: booksales@johncatt.com

Contents

What does a prep school education truly provide?

Mark Hartley, vice-chairman of the Independent Association of Prep Schools (IAPS), highlights the importance of choosing the right school during your child's most crucial years in education

Welcome to the 2017 edition of John Catt's *Preparatory Schools* guide. I am delighted to be able to scribe the foreword to this important publication prior to you reading the wealth of information that is written about a diverse range of excellent schools. The independent sector remains a highly successful one; it incorporates a significant number of schools that many parents aspire to send their children to, not only in the United Kingdom but also globally.

I very much hope that the information written will help you choose the right school to enhance your child's education journey through what I firmly believe are the most important years of their education.

Modern prep schools offer a superb standard of education for pupils, balancing traditional values with cutting edge teaching and learning, far from the cliché of old-fashioned uniforms, rigid discipline and academic rigour. With my IAPS hat on, one of the key strengths of IAPS is the wide variety of schools that you can choose from within its membership. Whether you are looking for a single sex or co-ed school, day or boarding, one with a particular religious affiliation or one that provides special educational provision and facilities, there is a school for you.

What is it that a prep school education truly provides? Small class sizes are certainly high on the agenda, as is a favourable staff to pupil ratio, but remember the high quality teaching provides high academic standards and so class sizes are not necessarily as small as they were some years ago. It is clear though that the education provision in our schools certainly embraces both innovation and technology with Heads looking to ensure that children are prepared for a future that may be a little different to what they see in the present day. Schools will also provide a huge number of extra-curricular opportunities, including the creative performing arts (drama and music), but also sport. This provides for all children the ability to find their passion and excel in one or more areas both in and outside the classroom. These opportunities for your child to discover a genuine strength should not be underestimated.

I firmly believe that the key skills and learning traits are just as important for parents to consider; courtesy, respect, kindness, perseverance, determination, resilience, responsibility collaboration are examples of this and are certainly what future employers will consider a necessity in addition to good communication skills. You will find them all in our schools, where a broad curriculum is available. The schools in this publication will have superb facilities, they will provide your child with individual attention, they will ask them to think for themselves and be curious by asking questions, but also provide a stimulating warm environment for them to reach their potential.

A colleague of mine noted that choosing a school can be a life-long decision. Although some of you might only be looking for a specific stage of education. Whatever stage you are looking at, the choices that you make not only are likely to impact on your child for years to come, they will shape the way that your child will develop and grow into a young adult and, more importantly, a confident learner prepared fully for senior school life, the teenage years and then into the job market.

> Modern prep schools offer a superb standard of education for pupils, balancing traditional values with cutting edge teaching and learning...

GDST schools.
Where girls can.

Choosing your daughter's school is one of the biggest decisions you, as parents will make. At the GDST we put girls first, ensuring that everything in their school lives is calibrated and designed to meet their educational and pastoral needs.

The GDST has always been a pioneer of girls' education in the UK. Our network of 26 schools and academies provides unmatched opportunities, connections and resources for girls between the ages of three and 18.

GDST schools in London

Blackheath High School
Bromley High School
Croydon High School
Kensington Prep School
Northwood College for Girls
Notting Hill & Ealing High School
Putney High School
South Hampstead High School
Streatham & Clapham High School
Sutton High School
Sydenham High School
Wimbledon High School

GDST schools and academies outside London

The Belvedere Academy, Liverpool
Birkenhead High School Academy
Brighton & Hove High School
Howell's School, Llandaff
Ipswich High School for Girls
Newcastle High School for Girls
Northampton High School
Norwich High School for Girls
Nottingham Girls' High School
Oxford High School
Portsmouth High School
The Royal High School, Bath
Sheffield High School
Shrewsbury High School

 gdst Girls' Day School Trust

A network of confident, composed, courageous, committed girls.

See www.gdst.net to find your closest GDST school or academy, and arrange a visit.

I have already highlighted some of the key elements of prep schools that make them different. All have these common attributes, although schools may be different in their approach.

If you are just starting the process then this directory will be one of the tools which will provide you with relevant information for you to consider, from personal experience, word of mouth will also play a huge part in your decision, so talk to friends and acquaintances to gain their insight. However, in the end it must be a decision that you make alone. In choosing a school there are a number of things for you to consider. Part of this consideration will be to balance what your head says with what your heart says, the latter being a feeling similar to perhaps knowing that a house was the right one to buy. The advice I would give is very similar to that I provide to my existing parents when they are looking at senior schools.

Having shortlisted a number of schools, visit them all or certainly as many as you can. Arrange private meetings and tours, although open days will give you an initial flavour. You need to gauge a true feel for the atmosphere and ethos of the school. Meet and speak with the children already there, for they will say it as it is, for all wear their school badge with pride and will share their thoughts honestly and with enthusiasm. It is key that you meet with the Head, for they are the ones that set the vision and inculcate it into the whole school. I will always tour prospective parents myself and allow them the time to ask the probing questions and really get into the bricks and mortar of the school. This time is important for any decision made, will be hugely important both emotionally and financially.

You may be looking to pay fees for a considerable number of years. It is not just the wealthy that can afford the obvious benefits. Access to independent education is increasingly being made available through means tested bursaries and scholarships. Do not be afraid to ask for help, for schools will listen. Back to advice; ask about extra-curricular provisions with the hope of seeing it in action and how do they facilitate learning outside of school, especially with trips and enrichment activities. It will be important to read inspection reports, but do not take them in isolation.

Every Head will try to convince you that their school is the best one. The school community, the main constituents being the pupils and staff should be able to provide you with a good understanding. In the end you must feel that you would trust the school to develop your child educationally in all areas. Sometimes, this is just a true gut feeling.

This directory is the starting point and I hope you enjoy reading through it as you begin your decision making for finding the right school for your child – good luck!

Mark Hartley is the Headmaster of Forres Sandle Manor in Hampshire
Mark was appointed as vice-chairman of IAPS in 2016
For more information about IAPS, see page 27

How to use this guidebook

Are you looking for...

Help and advice?
If so, take a look at our editorial section (pages 7 to 36). Here you will find articles written by experts in their field covering issues you may well come across when choosing a school for your child.

A school or college in a certain geographical region?
Then you need to go to the map on D88 to find the directory page reference to a particular region. We suggest that you look first in the directory for basic information about all the schools in each region, complete with contact details, so that you will be better informed about the choices available to you. From this section you will be directed to more detailed information in the profile section, where this is available.

A certain type of school or college in a particular area?
Look in the directories for the area you want (again, you can find a directory page reference from the regional map on D88). Underneath each school listed you will find icons that denote different types of schools or qualifications that they offer. You can find a key to these icons on the following page; this key is repeated at the front of each section of the directory.

A specific school or college?

If you know the name of the school or college but are unsure of its location, simply go to the index at the back of the guide where you will find all the schools listed alphabetically. You will find that some page numbers are prefixed with the letter D, this denotes that the school appears in the directory section. Page numbers not prefixed by the letter D denote schools that have chosen to include a fuller school profile, which will provide you with much more extensive information.

More information on relevant educational organisations and examinations?

In the editorial section you will find 'Initial advice', a helpful explanation of the various educational organisations relevant to preparatory schools. There are articles from the Boarding Schools Association (BSA), Girls' Schools Association (GSA), Headmasters' and Headmistresses' Conference (HMC), Independent Association of Preparatory Schools (IAPS), Independent Schools Association (ISA), Independent Schools Council (ISC) and the Society of Heads.

Keys to directory information

The diagrams below explain what the different icons used in the directory mean, and indicate the type of information given for each school in the directory.

Key to directory

County	**Wherefordshire**
Name of school or college	**College Academy**
Indicates that this school has a profile	*For further details see p. 00*
Address and contact number	Which Street, Whosville, Wherefordshire AB12 3CD **Tel:** 01000 000000
Head's name	**Head Master:** Dr A Person
Age range	**Age range:** 11–18
Number of pupils. B = boys G = girls	**No. of pupils:** 660 B330 G330
Fees per annum. Day = fees for day pupils. WB = fees for weekly boarders. FB = fees for full boarders.	**Fees:** Day £11,000 WB £16,000 FB £20,000 Ⓐ Ⓐ 🏛 £ 🖊 ⒮ⓢⓐ ⒝ⓢⓐ

Key to directory icons (abridged)

Key to symbols:
- 🏵 Boys' school
- 🏵 Girls' school
- 🌐 International school
- ⒤ⓐⓟⓢ Member of IAPS
- ⒢ⓢⓐ Member of GSA

- ⒤ⓢⓐ Member of ISA
- ⒣ⓜⓒ Member of HMC
- ⒝ⓢⓐ Member of BSA
- Ⓢ Member of Society of Heads

Schools offering:
- 🏛 Boarding accommodation
- £ Bursaries
- Ⓐ A levels
- ⒤ⓑ International Baccalaureate
- 🖊 Learning support

Choosing a school – things to consider

However much a school may appeal at first sight, you still need sound information to form your judgement

Schools attract pupils by their reputations, so most go to considerable lengths to ensure that parents are presented with an attractive image. Modern marketing techniques try to promote good points and play down (without totally obscuring) bad ones. But every Head knows that, however good the school prospectus is, it only serves to attract parents through the school gates. Thereafter the decision depends on what they see and hear. Research we have carried out over the years suggests that in many cases the most important factor in choosing a school is the impression given by the Head. As well as finding out what goes on in a school, parents need to be reassured by the aura of confidence that they expect from a Head. How they judge the latter may help them form their opinion of the former. In other words, how a Head answers questions is important in itself and, to get you started, we have drawn up a list of points that you may like to consider. Some can be posed as questions and some are points you'll only want to check in your mind. They are not listed in any particular order and their

significance will vary from family to family, but they should be useful in helping you to form an opinion.

Before visiting and asking questions, **check the facts** – such as which association the school belongs to, how big it is, how many staff *etc*. Is there any form of financial pie chart showing how the school's resources are used? The answers to questions like these should be in the promotional material you've been sent. If they aren't, you've already got a good question to ask!

Check the website. Is it up-to-date? Almost certainly not 100% because that's just about impossible, but it shouldn't be obsolete. And that first impression is very important.

When you get to the school you will want to judge the overall atmosphere and decide whether it will suit you and your child. Are any other members of the family going to help to pay the fees? If so, their views are important and the school's attitude towards them may be instructive.

When you make it to the inner sanctum, **what do you make of the Head as a person?** Age? Family? Staying?

Moving on? Retiring? Busted flush? Accessible to children, parents and staff? If you never get to see the Head, but deal with an admissions person of some sort, it may not mean you should rule the school out, but it certainly tells you something about the school's view of pupil recruitment.

Academic priorities – attitude towards league tables? This is a forked question. If the answer is 'We're most concerned with doing the best for the child', you pitch them a late-developer; if the answer is, 'Well, frankly, we have a very high entry threshold', then you say 'So we have to give you a foolproof academic winner, do we?'

Supplementary questions:

- What is the ratio of teachers to pupils?
- What are the professional qualifications of the teaching staff?
- What is the school's retention rate? In prep schools this means how many pupils do they lose at 11 when the school goes on to 13.
- How long is the school day – and week?
- What are the school's exam results?
- What are the criteria for presenting them?
- Were they consistent over the years?
- Is progress accelerated for the academically bright?
- How does the school cope with pupils who do not work?
- Where do pupils go when they leave?
- How important and well resourced are sports, extra-curricular and after school activities, music and drama?
- What cultural or other visits are arranged away from the school?

Other topics to cover:

- What is the school's mission?
- What is its attitude to religion?
- How well is the school integrated into the local community?
- How have they responded to the Charities Act initiatives?

- What are the responsibilities and obligations at weekends for parents, pupils and the school?
- Does the school keep a watching brief or reserve the option to get involved after a weekend incident?
- What is the school's attitude to discipline?
- Have there been problems with drugs, drink or sex? How have they been dealt with?
- What is the school's policy on bullying?
- How does the school cope with pupils' problems?
- What sort of academic and pastoral advice is available?
- What positive steps are taken to encourage good manners, behaviour and sportsmanship?
- What is the uniform?
- What steps are taken to ensure that pupils take pride in their personal appearance?
- How often does the school communicate with parents through reports, parent/teacher meetings or other visits?
- What level of parental involvement is encouraged both in terms of keeping in touch with staff about your own child and more generally, *eg* a Parents' Association?
- Is it possible to have the names and addresses of parents with children at the school to approach them for an opinion?

And finally – and perhaps most importantly – what does your child make of the school, the adults met, the other children met, pupils at the school in other contexts, and the website?

Andrew Hunter lists some further probing questions on pages 16-17

A sporting chance?

Angela Drew discusses how healthy exercise and competition are central to a child's experience of independent school life

School sport is the perfect channel for the boundless energy of junior school pupils but sport is also expensive. To employ expert coaches and maintain excellent facilities takes the kind of sustained financial commitment that is only given where schools consider sport to be a true priority. As a head of an independent girls' school, I often find in 11+ Entrance interviews that talented girls from our local state primary schools express an enthusiasm for sport and a real eagerness to try out our extensive sporting facilities yet may have never played in a competitive fixture against another school. The 2016 Olympics has been the cue for much soul searching about the legacy of Great Britain's own games only four years ago. Much was made in 2012 of the over-representation of independently-educated sportsmen and women in Team GB's home Olympics, with a third of medal winners coming from fee-paying schools where many benefitted from the bursaries and scholarships that enabled them to access that education. From 2012 to 2016, the proportion of Team GB who had been privately educated had risen from 20% to 28%.

For many parents, the only way of giving their children a sporting chance – the chance for sporting activity to be a natural part of daily school life – is to select an independent prep or junior school. In reality, much of the under representation of current and former state school pupils in sport from District and County level upwards is related to facilities and funding. Despite continued protestations that money is being invested in sport in schools (some £320 million promised for this year through the primary PE and sport premium) vital school playing fields continue to be lost to development with 95 school fields sold off in the three and a half years that followed the end of the 2012 Games – at a rate of two playing fields a month. There has also been a dramatic drop in the number of grass roots sports coaches capable of teaching school sport with a drop of 65% in Level One coaches between 2011 and 2015 and a drop of 23% in more advanced Level 2 coaches.

Crucially, the primary commitment of independent schools to sport is to participation and enjoyment. Schools are not fundamentally driven by a desire to create a small number of elite athletes but by a commitment to providing opportunities for all their pupils to participate in sport as a foundation for a healthy lifestyle and, yes, to the development of that very traditional public school word 'character' and its more modern equivalent 'resilience'. Sir Peter Lampl, Chair of the Sutton Trust, which works to improve educational opportunity for all young people, recognises that *'Too often we allow pupils to adopt a negative mentality that limits their development... independent schools enable their pupils to develop the essential life skills that give them a competitive edge, not just in sport but in professional life – to become better communicators, to develop social skills, confidence, high aspirations and more resilience.'* Teamwork is the ultimate 'transferrable skill'; friendships formed on the games field make youngsters happier and healthier in the short and long term and they make young people more likely to thrive in a work environment where collaboration and networking are increasingly valuable.

Given this capacity of sport to encourage achievement and aspiration in all aspects of a young person's life, I am particularly heartened as Headmistress of a girls' school, to see the prominence given to women's sporting achievement in the Olympics, not least to the utterly exhilarating victory of Great Britain's Women's Hockey Team. Building on the work of campaigns such as 'This Girl Can' and 'Like a Girl', we are now seeing more coverage of women's sport in the media and more female faces presenting sports programmes on television. British Olympic swimmer, Siobhan O'Connor, talks convincingly about the impact that the equal media coverage of men's and women's swimming has on the numbers of young women taking up the sport and her hopes for the positive impact that such equal coverage might have

on women's team sport. *'I would love for girls to believe in themselves and have the confidence to do what they would like to do without feeling like they shouldn't, whether that's sport, the arts or any other passion.'* But for girls' interest in sport to thrive, they need time in the curriculum and space in the playground to be dedicated to nurturing their sporting talents.'

Parents and teachers recognise the transformative effect of a child finding a passion early in life whether that is academic, sporting or artistic. Independent prep and junior schools' commitment to sport is emblematic of their dedication to educating the whole child, to providing breadth of opportunity for each child to explore their interests and to develop their talents. The omission of artistic and practical subjects from the EBACC (the basket of GCSE subjects by which the government will measure the success of state secondary schools) gives genuine cause for concern that the importance of sport, music, drama and the arts risks becoming undervalued in the school curriculum but the best schools will continue to commit to leaving their pupils with a lasting educational legacy. Prep school sport is so precious because it is so much more about instilling healthy social behaviours than it is about winning. Jesse Owens, the great Olympian, pointed to the enduring value of sport: *'Awards become corroded, friends gather no dust.'*

Angela Drew is Headmistress of Bromley High School. For more information, see page 50
www.bromleyhigh.gdst.net

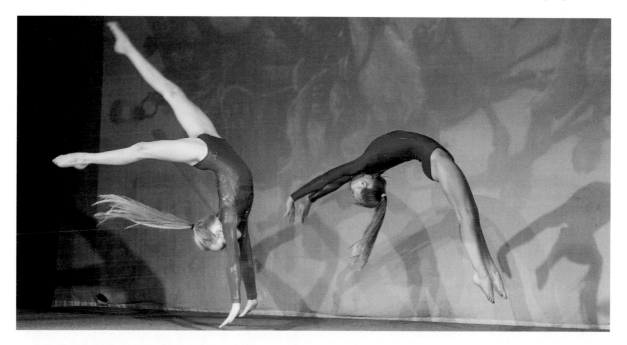

What is the purpose of education?

Charlie Minogue reflects upon the essential role that education plays in creating values and a community for the future of the children

We live in an increasingly competitive world and when the current generation of schoolchildren leaves to take their place within it, they will be judged against young people from across the globe as well as here in Britain. Such judgment will, in part, be based on examination results and it is an understandable response for schools and parents to push boys and girls towards achieving the highest possible grades. It is therefore tempting for schools and parents to pursue a narrow vision of education where excellent examination results are the only success factor but is this really all that education is about?

The 20th century American author Walker Percy once said, "you can get all A's but still flunk life" and there is, therefore, an alternative viewpoint that education is actually about the acquisition of skills and that obtaining knowledge should be secondary to developing the necessary attributes to enable a young person to cope with change in the future. Examination results matter less in this version of education; building transferable skills

such as leadership, flexibility of thought and responsible risk taking are considered to be much more important in preparing children to take their place in the world.

> *Knowledge is power, information is liberating*
> *– Kofi Annan*

I would argue that these two visions of education are not mutually exclusive. The acquisition of knowledge will always be important, "knowledge is power, information is liberating" said Kofi Annan and there is no doubt that having facts at one's fingertips is useful. Exams provide a mechanism for measuring the extent of our recall but it should be possible to acquire knowledge in such a way that skills are also taught. Excellent teachers have always known that children learn best when they have discovered things for themselves and the trick is to provide the conditions where this can happen. Developing

> A school community should actively model and celebrate such values as kindness and integrity and in doing so will produce young people who are more able to form positive relationships in the future.

curiosity is the key to engendering life-long learning and an attitude of mind that is able to cope with change whilst passing the inevitable exams.

I would also argue that an excellent education should go wider, even than this. The ability to form healthy relationships, whether they are personal or professional, will be crucial for individuals and for society going forwards. Schools play a crucial role when developing a strong moral compass in their pupils. A school community should actively model and celebrate such values as kindness and integrity and in doing so will produce young people who are more able to form positive relationships in the future.

I am very proud to lead such a community at Moor Park, a school that every year produces outstanding examination results to the full range of schools nationwide but at the same time teaches children to think for themselves within a strong moral framework. We are non-selective, use all of our beautiful 85-acre site for a bewildering range of extra-curricular activities (every child should find success in at least one area of school life) and yet still produce children who can pass exams, be curious about the world around them, hold a conversation and know right from wrong. The future need not be so worrying when education is like this.

Charlie Minogue is Headmaster of Moor Park.
For more information, see page 76
www.moorpark.org.uk

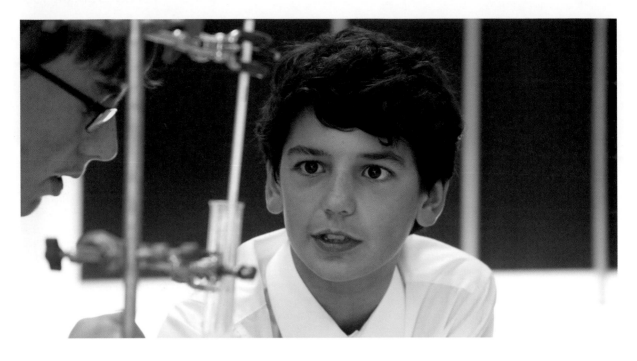

Probing questions to ask when considering a school

There are many things to consider, all of which are important if your child is to thrive in their 'home away from home' prep school environment, says Andrew Hunter, Headmaster of Merchiston Castle School

A) Academic

- What are the entry requirements? Is our child likely to obtain a place?

- How does the school approach the teaching of subjects for the most and least able students?

- What does your school do to ensure that bright pupils are not treading water, but are fully motivated and extended to suit their abilities?

- What provision, if any, does your school make for children with learning difficulties?

- How do your teachers ensure that a pupil achieves or surpasses his/her potential?

- How does the school compare with other schools within the UK?

- How advanced is your school in the provision of 'online learning' and teaching, alongside traditional learning and teaching methods?

B) Educating the whole person/co-curricular activities

- In this world of intensive pressure and academic results, how do you maintain and encourage a balanced education for the pupils in your school?

- How will the school get the best out of our child, who has a particular interest in sport/music/ drama/art...?

- Is religion a relevant or even significant part of education these days?

- How does your school challenge each of its pupils?

- What is the single most important quality you seek to bring out in the pupils?

- What do you consider to be the values uppermost in your school's philosophy?

- How does your school prepare its pupils for the move to senior school?

- How does your school encourage its pupils to try new activities?

C) Single Sex/Co-education

- Do boys need to be taught differently to girls?

- Is co-education always beneficial?

- What are the benefits of single sex education?

D) Boarding/Day issues

- What is your attitude to allowing students to leave school at weekends? What about those who remain behind?

- How do you reconcile the dilemma of providing high class boarding facilities and yet allowing regular visits home, when circumstances permit?

- What do you see as the future of boarding and do you foresee any significant changes on the horizon?

- How important is boarding experience prior to senior school?

- Beyond inspection reports, how do you know that your pupils are really cared for and that their needs are continually met?

E) Looking after pupils – pastoral issues

- How should or does your school deal with bullying?

- What are the school's policies on alcohol, drugs and smoking? What specific steps are taken at your school to control/prevent students from using drugs, alcohol and smoking?

- In a world where discipline appears to be a feature of the past, to what extent do you maintain a firm hand at your establishment?

- All good schools have an effective system of sanction and reward. How do you balance the need for an effective discipline policy against the minutiae of Human Rights legislation?

- Will my child receive extra support if necessary?

- To what extent are students affected by the standard and quality of their accommodation?

- How good is the catering? Do the pupils have an input into the choice of menu offered?

- What medical arrangements are in place?

- What are the staffing levels of the houses in your school?

F) After your visit to a school…

After your visit, try to discuss with your child your thoughts about the people you met, what you were told and what you saw. Then ask yourself and your child a number of follow-up questions:

- What views did you form of the Head?

- How did the aims and objectives of the school appear in practice?

- Was there a good rapport between pupils and staff?

- Were the pupils well mannered and enthusiastic about their school?

- Were the rules there to make it a more civilised and caring community?

- Were the staff communicative and did they enjoy their teaching?

- What contribution did they make to the life of the school outside the classroom?

- Were the buildings well maintained, and the grounds neat and attractive?

- Was there a generally positive atmosphere about the community?

- What did your child make of it all, and does the school meet your child's needs and abilities?

For more information about Merchiston Castle School, see page 84
www.merchiston.co.uk

The individual character of a prep school

The success of pupils is illustrated in everything but its core lessons, writes Catherine Ford, Head of Moreton First Prep School in Shropshire

"I love learning things when we don't have lessons," declared one young enthusiast during our Recycling Awareness Day. These are the days we remember when so much is learnt and not a book in sight!

Cast your mind back to your own days of chalk-dusted classrooms with rolling blackboards and your ink stained fingers. The lessons we remember from those times are not those that were planned to an outstanding level, complete with starter and plenary. Look beyond the lesson format and this is where we as educators can deliver the most significant lessons.

The individual character of a prep school and the success of its pupils are illustrated in everything but its core lessons. This is why at Moreton First we relish theme days such as this term's Arctic Day and Bee Awareness Day. This is why children can thrive in independent schools because of the importance placed on everything that happens in addition to carefully orchestrated lessons.

At Moreton First, we seek out and celebrate the hidden curriculum. Without the constraints of government-designed targets we can take time to stretch

and enlighten children in ways that will nurture them as global citizens. Some lessons are so fundamental to the development of empathy in our pupils that one day cannot encompass the magnitude of this 'core' lesson.

Whilst brainstorming for ideas, I discovered a website suggesting Cultural Awareness Day. Perhaps the solution to our end of year 'off piste' learning?

The suggestions were interesting, if not already familiar: invite parent speakers, celebrate the heritage of your pupils, discuss traditions of other cultures and countries, encourage discussions about other faiths, look at art from other cultures. Assigning one day or week to this theme was contrary to what we value at Moreton First. Cultural Awareness is already, quite rightly, an integral part of life here.

For two terms we have explored the whole school topic of Heritage, which was reflected in our recent Art Exhibition, and have welcomed stories and visitors who highlighted for us the wealth of understanding different cultures as celebrated in the homes and families of our own pupils.

We choose class reading books to represent a cross section of cultures and countries. This term Year Five read 'The Breadwinner' set against the backdrop of troubled times in Afghanistan and Year 4 studied 'Journey to Jo'burg', following the story of children living in a segregated country during the time of Apartheid.

How could one Awareness Day encompass everything the children have learned through our topics in Geography, which take the children on adventures to distant lands where childhood is vastly different from what they know? Or by the RS syllabus which celebrates all world religions? This month having learned about Sikhism our older pupils visited a Gurdwara in Birmingham and Year 4 went to a Mosque in Liverpool.

Perhaps the most exciting way that we promote Cultural Awareness must be the ease with which the children welcome pupils from other nations. Each visiting child contributes so much to us all by bringing their own culture into our school.

On my recent visit to schools in China, I received the warmest of welcomes and a deluge of questions about the opportunities offered by the British educational system. I was curious to understand the style of teaching large groups and how success was achieved. The answer would appear to lie in the Chinese culture, which venerates pride and respect. During my brief visit I was asked about the broad curriculum that is offered in schools such as Moreton First. This vast and ancient nation still considers Britain the trailblazer in educational practices.

To ensure all our children grow up to be global citizens holding a place in a multi-cultural society, interacting empathetically with others we must model respect and understanding of other cultures every day, not just during a theme week. In the playground I see evidence of the 'Cultural Awareness' as five-year-old Alina from Austria plays alongside visiting children from the Ukraine. Juan from Tenerife enjoys a game of football with his English and Welsh classmates while Reine from Paris is teaching her friends skipping rhymes from France.

I have to agree; we do learn really important things at school, especially when we are not in lessons.

Catherine Ford is the Head of Moreton First Prep School at Moreton Hall School
For more information about Moreton Hall, see page 77
www.moretonhallschool.com

WILDWIND

An Unforgettable Holiday Experience

Summer in Greece, winter in Mauritius

Over the past 30 years, Wildwind has offered the ultimate in beach based sailing holidays: fantastic sailing conditions, superlative kit, and staff that receive incredible praise every week of the season. Join us at our flagship summer location in Vassiliki on the Greek island of Lefkas, or come to our more exotic year-round centre on the beautiful Indian Ocean island of Mauritius.

Wildwind offers you a sailing experience you just can't get anywhere else!

Sharpen your skills with a spectacular sailing holiday

Learn to see the world (and yourself) in a whole new way during the summer or winter holidays!

It's a bit of a paradox: to truly relax, you must get active. Holidays are not just for lying next to the pool, but they're an opportunity to have different experiences, learn things about yourself that you didn't know yet, and get to see the world from a new angle. One way to do that is by going on a sailing holiday and making the most of it!

For more than 30 years, Wildwind has welcomed sailing enthusiasts and their families on the Greek island of Lefkas in the summer and on the tropical island of Mauritius at times when Europe is cold and icy. There's nothing like seeing your kids learn to conquer the water as they speed on a Laser or Catamaran, the wind in their hair and the sun on their skin. If you've ever sailed before, you know that's an experience that will stay with you for life.

World class boats and professional training

Wildwind's centre in Greece is known the world over for its unique wind conditions. Calm mornings are perfect for learning the ropes and practicing new skills, while the afternoons are almost without exception windy and ideal for blasting away. Wildwind offers the widest range of boats of any sailing holiday in Europe, from Hobie Tigers and Hobie 16's to the best-in-class Lasers. For those looking for an extra dose of speed, they have recently introduced foiling equipment that won't just find anywhere else.

Wildwind's team of RYA-qualified instructors is very professional, friendly and experienced; many of them have competed at national and international levels. Courses stretching the full range of the RYA syllabus are offered at no additional charge. RYA qualification means that the safety of you and your family is never compromised.

Kids' Club

The Wildwind Kids Club is run by some of their staff, organizing sailing classes and other fun activities for kids of

all ages. You have to see some of the videos on Facebook to believe the amount of fun they have!

Water sports and other adventures
If you and your family are keen to have as many experiences as you can on your holiday, Wildwind's Adventures programme offers multiple water sports, such as scuba diving, sea kayaking, paddle boarding and windsurfing – a new adventure every day! If anyone in your family is not a fan of the water, they can join the 'Healthy Options' programme with Yoga, Pilates and fitness instead. You don't need to stay in the centre, of course: both Lefkas and Mauritius are islands that are a joy to explore! If you visit Wildwind in Greece in the summer, you can go for a bike ride around the beautiful olive groves and surrounding mountains. You'll discover much of the area's natural beauty during the organized walks and cycle rides. The sea safari is a truly unique experience, with numerous stops at secluded beaches for sun-bathing, snorkelling, and swimming. If you're lucky, you'll catch sight of the dolphins and flying fish along the way. Wildwind's winter location in the Indian ocean is a gem to discover, too. The island of Mauritius has a rich multi-cultural history and the population is surely one of the most friendly and welcoming in the world.

Comfortable accommodation
The included beachfront accommodation is located just yards from the sea's edge, with multiple options to choose from. You'll find small family run hotels and self-catering studios and apartments in beautiful landscaped gardens in Greece, and a comfortable three star-hotel with exotic views from the floor-to-ceiling windows and balconies in Mauritius.

Lots of fun, but zero pressure
Wildwind's relaxed social atmosphere means that nobody will feel any pressure to participate. You can take part as much or as little in any of the activities you'd like. There are cocktail evenings and barbeque nights, live music and always plenty of banter to go around. Wildwind is known as a great opportunity to make new friends for life, meeting guests from many different countries. Both Greece and Mauritius are famous for their tasty and healthy cuisine... yumm!

Booking information
To plan a week or two with Wildwind, call their friendly UK office on 0844 499 2898 or visit their website wildwind.co.uk, which contains plenty of information to give you a taste of what you can expect.

Initial advice

Educational institutions often belong to organisations that encourage high standards. Here we give a brief guide to what some of the initials mean.

BSA

The Boarding Schools' Association

Since its foundation in 1966, the Boarding Schools' Association (BSA) has had the twin objectives of the promotion of boarding education and the development of quality boarding through high standards of pastoral care and boarding accommodation. Parents and prospective pupils choosing a boarding school can, therefore, be assured that the 500 schools in membership of the BSA are committed to providing the best possible boarding environment for their pupils.

A school can only join the BSA if it is in membership of one of the ISC (Independent Schools Council) constituent associations or in membership of SBSA (State Boarding Schools' Association). These two bodies require member schools to be regularly inspected by the Independent Schools' Inspectorate (ISI) or Ofsted. Boarding inspection of independent schools has been conducted by ISI since September 2012. Ofsted retains responsibility for the inspection of boarding in state schools. Boarding inspections must be conducted every three years. Boarding is judged against the National Minimum Standards for Boarding Schools (revised 2011) with considerable input from the BSA.

Relationship with government

The BSA is in regular communication with the Department for Education (DfE) on all boarding matters. The Children Act (1989) and the Care Standards Act (2001) require boarding schools to conform to national legislation and the promotion of this legislation and the training required to carry it out are matters on which the DfE and the BSA work closely. The key area is in training.

Boarding training

The programme of training for boarding staff whose schools are in membership of the BSA has been supported and sponsored in the past by the DfE. The BSA maintains the high standards expected as a consequence of that support. The Utting Report on the Safeguards for Children Living Away from Home highlighted the importance of the development of 'policy, practice and training for services for children who live away from home'. It focuses on the right of parents to expect that staff looking after children are competent to do so, and points out the responsibility of central government to secure consistent national standards in promoting the welfare of children away from home. The Singleton Review (March 2009) reiterated the importance of rigorous safeguarding of such children.

In addition the BSA organises five conferences and more than 50 seminars a year for governors, Heads, deputies, housemasters and housemistresses, and matrons and medical staff where further training takes place in formal sessions and in sharing good practice. The BSA provides the following range of training and information:

- Professional qualifications for both teaching and non-teaching staff in boarding schools. The BSA has been responsible for the development of courses leading to university validated Certificates of Professional Practice in Boarding Education. These certificates, the result of at least two years' study, are awarded by the University of Roehampton.

- A rolling programme of day seminars on current boarding legislation and good practice.

State Boarding Schools Association

The BSA issues information on the 38 state boarding schools in England and Wales and the BSA should be contacted for details of these schools. In these schools parents pay for boarding but not for education, so fees are substantially lower than in an independent boarding school.

National Director: Robin Fletcher MBA, MPhil, FRSA
Director of Training: Alex Thomson OBE, BSc(Hons), PGCE, DipEd, FCIPD
Boarding Schools' Association
4thFloor
134-136 Buckingham Palace Road
London SWIW 9SA
Tel: 020 7798 1580
Fax: 020 7798 1581
Email: bsa@boarding.org.uk
Website: www.boarding.org.uk

GSA

The Girls' Schools Association, to which Heads of leading girls' schools belong

The Girls' Schools Association represents the heads of many of the top performing day and boarding schools in the UK independent schools sector and is a member of the Independent Schools Council.

The GSA encourages high standards of education for girls and promotes the benefits of being taught in a largely girls-only environment. GSA schools are internationally respected and have a global reputation for excellence. Their innovative practice and academic rigour attract pupils from around the world. As a whole, students at GSA schools tend to achieve disproportionately high results and are more likely to study and do well in STEM (science, technology, engineering, maths) subjects than girls in other schools. A high percentage – 96% – progress to higher education.

Twenty first century girls' schools come in many different shapes and sizes. Some cater for 100% girls, others provide a predominantly girls-only environment with boys in the nursery and/or sixth form. Some follow a diamond model, with equal numbers of boys but separate classrooms between the ages of 11 to 16. Educational provision across the Association offers a choice of day, boarding, weekly, and flexi boarding education. Schools range in type from large urban schools of 1000 pupils to small rural schools of around 200. Many schools have junior and pre-prep departments, and can offer a complete education from three/four to 18. A significant proportion of schools also have religious affiliations. Heads of Girls' Day School Trust (GDST) schools are members of the GSA.

The Association aims to inform and influence national educational debate and is a powerful and well-respected voice within the educational establishment, advising and lobbying educational policy makers on core education issues as well as those relating to girls' schools and the education of girls. The Association liaises with the Department for Education, the Office for Standards in Education, the Qualifications and Curriculum Authority and other bodies.

The GSA also provides its members and their staff with professional development courses, conferences, advice and opportunities to debate and share best practice, ensuring that they have every opportunity to remain fully up-to-date with all aspects of their profession.

As the GSA is one of the constituent bodies of the Independent Schools' Council (ISC), its schools are required to undergo a regular cycle of inspections to ensure that these rigorous standards are being maintained. GSA schools must also belong to the Association of Governing Bodies of Independent Schools, and Heads must be in membership of the Association of School and College Leaders (ASCL).

The Association's secretariat is based in Leicester.

Suite 105, 108 New Walk, Leicester LE1 7EA
Tel: 0116 254 1619
Email: office@gsa.uk.com
Website: www.gsa.uk.com
Twitter: @GSAUK
President 2017: Charlotte Avery, St Mary's Cambridge
Interim Operations Director: Christine Edmundson

HMC

The Headmasters' and Headmistresses' Conference, to which the Heads of leading independent schools belong

Founded in 1869 the HMC exists to enable members to discuss matters of common interest and to influence important developments in education. It looks after the professional interests of members, central to which is their wish to provide the best possible educational opportunities for their pupils.

The Heads of some 281 leading independent schools are members of The Headmasters' and Headmistresses' Conference, whose membership now includes Heads of boys', girls' and coeducational schools. International membership includes the Heads of around 54 schools throughout the world.

Initial advice

The great variety of these schools is one of the strengths of HMC but all must exhibit high quality in the education provided. While day schools are the largest group, about a quarter of HMC schools consist mainly of boarders and others have a smaller boarding element including weekly and flexible boarders.

All schools are noted for their academic excellence and achieve good results, including those with pupils from a broad ability band. Members believe that good education consists of more than academic results and schools provide pupils with a wide range of educational co-curricular activities and with strong pastoral support.

Only those schools that meet with the rigorous membership criteria are admitted and this helps ensure that HMC is synonymous with high quality in education. There is a set of membership requirements and a Code of Practice to which members must subscribe. Those who want the intimate atmosphere of a small school will find some with around 350 pupils. Others who want a wide range of facilities and specialisations will find these offered in large day or boarding schools. Many have over 1000 pupils. About 30 schools are for boys only, others are coeducational throughout or only in the sixth form. The first girls-only schools joined HMC in 2006. There are now about 25 girls-only schools.

Within HMC there are schools with continuous histories as long as any in the world and many others trace their origins to Tudor times, but HMC continues to admit to membership recently-founded schools that have achieved great success. The facilities in all HMC schools will be good but some have magnificent buildings and grounds that are the result of the generosity of benefactors over many years. Some have attractive rural settings, others are sited in the centres of cities.

Pupils come from all sorts of backgrounds. Bursaries and scholarships provided by the schools give about a third of the 220,000 pupils in HMC schools help with their fees. These average about £30,000 per annum for boarding schools and £13,000 for day schools. About 170,000 are day pupils and 43,000 boarders.

Entry into some schools is highly selective but others are well-suited to a wide ability range. Senior boarding schools usually admit pupils after the Common Entrance examination taken when they are 13.

Most day schools select their pupils by 11+ examination. Many HMC schools have junior schools, some with nursery and pre-prep departments. The growing number of boarders from overseas is evidence of the high reputation of the schools worldwide.

The independent sector has always been fortunate in attracting very good teachers. Higher salary scales, excellent conditions of employment, exciting educational opportunities and good pupil/teacher ratios bring rewards commensurate with the demanding expectations. Schools expect teachers to have a good education culminating in a good honours degree and a professional qualification, though some do not insist on the latter especially if relevant experience is offered. Willingness to participate in the whole life of the school is essential.

Parents expect the school to provide not only good teaching that helps their children achieve the best possible examination results, but also the dedicated pastoral care and valuable educational experiences outside the classroom in music, drama, games, outdoor pursuits and community service. Over 90% of pupils go on to higher education, many of them winning places on the most highly-subscribed university courses.

All members attend the Annual Conference, usually held in a large conference centre in September/October. There are ten divisions covering England, Wales, Scotland and Ireland where members meet once a term on a regional basis, and a distinctive international division.

The chairman and committee, with the advice of the general secretary and membership secretary, make decisions on matters referred by membership-led sub-committees, steering groups and working parties. Close links are maintained with other professional associations in membership of the Independent Schools Council and with the Association of School and College Leaders.

Membership Secretary: Ian Power
Tel: 01858 465260
General Secretary: Dr William Richardson
Tel: 01858 469059
12 The Point
Rockingham Road
Market Harborough
Leicestershire LE16 7QU
Email: gensec@hmc.org.uk
Website: www.hmc.org.uk

Leading
Independent
Schools

IAPS

The Independent Association of Preparatory Schools (IAPS) is a membership association representing leading headteachers and their prep schools in the UK and overseas

With more than 650 members, IAPS schools represent a multi-billion pound enterprise, educating more than 160,000 children and employing more than 20,000 staff.

Schools are spread throughout cities, towns and the countryside and offer pupils the choice of day, boarding, weekly and flexible boarding, in both single sex and coeducational settings. Sizes vary from 100 to more than 800 per school, with the majority between 150 and 400. Most schools are charitable trusts, some are limited companies and a few are proprietary. There are also junior schools attached to senior schools, choir schools, those with a particular religious affiliation and those that offer specialist provision as well as some schools with an age range extending to age 16 or above.

IAPS only accredits those schools that can demonstrate that they provide the highest standards of education and care. Member schools offer an all-round, values-led, broad education, which produces confident, adaptable, motivated children with a lifelong passion for learning. In order to be elected to membership, a Head must be suitably qualified and schools must be accredited through a satisfactory inspection. IAPS offers its members and their staff a comprehensive and up-to-date programme of professional development courses to ensure that high professional standards are maintained.

Pupils are offered a rich and varied school life. The targets of the National Curriculum are regarded as a basic foundation, which is greatly extended by the wider programmes of study offered. Specialist subject teaching begins at an early age and pupils are offered a range of cultural and sporting opportunities. Together with more than 30 recreational games, music, art and drama form part of curricular and extra-curricular activities. In addition, IAPS organises holiday and term-time sporting competitions for pupils to take part in, including skiing, sailing, judo, swimming, golf, fencing and squash, amongst many others.

IAPS has well-established links with senior independent schools, and experience in methods of transfer and entry to them. As the voice of independent prep school education, it has national influence and actively defends and promotes the interests of its members. It lobbies the government on their behalf and promotes prep school issues on a national and international stage. IAPS works directly with ministers and national policy advisers to ensure that the needs of the prep school sector are met.

IAPS
11 Waterloo Place,
Leamington Spa,
Warwickshire CV32 5LA
Tel: 01926 887833
Email: iaps@iaps.uk
Website: iaps.uk

Excellence in Education
The Independent Association
of Prep Schools

ISA

The Independent Schools Association, with membership across all types of school

The Independent Schools Association (ISA), established in 1879, is one of the oldest of the Headteachers' associations of independent schools that make up the Independent Schools' Council (ISC). It began life as the Association of Principals of Private Schools, which was created to encourage high standards and foster friendliness and cooperation among Heads who had previously worked in isolation. In 1895 it was incorporated as The Private Schools Association and in 1927 the word 'private' was replaced by 'independent'. The recently published history of the association, Pro Liberis, demonstrates the strong links ISA has with proprietorial schools, which is still the case today, even though boards of governors now run the majority of schools.

Membership is open to any Head or Proprietor, provided they meet the necessary accreditation criteria, including inspection of their school by a government-approved inspectorate. ISA's Executive Council is elected by members and supports all developments of the Association through its committee structure and the strong regional network of co-ordinators and area committees. Each of ISA's seven areas in turn supports members through regular training events and meetings.

ISA celebrates a wide-ranging membership, not confined to any one type of school, but including all: nursery, pre-preparatory, junior and senior, all-through schools, coeducational, single-sex, boarding, day and performing arts and special schools.

Promoting best practice and fellowship remains at the core of the ISA, as it did when it began 130 years ago. The association is growing, and its 384 members and their schools enjoy high quality national conferences and courses that foster excellence in independent education. ISA's central office also supports members and provides advice, and represents the views of its membership at national and governmental levels.

Pupils in ISA schools enjoy a wide variety of competitions, in particular the wealth of sporting, artistic and academic activities at area and national level.

President: Lord Lexden
Chief Executive: Neil Roskilly, BA PGCE NPQH FRSA FRGS

ISA House,
5-7 Great Chesterford Court,
Great Chesterford, Essex CB10 1PF
Tel: 01799 523619
Fax: 01799 524892
Email: isa@isaschools.org.uk
Website: www.isaschools.org.uk

The Society of Heads

The Society of Heads represents the interests of the smaller independent secondary schools.

The Society of Heads represents the interests of the smaller, independent, secondary schools. The Society celebrated its 50th Anniversary in 2011. The Society has as its members over 110 Heads of well-established secondary schools, many with a boarding element, meeting a wide range of educational needs. All member schools provide education up to 18, with sixth forms offering both A and AS levels and/or the International Baccalaureate. Also some offer vocational courses. Many have junior schools attached to their foundation. A number cater for pupils with special educational needs, whilst others offer places to gifted dancers and musicians. All the schools provide education appropriate to their pupils' individual requirements together with the best in pastoral care.

The average size of the schools is about 350, and all aim to provide small classes ensuring favourable pupil:teacher ratios. The majority are coeducational and offer facilities for both boarding and day pupils. Many of the schools are non-denominational, whilst others have specific religious foundations.

The Society believes that independent schools are an important part of Britain's national education system. Given their independence, the schools can either introduce new developments ahead of the maintained sector or offer certain courses specifically appropriate to the pupils in their schools. They are able to respond quickly to the needs of parents and pupils alike.

Schools are admitted to membership of the Society only after a strict inspection procedure carried out by the Independent Schools Inspectorate. Regular inspection

visits thereafter ensure that standards are maintained.

The Society is a constituent member of the Independent Schools Council and every full member in the Society has been accredited to it. All the Society's Heads belong to the Association of School and College Leaders (ASCL) (or another recognised union for school leaders) and their schools are members of AGBIS.

The Society's policy is: to maintain high standards of education, acting as a guarantee of quality to parents who choose a Society school for their children; to ensure the genuine independence of member schools; to provide an opportunity for Heads to share ideas and common concerns for the benefit of the children in their care; to provide training opportunities for Heads and staff in order to keep them abreast of new educational initiatives; to promote links with higher and further education and the professions, so that pupils leaving the Society's schools are given the best advice and opportunities for their future careers; and to help Heads strengthen relations with their local communities.

The Society of Heads' Office,
12 The Point, Rockingham Road,
Market Harborough,
Leicestershire LE16 7QU
Tel: 01858 433760
Fax: 01858 461413
Email: gensec@thesocietyofheads.org.uk
Website: www.thesocietyofheads.org.uk

The Independent Schools Council

The Independent Schools Council (ISC) works with its members to promote and preserve the quality, diversity and excellence of UK independent education both at home and abroad

What is the ISC?

Through our member associations we represent 1,280 independent schools in the UK and overseas. These schools are ranked among the best in the world and educate more than half a million children each year.

ISC's work is carried out by a small number of dedicated professionals in our offices in Central London. We are assisted by the contributions from expert advisory groups in specialist areas.

ISC schools

ISC schools are at the forefront of educational achievement in every way. They are the most academically successful schools and offer excellent teaching, extensive facilities and an astonishing breadth of co-curricular activities. There are schools to suit every need, whether you want a day or boarding school, single sex or co-education, a large or a small school, or schools offering specialisms, such as in the Arts.

Our schools are very diverse: some of our schools are selective and highly academic, offering a chance to stretch the bright child. Others have very strong drama or music departments full of creative opportunities in plays, orchestras and choirs. For children with special needs such as dyslexia or autism there are many outstanding independent schools that offer the best provision in the country.

And of course, our schools have very strong track records of high achievement at sport, offering superb facilities, excellent coaches and a full fixture list. Independent schools excel at the traditional sports like football and rugby, but also offer more unusual sports like rowing, fencing and even rock climbing.

There is also a wealth of co-curricular opportunity available. Whether your child is into debating, sailing, the Model United Nations or is interested in army training in the Combined Cadet Force, most schools offer numerous clubs and activities. It all adds up to an exciting, broad and stimulating all-round education.

Academic results

In 2016, 49% of A level subjects taken at independent schools were graded A*/A – this is double the national average of 26%. Last year also saw more than a third of independent school GCSE entries being awarded an A*, compared to 7% nationally. This would be less impressive if fee-charging schools were very selective academically, but most are not. A high proportion of ISC schools support alternative qualifications which are more demanding than GCSEs and A levels and thus a better offer for able pupils. In 2016 outstanding results were achieved; for example, nearly a third of pupils who took the IB Diploma obtained 40 points or more, equivalent to 4.5 A grades at A level. Based on grades achieved (DfE tables 2015), 84 of the top 100 schools are ISC independent schools.

Fee Assistance

ISC schools are sympathetic to the financial challenges facing many parents and the amount of bursaries and scholarships available has grown to reflect this. A third of pupils receive fee assistance, the value of this help totals over £850m.

ISC Associations

There are seven member associations of ISC each with its own distinctive ethos reflected in their entrance criteria and quality assurance:

Girls' Schools Association (GSA) – see page 25
Headmasters' and Headmistresses' Conference (HMC) - see page 25
Independent Association of Prep Schools (IAPS) – see page 27
Independent Schools Association (ISA) – see page 27
The Society of Heads – see page 28
Association of Governing Bodies of Independent Schools (AGBIS)
www.agbis.org

Independent Schools' Bursars Association (ISBA)
www.isba.org.uk
The ISC can be contacted at:
First Floor,
27 Queen Anne's Gate,
London,
SW1H 9BU
Telephone: 020 7766 7070
Fax: 020 7766 7071
Website: www.isc.co.uk

independent
schools
council

Help in finding the fees

Chris Procter, joint managing director of SFIA, outlines a planned approach to funding your child's school fees

Recent research shows that school fees have increased by three times the rate of inflation over the past five years. In addition, the latest Independent Schools Council (ISC) survey, completed by all 1,280 schools in UK membership, shows that fees have increased by 553% in the last 25 years, compared to a rise in consumer prices of 201% and wage rises of 217%.

There are now 518,432 pupils being educated privately, the highest number since records began in 1974. The proportions of day (86.4%) and boarding pupils (13.6%) show a continuing shift towards boarding schools. The share of girls and boys at ISC schools is very nearly equal, with boys representing 51% of all pupils.

The overall average boarding fee is £10,317 and the overall average day fee is £4,541. However, fees charged by schools vary by region – for example the average boarding fee ranges from £9,566 per term in Wales to £11,940 per term in Greater London; the average day fee ranges from £3,568 per term in the North to £5,299 per term in Greater London.

The overall cost (including university fees) might seem daunting: the cost of educating one child privately could well be very similar to that of buying a house but, as with house buying, the school fees commitment for the majority of parents can be made possible by spreading it over a long period rather than funding it all from current resources.

It is vital that parents do their financial homework, plan ahead, start to save early and regularly. Grandparents who have access to capital could help out; by contributing to school fees they could also help to reduce any potential future inheritance tax liability.

Parents would be well-advised to consult a specialist financial adviser as early as possible, since a long-term plan for the payment of fees – possibly university as well – can prove very advantageous from a financial point of view and offer greater peace of mind. Funding fees is neither science, nor magic, nor is there any panacea. It is quite simply a question of planning and using whatever resources are available, such as income, capital, or tax reduction opportunities.

The fundamental point to recognise is that you, your circumstances and your wishes or ambitions, for your children or grandchildren are unique. They might well be similar to those of other people but they will still be uniquely different. There will be no single solution to your problem. In fact, after a review of all your circumstances, there might not be a problem at all.

So, what are the reasons for seeking advice about education expenses?

- To reduce the overall cost?

- To get some tax benefit?

- To reduce your cash outflow?

- To invest capital to ensure that future fees are paid?

- To set aside money now for future fees?

- To provide protection for school fees?

- Or just to make sure that, as well as educating your children, you can still have a life?!

Any, some, or all of the above – or others not listed – could be on your agenda, the important thing is to develop a strategy.

At this stage, it really does not help to get hung up on which financial 'product' is the most suitable. The composition of a school fees plan will differ for each family depending on a number of factors. That is why there is no one school fees plan on offer.

The simplest strategy but in most cases, the most expensive option, is to write out a cheque for the whole bill when it arrives and post it back to the school. Like most simple plans, that can work well, if you have the money. Even if you do have the money, is that really the best way of doing things? Do you know that to fund £1,000 of school fees as a higher rate taxpayer paying 40% income tax, you currently need to earn £1,667, this rises to £1,818 if you are an additional rate taxpayer where the rate is 45%.

How then do you start to develop your strategy? As with most things in life, if you can define your objective, then you will know what you are aiming at. Your objective in this case will be to determine how much money is needed and when.

You need to draw up a school fees schedule or what others may term a cash flow forecast. So, you need to identify:

- How many children?

- Which schools and therefore what are the fees? (or you could use an average school fee)

- When are they due?

- Any special educational needs?

- Inflation estimate

- Include university costs?

With this basic information, the school fees schedule/ cash flow forecast can be prepared and you will have defined what it is you are trying to achieve.

Remember though, that senior school fees are typically more than prep school fees – this needs to be factored in. Also be aware that the cost of university is not restricted to the fees alone; there are a lot of maintenance and other costs involved: accommodation, books, food, to name a few. Don't forget to build in inflation, I refer you back to the data at the beginning of this article.

You now have one element of the equation, the relatively simple element. The other side is the resources you have available to achieve the objective. This also needs to be identified, but this is a much more difficult exercise. The reason that it is more difficult, of course, is that school fees are not the only drain on your resources. You probably have a mortgage, you want to have holidays, you need to buy food and clothes, you may be concerned that you should be funding a pension.

This is a key area of expertise, since your financial commitments are unique. A specialist in the area of school fees planning can help identify these commitments, to record them and help you to distribute your resources according to your priorities.

The options open to you as parents depend completely upon your adviser's knowledge of these complex personal financial issues. (Did I forget to mention your tax position, capital gains tax allowance, other tax allowances, including those of your children and a lower or zero rate tax paying spouse or partner? These could well be used to your advantage.)

A typical school fees plan can incorporate many elements to fund short, medium and long-term fees. Each plan is designed according to individual circumstances and usually there is a special emphasis on what parents are looking to achieve, for example, to maximise overall savings and to minimise the outflow of cash.

Additionally it is possible to protect the payment of the fees in the event of unforeseen circumstances that could lead to a significant or total loss of earnings.

Short-term fees

Short-term fees are typically the termly amounts needed within five years: these are usually funded from such things as guaranteed investments, liquid capital, loan plans (if no savings are available) or maturing insurance policies, investments etc. Alternatively they can be funded from disposable income.

Medium-term fees

Once the short-term plan expires, the medium-term funding is invoked to fund the education costs for a further five to ten years. Monthly amounts can be invested in a low-risk, regular premium investment ranging from a building society account to a friendly society savings plan to equity ISAs. It is important to understand the pattern of the future fees and to be aware of the timing of withdrawals.

Long-term fees

Longer term funding can incorporate a higher element of risk (as long as this is acceptable to the investor), which will offer higher potential returns. Investing in UK and overseas equities could be considered. Solutions may be the same as those for medium-term fees, but will have the flexibility to utilise investments that may have an increased 'equity based' content.

Finally, it is important to remember that most investments, or financial products either mature with a single payment, or provide for regular withdrawals; rarely do they provide timed termly payments. Additionally, the overall risk profile of the portfolio should lean towards the side of caution (for obvious reasons).

There are any number of advisers in the country, but few who specialise in the area of planning to meet school and university fees. SFIA is the largest organisation specialising in school fees planning in the UK.

This article has been contributed by SFIA and edited by Chris Procter, Managing Director.

Chris can be contacted at: SFIA, 29 High Street, Marlow, Buckinghamshire, SL7 1AU
Tel: 01628 566777
Fax: 0333 444 1550
Email: enquiries@sfia.co.uk
Web: www.sfia.co.uk

What benefit is there in the boarding experience?

Tracey Gray, from Merchiston Castle School, discusses the benefits a boarding experience can introduce into a child's life

Boarding is far from the experience of the past, where children were dropped at the School gates in August and picked up at Christmas time. There are many opportunities for parents to visit, or for pupils to go out and meet their friends and family.

Boarders themselves recognise that they often have a more diverse social life, a wider variety of interests and closer relationships with their friends than day pupils. Parents often note that their children who board develop high levels of confidence, independence, social skills, cultural awareness, self-motivation, and a genuine respect for others."

Boarding offers 'True wrap around care'! The environment and ethos allows activities to run into the evening – from indoor football to school debates and trips out of school. It is easier for the pupils wanting to buy into this to get the amount of sleep they need, without time and energy spent on commuting. It allows for growth of independence in a secure, caring environment and with the added benefit of access to an international set of friendships, increasingly significant in a global world. There is also the advantage of supervised prep sessions, helping build the work ethos and providing additional help in their academic work. Pupils are certainly happy, living together with their friends, working together and relaxing together, enjoying a huge range of activities.

Constancy of environment and friends is extremely important so pupils should have opportunities available to them to take up activities that may well turn into life-long interests; a safe environment where they are 'cared for' and yet allowed to grow to seek their own individual 'strengths'; a greater range of role-models to serve each boarder; resilience to cope with broader demands of today's world; acquisition of fundamental transferable skills that will make them highly desirable employees.

For more information about Merchiston Castle School, see page 84
www.merchiston.co.uk

Why camp? Why bother?

Since the advent of adventure tourism the role of the outdoors in personal growth has remained pertinent. Stepping out into the wilderness to experience the sublime and to broaden one's horizons has continued to capture the interest of generations. We often see the trepidation on parents' faces as they bid farewell to their child thinking "Have I made the right decision ?".

Camp is an experience your child will never forget!

At Les Elfes camp our favourite part of the week is the weekend. Unlike many other young professionals our weekends are the busiest working days, hectic, exciting and often punctuated with campers' tears. It may seem strange that the highlight of my week is when our campers are upset but the weekend signifies a huge shift in the emotional frame of our young Elves.

Upon arrival campers are jet-lagged, tired and missing home. Our campers come from 60 countries around the world. It takes a little time to settle in, so... we have tears. The reason we cherish this time is not because the students continue to cry throughout their time with us but, quite the opposite, because there are only two times that our campers cry. When they arrive and when they have to leave!

Whether they entered camp ready to embrace the experience or clawing at the reception door like a cat heading for an unwelcome shower by the time they leave, they are changed. Their perception of their own abilities, their capacity for independence and their relationship with other campers have all shifted and, it's in these weekend change-overs that this journey is most apparent.

At Les Elfes we understand that the next generation are expert programmers, they are the ones we call upon to set up our new phones and to show us how to use our video editing software. They think Facebook is for old people and receive 20+ snapchats per day. Camp allows our youngsters to look up from the world on their screens and to experience the mountains in panoramic-real-life view. To stand on top of a mountain knowing it was their own legs and perseverance that got them there.

We frame our activities and design our programmes to offer a steady progression for our campers. Our philiosophy at Les Elfes International is to:

- Provide adventurous activities built on a well-established foundation of professional and safe practices.

- Inspire holistic personal development through culturally diverse experiences.

- Outdoor learning which enables young people to discover their true potential to be dynamic & prosperous in their future lives.

At camp our Elfes learn to cope with adversity, harness equanimity and gain confidence in expressing themselves. Social media will still be there when they go home, but so will the knowledge that their resilience and personal strength can enable them to achieve astounding things!

Experience it today. Remember forever!

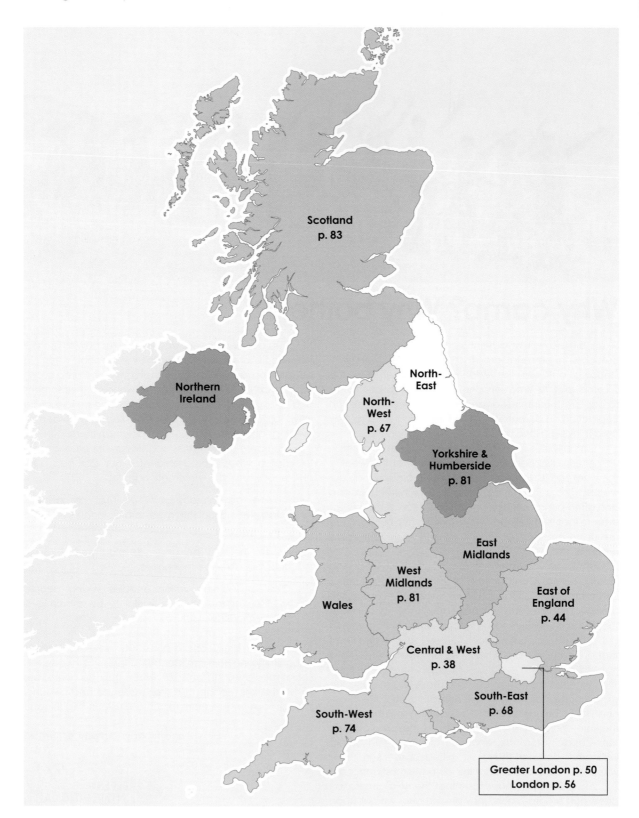

Scotland
p. 83

Northern
Ireland

North-
East

North-
West
p. 67

Yorkshire &
Humberside
p. 81

East
Midlands

West
Midlands
p. 81

Wales

East of
England
p. 44

Central & West
p. 38

South-East
p. 68

South-West
p. 74

Greater London p. 50
London p. 56

Prep schools in the UK

Please note that, to facilitate the use of this guide, we have introduced the geographical region 'Central & West' (see map opposite). This is not an officially designated region, and has been created solely for the purposes of this publication.

Clifton College Preparatory School

CLIFTON
COLLEGE
ESTABLISHED 1862

(Founded 1908)

The Avenue, Clifton, Bristol, BS8 3HE

Tel: +44 (0)117 405 8396

Fax: +44 (0)117 315 7504

Email:

prepadmissions@cliftoncollege.com

Website: www.cliftoncollege.com/prep

Head of Preparatory School:

Mr John Milne

School type: Coeducational Day & Boarding Preparatory

Age range of pupils: 2–13

No. of pupils enrolled as at 01/01/2017: 495

Boys: 282 **Girls:** 213

No. of boarders: 40

Fees per annum as at 01/01/2017:

Day: £12,465–£16,485

Flexi Boarding: £15,465–£19,485

Full Boarding: £21,420–£27,240

Average class size: 18

Teacher/pupil ratio: 1:7

The Preparatory School was opened in 1908 and is now the region's largest boarding and day preparatory school, catering for almost 500 pupils.

Clifton College Preparatory School is ranked as a top 100 independent preparatory school (Sunday Times 2016). We offer first class teaching and outstanding pastoral care for girls and boys aged 2 to 13. There is no 'one size fits all' approach, each child is treated as an individual and is encouraged to explore and develop their unique talents and skills. Our children are our best ambassadors. They are socially confident, intellectually agile, adventurous, well-mannered and decent young people.

We offer a tailored, all-round education with diverse and targeted co-curricular activities and excellent facilities.

Each year the Preparatory School sees more than 100 new pupils join from a wide range of schools nationwide and overseas.

The main entry points are at Nursery, Year 3 and Year 7, though pupils are welcome to join into any of the year groups.

Exceptional pastoral care

From eight years old, pastoral care is House-based, with Housemasters and Housemistresses and their teams offering a 'home from home'. Our Pre-Prep pupils' pastoral care is provided by their dedicated classroom teachers; Year 3 pupils also have their own common room, which acts as an introduction to the House system. Each child has a tutor who meets with them weekly to discuss academic, co-curricular or any other matters.

Inspirational teaching

We provide a rigorous and stimulating academic curriculum and we select teachers that lead in their field and share best practice. They encourage intellectual curiosity and independent learning, engendering academic self-belief and confidence in our pupils.

Diverse and targeted co-curricular activities

Our ethos encourages participation and all of our pupils engage with a diverse range of co-curricular activities and experiences. Through these activities we provide opportunities and challenges for pupils to find new strengths and talents and encourage collaboration.

Traditional values, modern facilities

The College successfully combines heritage with modernity, enjoying the best of both. Landscaped greenery surrounds our magnificent Grade II listed buildings which are on the outskirts of a vibrant international city. The Chapel is one of our most cherished buildings and The Redgrave is the third largest theatre in Bristol. Our superb sporting facilities include The Close and the 90-acre site known as 'Beggar's Bush' which is Bristol's biggest outdoor sports complex, providing all the latest sporting facilities.

All our pupils benefit from the Preparatory School being a boarding school, with early drop off and late pick up for our day pupils, enabling them to take part in a huge array of co-curricular activities. Our flexible and full boarding options mean that parents can choose the level of care that works best for their family, confident in the knowledge that their child will be happy, safe and secure.

Clifton College provides a supportive and welcoming atmosphere and allows pupils to benefit from the security and confidence that comes from belonging to the same school from the ages of 2 to 18. As pupils grow with the Preparatory School, their sense of independence and responsibility prepares them for their journey into the Upper School.

All-round success

We aim to unlock your son or daughter's potential to enable them to become the best version of themselves they can be. Alongside high academic achievement, our pupils also excel in art, music, sport and drama. Recent Clifton College graduates have gone on to study music at the Royal Academy of Music, perform Shakespeare at the Globe Theatre, and win gold at the Olympics!

Come and visit us

We understand that choosing a school is an important decision for both parents and children, so come along to one of our Open Days or book a personal visit and see why a Clifton child is a happy child. For more information on Clifton College, or to request a prospectus or book a visit, please go to www.cliftoncollege.com

Leehurst Swan Prep School

Leehurst Swan School

Campbell Road, Salisbury, Wiltshire SP1 3BQ

Tel: 01722 333094

Email: registrar@leehurstswan.org.uk

Website: www.leehurstswan.org.uk

Headmaster: Mr Roger Leake BSc (Hons), PGCE, CBiol, MSB

Appointed: September 2006

School type: Coeducational Day

Age range of pupils: 6 weeks–16 years

Fees per annum as at 01/01/2017:

Day: £8,190–£13,770

Average class size: 17

Leehurst Swan Prep School

Leehurst Swan is a school where pupils achieve and thrive in the heart of Salisbury. We are a co-educational day school, highly praised for its ethos, pastoral care, academic standards and breadth of extra-curricular activities. Pupils enjoy coming to school and being part of our community.

Pupils in the Prep School receive specialist teaching in key subjects and use modern teaching facilities. A state-of-the-art dedicated Prep building, completed in 2014, offers bright, spacious classrooms, and provides an interactive and thoroughly stimulating learning environment.

Our children experience success (academically, artistically and sportingly) whilst growing in confidence and self-esteem. The school is well known for excellent results in the 11+ entrance selection for the grammar schools.

We foster the values of hard work, thoughtfulness, kindness and generosity. Leehurst Swan is a warm-hearted community where learning and laughter is an essential part of the school day. Children receive the best start in life, enabling them to thrive in Senior School and beyond.

Leehurst Swan School provides for children in The Nest, at age 6 weeks, through to GCSE for pupils aged 16. The benefits of an all-through education are widely recognised, eliminating the problems of transfer between the stages of education. Scholarships are awarded for entry into Year 3 and Year 7.

The best way to experience Leehurst Swan is by viewing the digital prospectus at http://prospectus.leehurstswan.org.uk and making an appointment on 01722 333094.

Monkton Prep School

(Founded 1888)
Church Road, Combe Down, Bath,
Bath & North-East Somerset BA2 7ET

Tel: +44 (0)1225 837912
Email: admissions@monktonprep.org.uk
Website: www.monktonprep.com
Headmaster: Mr M Davis
Appointed: January 2017
School type: Coeducational Day & Boarding
Age range of pupils: 7–13 (boarding from 8)
No. of pupils enrolled as at 01/01/2017: 240

Fees per term as at 01/01/2017:
Prep (Day age 7-11):
£3,750–£3,860 per term
Prep (Boarding age 7-11):
£7,300 –£7,575 per term
Prep (Day age 11-13): £5,460 per term
Prep (Boarding age 11-13): £7,870 per term
Average class size: 15-20
Teacher/pupil ratio: 1:15-20

Setting standards for life

Monkton Prep School, in the World Heritage City of Bath, is an independent, co-educational day and boarding school for pupils aged 7–13. We pride ourselves on our academic excellence, our strong pastoral care and our Christian ethos. At Monkton, we are setting standards for life; giving young people the qualities of character and values they need to become valued friends, confident team players and inspiring leaders.

A broad and varied curriculum

The syllabus in each subject is aimed at, and beyond, the requirements of National Curriculum up to the end of Year 6, and also the Common Entrance and Scholarship examinations at 13+. The Prep School has subject specialist teachers which enables both great breadth and depth of teaching. All pupils in our Year 7 and 8 year groups at Monkton have the opportunity to be leaders and mentors and take on responsibilities; this is an integral part of their education. Many opportunities are provided for children to grow as leaders, as independent thinkers and in their self-confidence, so they are well-prepared for the next step.

A wide range of activities

The activity programme is a key and exciting part of life at Monkton. The choice is extremely varied and includes gymnastics, swimming, choir, football and animation to name just a few. There are some brilliant events throughout the year and these together with music, drama and sporting competitions provide many opportunities for pupils to learn and grow individually and as part of a team.

Pastoral care

The happiness and well-being of each child is central to what we do. Through our inclusive approach each pupil is encouraged to try new things, develop their skills and talents and achieve in every area of school life. At Monkton we believe that every child is an individual, and we provide an education that encourages the development of every child academically, emotionally and spiritually to enable them to go out into the world and play their part in transforming the community and society around them.

'A happy place, where much is expected and much achieved'
The Good Schools Guide

St Margaret's Preparatory School

ST MARGARET'S
PREPARATORY SCHOOL CALNE

(Founded 1873)
Curzon Street, Calne, Wiltshire SN11 0DF

Tel: 01249 857220
Email: office@stmargaretsprep.org.uk
Website: www.stmargaretsprep.org.uk
Headmistress: Mrs Karen Cordon
School type: Co-educational Day
Age range of pupils: 3–11

No. of pupils enrolled as at 01/01/2017: 200
Boys: 90 **Girls:** 110
Fees per term as at 01/01/2017:
Day: £4,614–£12,600
Average class size: 14-18

You will undoubtedly want your children to be happy and enjoy a broad and stimulating education that's rich in opportunities, but what makes St Margaret's special?

Your child will join a school with real spirit and energy, which lives each day to the full. We purposefully pack excitement and learning experiences into every moment. Our staff are passionate about teaching and lessons are fun, vibrant and engaging. The children's love of learning is infectious and we hope it'll rub off on you too!

Wherever your child's strengths and interests lie, we have the facilities to support them. Learning spaces are contemporary, vibrant and well-equipped; these have been purpose-built in the last 10 years. These include dedicated specialist teaching rooms; a 25m indoor swimming pool; sports pitches; all-weather Astroturf; Chapel; dining hall; theatre and an outstanding Library and Computer Suite where interactive learning takes place. Additionally, outdoor space is plentiful and children enjoy time spent in the school garden; wildlife area, courtyard classroom or one of the many play areas.

Teaching throughout the school is tailored to meet the needs of the individual child. Children are encouraged to reflect and evaluate their own learning and with support identify their next steps. Specialist teachers offer a wide range of experiences and as a result, our teaching delivers truly personalised learning for each child. An extensive range of mobile technology enhances learning across the curriculum.

St Margaret's is a place where friendships and special memories are created and where a love of learning is established. Your children will understand that success requires hard work, personal responsibility, respect and consideration for others. These qualities will remain with them, equipping him or her for future challenges and providing an edge in years to come.

St Margaret's is an independent day school for boys and girls aged from 3-11 based in Calne, Wiltshire.

Visitors are warmly welcomed throughout the year.

Westonbirt Prep School

WESTONBIRT
— PREP SCHOOL —

Westonbirt, Tetbury, Gloucestershire
GL8 8QG
Tel: 01666 881400
Email: admissions@westonbirt.org
Website: www.westonbirt.org

Headmaster: Mr Sean Price
School type: Coeducational Day
Age range of pupils: 3–11
Fees per term as at 01/01/2017:
Day: £2,800–£3,750

Westonbirt Prep is an independent Preparatory and Nursery School for boys and girls aged 3-11 years. Set in 210 acres of stunning parklands, shared with Westonbirt Senior School, pupils are inspired by the beauty that surrounds them and benefit from the resources of a much larger school while maintaining the atmosphere of a small family setting.

Why Westonbirt Prep?

Smaller class sizes and the excellent ratio of staff to pupils allow children to be well supported throughout their development and for their individual abilities to be valued. Boys and girls are praised for their efforts and good behaviour and are encouraged to develop a sense of independence, mutual consideration, manners and respect for others. Our commitment to children's broader personal development combined with a structured preparation for Senior School makes us stand out.

Academic success

Prep school pupils go on to their first choice of Senior School including Westonbirt School, Grammar Schools and other top Independent schools. Academic success is strong. Emphasis is placed on sport, music, drama and art as well as wide ranging opportunities outside the classroom, including their own Forest School area.

The Good Schools' Guide

The Good Schools' Guide highlighted parents' observations that children were encouraged to find their voice at the school; "When she started my daughter was very shy, but she's flourished and has so much more confidence now."

Exceptional grounds and facilities

Westonbirt Prep successfully combines the educational quality and individual attention of an intimate, family school with the facilities and opportunities of a much larger school. The Prep school offers a £3m sports centre, indoor pool, state-of-the-art music technology suite and there is even a golf course! Pupils are given every advantage in their educational and personal development.

King's Ely Junior

(Founded 970)
Ely, Cambridgeshire CB7 4DB

Tel: 01353 660707
Email: admissions@kingsely.org
Website: www.kingsely.org
Head: Mr Richard Whymark
Appointed: September 2008
School type: Co-educational Day & Boarding

Age range of pupils: 7–13
No. of pupils enrolled as at 01/01/2017: 345
Fees per annum as at 01/01/2017:
Day: £13,180–£14,382
Full Boarding: £21,013–£22,181
Average class size: 17
Teacher/pupil ratio: 1:14

NESTLED in the heart of the beautiful cathedral city of Ely in Cambridgeshire, King's Ely Junior is an inspiringly innovative and visionary preparatory school, yet one that is built on a fascinating history stretching back over 1,000 years.

A co-educational independent day and boarding school for pupils aged 7-13, King's Ely Junior is full of the same excitement and energy that pervade the whole of King's Ely. We pride ourselves on being a happy yet purposeful community where compassionate teachers teamed with first-rate facilities mean children flourish, both academically and socially.

The curriculum at King's Ely Junior is broad and balanced. We inspire our pupils to push the parameters of their learning.

Children set their sights high and begin to take responsibility for their learning, while building strong partnerships with their teachers to ensure continuing personal success.

Our holistic ethos is reflected in the energy invested in our co-curricular offerings. Music, performing and creative art, sport and outdoor education are each embedded in the culture of King's Ely Junior. Embracing and fueling our pupils' talents and enthusiasms in any realm helps to promote strong self-esteem and a positive attitude towards learning and development.

Our boarders and the Ely Cathedral Boy Choristers live in picturesque, homely accommodation in the college of the

cathedral, led by caring housemasters and housemistresses. King's Ely Junior International provides an exciting opportunity for international pupils to fully integrate into school life while receiving specialist language tuition.

We do not have a template for how a King's Ely Junior pupil should be. We believe in drawing out their inner talents and personalities, allowing every child to succeed and we welcome pupils from all backgrounds. Our close bond with Ely Cathedral supports our pupils and encourages them to grow into reflective and compassionate young people. Along the way they learn and live the values of Energy, Courage and Integrity.

Littlegarth School

LITTLEGARTH
A truly independent school & nursery

(Founded 1940)

Horkesley Park, Nayland, Colchester,
Essex CO6 4JR
Tel: 01206 262332
Fax: 01206 263101
Email: office@littlegarth.essex.sch.uk
Website: www.littlegarth.essex.sch.uk
Headmaster: Mr Peter H Jones

Appointed: September 2003
School type: Coeducational Day
Age range of pupils: 2–11 years
No. of pupils enrolled as at 01/01/2017: 318
Fees per term as at 01/01/2017:
Day: £2,700–£3,140
Average class size: 19 approx

Set in 28 acres of glorious grounds in the beautiful Stour Valley, Littlegarth offers the ideal environment for children between the ages of 2 and 11 to begin their exciting educational journey of discovery. Littlegarth is a co-educational Charitable Trust School which was founded in 1940 in Dedham and moved to Horkesley Park in 1994. Membership of IAPS and ISA helps to ensure that the children are provided with a thorough and successful all-round education in a warm, caring and secure environment.

Littlegarth boasts a flourishing Nursery which prepares the children carefully for admission to the Pre-Prep, although children are able to join the school at any age, subject to availability. A well-qualified team of Early Years staff combined with specialist teaching in French, drama, music and sport from Nursery age helps to ensure that children develop key skills across a range of activities from an early age.

Success breeds confidence and a determination to succeed in those activities that children find more difficult. Our outstanding results at 11+ for entry to local grammar and independent senior schools highlight the pleasing record of success that Littlegarth children have achieved in recent years.

We pride ourselves in providing an excellent all-round education with a particular focus on developing a passion for the core subjects. The staff team work closely to provide an individualised programme of learning for each child and to achieve this goal, our relationships with parents are strong and mutually supportive.

In the Pre-Prep, specialist class teachers and teaching assistants nurture the enthusiasm of each child so that they are confident enough to develop their academic skills. As children move through the school, subject specialist teachers provide inspiration across the curriculum and in 2017, six new classrooms, a large library and IT room and purpose built art, music, drama and learning support facilities will further enhance the outstanding specialist facilities of the school.

An excellent Sports Hall and expansive outdoor sports facilities have helped the school to build an outstanding reputation for sporting success and our four acre woodland incorporating an outdoor stage for performing arts provides the ideal outdoor environment for Forest School and a wide variety of other outdoor learning experiences!

An extensive range of after-school clubs, combined with numerous school trips provide further opportunities to build on the children's love for learning. For further details please visit our website or visit us to see just what makes Littlegarth so special.

St Cedd's School

St Cedd's School

(Founded 1931)

178a New London Road, Chelmsford, Essex CM2 0AR
Tel: 01245 392810
Fax: 01245 392815
Email: hbrierley@stcedds.org.uk
Website: www.stcedds.org.uk
Head: Dr Pamela Edmonds
Appointed: January 2011

School type: Coeducational Day
Age range of pupils: 3–11
No. of pupils enrolled as at 01/01/2017: 400
Boys: 200 **Girls:** 200
Fees per annum as at 01/01/2017:
Day: £8,550–£9,720
Average class size: 24

St Cedd's School is a co-educational 3-11 IAPS Charitable Trust School offering pupils the opportunity to aspire and achieve in a caring environment that nurtures talent and supports individual endeavour. This is a school in which every child matters. We value and celebrate their many diverse talents and qualities and the grounded confidence the pupils develop results in great personal achievement.

Individual pupil progress

Most children exceed the Early Learning Goals by age 5 and the progress of pupils, of all abilities, throughout the school is rapid. Our internal assessment results and 11+ results far exceed national averages and annually we celebrate an unrivalled success rate to selective grammar and independent senior schools with an impressive track record of scholarship awards. This level of achievement is significant given that we are academically non-selective. Assessments on entry are designed to capture the strengths, weaknesses and areas for development of each child so that the education is tailored to their individual needs.

Centre of excellence

The Independent Schools Inspectorate (ISI) put St Cedd's School at the top level in every category of inspection in February 2013 which places the school amongst the very best 3-11 preparatory schools in the country. The accolade confirms what we witness every day; high academic achievement, excellent records of attainment in music, drama and sport, a sense of purpose and ambition that shows itself in the attitude and actions of the pupils and staff, an outstanding pastoral care system and first-rate arrangements for welfare, health and safety.

Broad and balanced curriculum

With over 70 after-school activities to choose from, extra study opportunities are balanced with a firm focus on academic work. This synergy supports the development of confident self-assured pupils ready for the challenges ahead. PE, music, art, French and science are taught by specialists with the teaching of PE, music and French starting in Nursery. Acknowledging the breadth of talents of pupils is an important aspect of life at St Cedd's School. To this end, our baccalaureate-style Year 6 curriculum,

HOLDFAST, leads to awards in recognition of 'Holistic Opportunities to Learn and Develop, Furthering Achievement, Service and Talent'.

As a member of the Choir Schools Association our Choristers sing in the Cathedral Choir.

Nurturing the future

For more than 80 years, boys and girls have been enjoying a quality of education that is among the very best you will find. Give your child the best start in our Nursery where the boys and girls thrive in a colourful and nurturing environment that widens their horizons and instils in them a love of learning. Places may also be available in other year groups.

Breakfast Club operates from 7:30am-8:00am and a wrap-around care programme is open to 6:00pm. Fees include lunch and the majority of after-school clubs.

To attend an open day, request a prospectus, or to arrange an individual tour, please contact Helen Brierley on 01245 392810 or email hbrierley@stcedds. org.uk.

Tring Park School for the Performing Arts

TringPark
School for the Performing Arts

(Founded 1919)

Tring Park, Tring, Hertfordshire HP23 5LX

Tel: 01442 824255

Fax: 01442 891069

Email: info@tringpark.com

Website: www.tringpark.com

Principal:
Mr Stefan Anderson MA, ARCM, ARCT

Appointed: September 2002

School type:
Coeducational Boarding & Day

Religious Denomination:
Non-denominational

Age range of pupils: 8–19

No. of pupils enrolled as at 01/01/2017: 335

Boys: 97 **Girls:** 243 **Sixth Form:** 217

No. of boarders: 205

Fees per annum as at 01/01/2017:

Day: £14,070–£22,410

Full Boarding: £23,715–£33,540

Tring Park School for the Performing Arts is an independent, co-educational boarding and day school for over 330 pupils from ages 8-19. It offers a unique opportunity for gifted young people to specialise in ballet, dance, drama, musical theatre or commercial music, whilst gaining an excellent academic education to GCSE, BTEC and A Level.

The Prep department at Tring Park caters for pupils aged 8 – 11 years and is set within an inspiring, creative environment in a Rothschild mansion steeped in fascinating history. The Prep department offers an enriched, integrated curriculum with a unique balance between academic and vocational studies to suit the 'budding' performer plus:

- a friendly, encouraging environment

enabling pupils to flourish and perform to the best of their ability building confidence to ensure progress in all areas of the curriculum giving your child an opportunity to succeed academically, whilst training in vocational activities during the school day.

- specialist teaching in dance, drama and music
- small classes set in a unique historic building
- personalised learning tailored to meet your child's needs

Pupils at Tring Park perform regularly in the school's Markova Theatre as well as in London and Europe. Performances have included Gershwin's *Crazy for You* and *Jesus Christ Superstar* at London's

Shaw Theatre. The school provides young dancers to perform in the English National Ballet Christmas production of *Nutcracker* at the London Coliseum and dancers are also invited to perform with ENB on its tour of *Le Corsaire*.

Alumni include Daisy Ridley – star of *Star Wars VII*, Lily James – star of *Cinderella*, Drew McOnie – Choreographer in Residence at The Old Vic Theatre and Jessica Brown Findlay – *Downton Abbey* and *The Oresteia* in the West End.

Prep Taster Morning: 2 February 2017

Auditions: contact registrar@tringpark.com or Tel. 01442 824255

Open Days: www.tringpark.com/opendays

www.tringpark.com

Tring Park School is a registered charity no. 1040330

Westbrook Hay Prep School

(Founded 1892)
London Road, Hemel Hempstead,
Hertfordshire HP1 2RF

Tel: 01442 256143
Fax: 01442 232076
Email: admin@westbrookhay.co.uk
Website: www.westbrookhay.co.uk
Headmaster: Keith D Young BEd(Hons)
Appointed: September 1996
School type: Coeducational Day

Age range of pupils: 3–13
No. of pupils enrolled as at 01/09/2016: 300
Boys: 200 **Girls:** 100
Fees per annum as at 01/09/2016:
Day: £9,780–£14,085
Average class size: 18

A thriving independent prep school for boys and girls, from three to 13 years old, Westbrook Hay is located between Hemel Hempstead and Berkhamsted, and set in 26 acres of beautiful parkland overlooking the Bourne Valley. Modern, spacious classrooms are coupled with small class sizes to provide an interactive and thoroughly stimulating learning environment.

These small class sizes, together with visionary teaching, fabulous facilities and a broad curriculum enable our children to gain the all-important confidence to succeed. As every parent will know, school is so much more than simply what is taught in lessons. At Westbrook Hay we aim to provide a learning experience that goes far beyond that of the classroom.

Our new and visiting parents are struck by the wonderful atmosphere at Westbrook Hay. The children are clearly confident, happy and secure in their environment, and view the school as an extended family to support them.

The greater opportunities provided in technology, art, games, music, dance, drama and a whole range of other extracurricular activities help to balance the school's high academic expectations and allow the children further opportunities to express themselves and try new things, learning vital skills along the way.

There is a fabulous purpose-built lower school that offers our youngest children superb space and facilities, giving them the best possible start to their education. We have a state-of-the-art IT suite, with two fully equipped rooms for IT lessons and use across the curriculum. A new Performing Arts Centre with a 300 seat theatre and full music and performance opportunities was opened in 2016.

In the preparation of our children for entry to their chosen senior school, we proudly boast 100% success. Most children go on to local independent schools and are prepared not only for entry but, when appropriate, for scholarship.

The Independent Schools Inspectorate (ISI) carried out a very successful inspection and regarded our school as 'Excellent' and our Early Years Foundation Stage as 'Outstanding', the highest possible recognition from the ISI for both age groups.

The best way to experience Westbrook Hay is by attending one of our Open Mornings or by making an appointment with our Headmaster, Keith Young. Please visit: www.westbrookhay.co.uk or telephone 01442 256143.

Bromley High School GDST
A GDST School

FIDES et OPERA

(Founded 1883)

Blackbrook Lane, Bickley, Bromley, Kent
BR1 2TW

Tel: 020 8781 7000/1
Fax: 020 8781 7002/3
Email: bhs@bro.gdst.net
Website: www.bromleyhigh.gdst.net
Head:
Mrs A M Drew BA(Hons), MBA (Dunelm)
Appointed: September 2014
Head of Junior School:
Mrs Claire Dickerson BA (Hons) (Anglia)

School type: Independent Selective Day School for Girls
Age range of girls: 4–18
No. of pupils enrolled as at 01/01/2017: 912
Sixth Form: 125
Senior School (ages 11-18): 600
Junior School (ages 4-11): 312
Fees per annum as at 01/01/2017:
Day: £12,855–£15,942
Average class size: 20-25

Childhood is a time for curiosity, imagination and friendships. At Bromley High Junior School we provide a secure and happy environment in which we nurture these qualities. We believe in preparing the girls for the challenges beyond school and value the importance of a holistic approach.

The curriculum is designed to encourage independent thought, with opportunities for the girls to take risks to deepen their learning and embrace new experiences. We achieve high standards by providing excellent teaching, with specialist teachers and facilities in many areas including music, sport, science, computing and languages. Physical education is an integral part of school life with many different sports on offer and opportunities to compete at all levels. The learning is enriched with a diverse programme of visits and events and a wide range of extra-curricular activities are on offer.

Creativity plays a key part in each girl's day. Girls may find themselves immersed in a Tudor Court or a Victorian classroom or even joining a Chinese Dance workshop. They may present their ideas on becoming a House Captain or be inspired by Tim Peak and take part in an evening 'star-gazing' event! Our beautiful school grounds provide opportunities for outdoor learning. Forest School enables the girls to encounter the beauty, joy, awe and wonder of the natural environment.

We understand that parents want their daughter to be happy and part of a caring, diverse community within an excellent learning environment. Being an all through school, educating girls from childhood to adulthood brings many benefits. One school means one choice for parents as their daughters reach school age. After that the girls' educational, emotional and social progress is tracked and developed until they leave us for University, having formed long lasting relationships.

At all stages girls are encouraged to set good examples and to behave in a courteous way in order to promote self-respect. They take responsibility for their actions and show a willingness to help, support and guide others in their work within the school.

You would be very welcome to visit the Junior School at any time, and I look forward to meeting you.

Claire Dickerson, Junior Head, Bromley High School

For 4+, 7+, 11+, and 16+ Entry please visit us at our Open Events on Friday 19th May and Saturday 7th October 2017.

Please contact the school via our website: www.bromleyhigh.gdst.net or our admissions office on admissions@bro.gdst.net or Tel 020 8781 7066 to arrange a visit.

Croydon High School GDST

CHS
Croydon High School
ESTD. 1874

(Founded 1874)
Old Farleigh Road, Selsdon, South Croydon, Surrey CR2 8YB

Tel: 020 8260 7500
Fax: 020 8260 7461
Email: admissions@cry.gdst.net
Website: www.croydonhigh.gdst.net
Head of Junior School:
Mrs Sophie Bradshaw
Appointed: January 2015
School type: Girls' Day

Age range of girls: 3–18
No. of pupils enrolled as at 01/01/2017: 580
Sixth Form: 110
Fees per term as at 01/01/2017:
Nursery: £1,557 (Part time)–£3,115 (Full time)
Junior School: £3,917 –£4,073 per term
Senior School: £4,986 –£5,172 per term

If you are looking for the best... aim high ...Aim for Croydon High Junior School

Croydon High School in Selsdon, Surrey is an exceptional independent day school for girls aged 3 to 18. Part of the Girls' Day School Trust, the leading network of independent girls schools in the UK, Croydon High has been delivering outstanding education to local girls since 1874.

The Junior School, on the same spacious 22 acre site as the seniors, shares the excellent sports facilities, with indoor swimming pool, tennis and netball courts and a floodlit all weather artificial hockey pitch. Visitors remark on how happy, confident and well-mannered the girls are and on their sense of purpose and focus on their work.

Girls join Nursery aged 3 for mornings or full days, in recently refurbished classrooms offering a warm and caring environment where learning is both challenging and fun. Moving on to Reception, the acquisition of literacy and numeracy competence is promoted, whilst building confidence and finding out what sparks each girl's imagination.

Light, bright purpose-built classrooms and bespoke Music and Drama suites are well resourced and spacious. In the innovative 4D room, a combination of sound, light, music and touch inspires junior school pupils to produce wonderful written and creative work.

Thanks to a legacy from a former Music teacher, all girls in Year 3 have the opportunity to learn a stringed instrument with free tuition for a year and many continue with this. Many also attend the wide range of extra-curricular clubs. Pastoral care is an absolute priority with the school supporting girls as they develop socially, always encouraging them to 'have a go'. Success and effort are celebrated equally.

Inspirational teaching and a focus on the individual maximises potential and prepares girls academically and emotionally to make a seamless transition to the senior school in Year 7.

For more details or to arrange to visit the school, please contact Clare Macmillan on c.macmillan@cry.gdst.net or 020 8260 7508

www.croydonhigh.gdst.net

Staines Preparatory School

(Founded 1935)

3 Gresham Road, Staines upon Thames, Middlesex TW18 2BT
Tel: 01784 450909
Email: admissions@stainesprep.co.uk
Website: www.stainesprep.co.uk
Head of School: Ms Samantha Sawyer B. Ed (Hons), M.Ed, NPQH
Appointed: September 2014

School type: Coeducational Day
Age range of pupils: 3–11
No. of pupils enrolled as at 01/01/2017: 377
Boys: 200 **Girls:** 177
Fees per annum as at 01/01/2017:
Day: £9,270–£10,680
Average class size: 16 (max 20)

Founded in 1935, Staines Preparatory School has been delivering high quality education to the children of Surrey for over 80 years. We are a happy, welcoming and non-selective school that prides itself on creating a genuine family atmosphere allied to a first rate educational experience.

We have a strong track record of our pupils going on to competitive grammar and independent schools and as you can see if you visit us, all our children are confident, well-adjusted, global citizens. Our educational experience is both challenging and fun, giving our pupils the tools to achieve well above the national average.

This supportive and nurturing environment enables children to fulfil their potential and become confident, independent lifelong learners across all areas of the curriculum. W have a 'Growth Mind-set' culture at Staines Preparatory School. This has had a positive impact on different approaches to learning. There have been various parental workshops and seminars on how parents can support their child's learning across the curriculum, delivered by staff and external speakers. The pupils at Staines Prep learn the value of commitment to successful learning. In addition to this, our pupils develop discipline and a sense of responsibility.

Beyond the original school façade, we have a multi-million pound development consisting of new classrooms, a science lab which many secondary schools would be envious of, a large sports hall and theatre space, which all pupils take advantage of. We are committed to delivering the highest quality educational experience and our independent status allows us to provide a bespoke learning opportunity alongside the National Curriculum.

Our newly constructed Environmental Area 'The Sanctuary', allows the children to bring science to life. They can pond dip, bird watch and even experience a barefoot walk whilst learning to safely explore the great outdoors. We use Forest School principles to teach skills that can be used in the classroom and beyond, encouraging team work, responsibility and communication, as well as building self-esteem and independence. The children are not limited in what they can do but instead are taught how to access and manage the risks in nature.

We provide wraparound care from 7.30am until 6pm and are less than 5 minutes' walk from Staines railway station, making pick-up and drop-off that little bit easier. We understand how hard our parents work, and we aim to support them to provide the best start in life for their children with a Staines Prep education.

To come and experience the school first hand, we can arrange a private tour to fit in around your commitments, or visit us at one of our popular Open Mornings which run throughout the year. Details of these can be found on our website.

Woodford Green Preparatory School

EST 1932

Glengall Road, Woodford Green, Essex
IG8 0BZ
Tel: 020 8504 5045
Email: admissions@wgprep.co.uk
Website: www.wgprep.co.uk
Headmaster: Mr J P Wadge
Appointed: September 2015

School type: Co-educational Day
Age range of pupils: 3–11
No. of pupils enrolled as at 01/01/2017: 381
Fees per term as at 01/01/2017:
Day: £3,140
Average class size: 24
Teacher/pupil ratio: 1:12

Known locally as the "Red School" because of the scarlet uniforms, Woodford Green Preparatory School was founded in 1932 to provide a non-denominational Christian education for boys and girls, a tradition that has been maintained throughout and is now enriched by a vibrant, multi-cultural environment. The school is highly regarded by parents as successful in terms of ensuring children are safe, happy and well prepared for achieving excellent results in 11+ entrance examinations. We aim to provide a learning community that lights the flame within and empowers all children to reach their educational and personal potential.

Our latest independent school inspection report highlights our outstanding work. Our school ensures that "pupils' personal development is excellent" and that "the quality of pupils' achievements and learning is excellent and reflects the school's aims". It was also noted by the inspectors that our children "are confident, self-aware and have high esteem. Pupils have a keen moral sense, awareness of others and accept responsibility willingly".

The friendly, supportive environment, in which excellent work and behaviour fosters interest and independence, encourages all children to do their very best. We have purpose-built areas for science, sport, art, music, computing and French, complemented by specialist teachers. We have excellent teachers and modern facilities throughout the school, including a fabulous library which is regularly used by the whole school to foster a love of reading. In the Early Years, fully qualified staff ensure that children have an outstanding foundation for the rest of the school to build on.

Our links with parents are very good as we strive to give parents excellent opportunities to be involved in school life and their children's progress.

We look forward to welcoming you to our very happy and successful school.

Bassett House School

BASSETT
HOUSE SCHOOL

(Founded 1947)

60 Bassett Road, London, W10 6JP
Tel: 020 8969 0313
Email: info@bassetths.org.uk
Website: www.bassetths.org.uk
Headmistress: Mrs Philippa Cawthorne MA (Soton) PGCE Mont Cert
Appointed: January 2014

School type: Co-educational Day
Age range of pupils: 3–11
No. of pupils enrolled as at 01/01/2017: 190
Fees per annum as at 01/01/2017:
Day: £8,205–£17,100
Average class size: 20
Teacher/pupil ratio: 1:7

At Bassett House, 2017 marks 70 years of educating young children to achieve their very best. The school was founded in 1947 by Sylvia Rentoul, who passionately believed children should be recognised as individuals, and encouraged to express themselves, helping them to grow their achievements and self-confidence.

Focused attention remains our hallmark. We believe tailor-made teaching opens up young minds to endless possibilities, encouraging them to think creatively. Our high staff-to-pupil ratios, specialist teaching staff, excellent equipment, cutting-edge IT, vibrant music and drama and varied extra-curricular activities help develop our children into successful, well-rounded, confident and happy individuals. Residential trips create a sense of adventure and build self-reliance. When they leave aged 11, Bassett House children are ready to thrive at London's best senior schools.

We collaborate closely with our sister schools, Orchard House and Prospect House, sparking off new ideas to promote ever more successful teaching practices. The three schools share a common ethos but each retains its unique personality.

The schools (brought together under the umbrella of House Schools Group) are proudly non-selective. True to our belief, children are not tested and judged at the tender age of 3 or 4 years. Our outstanding results repeatedly show all children can fulfil their potential, regardless of early learning ability. We encourage our high fliers to skyrocket, whilst children who need a little extra help are given the support they need to reach their fullest potential.

All activities take place in a warm and nurturing atmosphere, because we never forget happiness is the key to children giving of their best.

Our last full ISI inspection awarded us 'excellent' and 'outstanding' in all areas and we flew through our 2016 compliance inspection.

This year, as we celebrate our 70th birthday, we look forward to another year of stellar success in education.

Devonshire House Preparatory School

(Founded 1989)
2 Arkwright Road, Hampstead, London, NW3 6AE

Tel: 020 7435 1916
Email: enquiries@
devonshirehouseprepschool.co.uk
Website:
www.devonshirehouseschool.co.uk
Headmistress: Mrs S. Piper BA(Hons)
School type: Preparatory, Pre-preparatory & Nursery Day School

Religious Denomination:
Non-denominational
Age range of boys: 2½–13
Age range of girls: 2½–11
No. of pupils enrolled as at 01/01/2017: 650
Boys: 350 **Girls:** 300
Fees per annum as at 01/01/2017:
Day: £9,405–£17,220

Academic & leisure facilities

The school is situated in fine premises in the heart of Hampstead with its own walled grounds. The aim is to achieve high academic standards whilst developing enthusiasm and initiative throughout a wide range of interests. It is considered essential to encourage pupils to develop their own individual interests and a good sense of personal responsibility.

Curriculum

Early literacy and numeracy are very important and the traditional academic subjects form the core curriculum. The younger children all have a class teacher and classroom assistant and their day consists of a mixture of formal lessons and learning through play. Whilst children of all ages continue to have a form teacher, as they grow older an increasing part of the curriculum is delivered by subject specialists. The combined sciences form an increasingly important part of the timetable as the children mature. The use of computers is introduced from an early stage, both as its own skill and as an integrated part of the pupils' education.

Expression in all forms of communication is encouraged, with classes having lessons in art, music, drama and French. Physical exercise and games also play a key part of the curriculum. Much encouragement is given to pupils to help widen their horizons and broaden their interests. The school fosters a sense of responsibility amongst the pupils, and individuality and personal attention for each pupil is considered essential to make progress in the modern world.

The principal areas of the National Curriculum are covered, though subjects may be taken at a higher level, or at a quicker pace. For the girls approaching the eleven plus senior schools' entry examinations, special emphasis is given to the requirements for these, and in the top two years for the boys, Common Entrance curriculum is taught. The pupils achieve great success in these examinations and a number also sit successfully for senior school scholarships.

The school has its own nursery, The Oak Tree Nursery, which takes children from two-and-a-half years of age.

Entry requirements

The Oak Tree Nursery: For children entering the Oak Tree Nursery, places are offered on the basis on an informal assessment made at the nursery. Children in The Oak Tree Nursery transfer directly to the Junior School.

The Junior School: For children entering the junior school from the ages of three to five, places are offered on the basis of assessment made at the school. From the age of six places are usually subject to a written test taken at school. At eight, children transfer directly into the upper school. Parents and their children are welcome to visit for interview and to see around the school.

The Upper School: Entry to the upper school is principally from the junior school. For pupils seeking to join the school from elsewhere places are normally subject to a written entrance test.

Hawkesdown House School Kensington

Hawkesdown House School
Endeavour • Courage • Truth

27 Edge Street, Kensington, London, W8 7PN

Tel: 020 7727 9090
Email: admin@hawkesdown.co.uk
Website: www.hawkesdown.co.uk
Acting Head: Mrs L Quilter B.Ed
Appointed: April 2016
School type: Boys' Independent Pre-Prep Day

Religious Denomination: Non-denominational
Age range of boys: 3–8
No. of pupils enrolled as at 01/01/2016: 141
Fees per annum as at 01/01/2017:
Day: £15,270–£17,565
Average class size: 18-20
Teacher/pupil ratio: 1:9

Hawkesdown House is an independent Pre-Prep school for boys from the age of four to eight with a Nursery Class for boys of three years old. It is housed in a fine building in Edge Street, off Kensington Church Street, and most families live within walking distance. Founded in 2001, the School's reputation has spread by word of mouth and it is an important part of the community.

The Acting Headmistress, Mrs Lisa Quilter, spent two years teaching Form 3 as Deputy Head before taking over the helm. Working alongside Mr Jeremy Edwards, In School Principal and previously Head of Eaton House the Manor, both are advocates for single sex education and

an environment where 'boys can be boys'.

Mrs Quilter leads a young and enthusiastic staff who all have high expectations of the boys. *"Our main curriculum focus is on literacy and numeracy but our syllabus is wonderfully broad. Music, chess, judo, fencing and Mandarin are just some of the subjects on offer."* The boys are encouraged to leave Hawkesdown House with a 'Joy of Learning', 'All in' attitude, 'Confidence' and 'Kindness', values which are instilled with the help of JACK, the School's teddy bear.

After school clubs, School Council and a House system offer the boys many opportunities to contribute to school life.

The Friday assembly for parents, where the boys' achievements are celebrated, is always packed. *"Hawkesdown House is a big family"* says Mrs Quilter, *"we are immensely proud of our boys and everyone here is valued for their contribution and effort."*

The School is dedicated to providing an outstanding early education for the boys, who are prepared for examinations at eight years old to London's most selective Prep Schools including Westminster Under, St. Paul's Juniors and Sussex House.

Parents who would like further information or to visit the School should contact the School Office for a prospectus or an appointment.

Lyndhurst House Prep School

**LYNDHURST HOUSE
PREPARATORY SCHOOL**

(Founded 1952)

24 Lyndhurst Gardens, Hampstead,
London, NW3 5NW
Tel: 020 7435 4936
Email: office@lyndhursthouse.co.uk
Website: www.lyndhursthouse.co.uk
Headmaster: Andrew Reid MA(Oxon)
Appointed: September 2008

School type: Boys' Day
Age range of boys: 4–13
No. of pupils enrolled as at 01/01/2017: 165
Fees per term as at 01/01/2017:
Day: £5,735–£6,410
Average class size: 18
Teacher/pupil ratio: 1:8

Lyndhurst House Pre-Prep & Prep School for boys was founded by Vernon Davies in 1952, in a tall, handsome Willett-style building in leafy Lyndhurst Gardens, Hampstead.

For over 60 years Lyndhurst has played a full part in the range of local independent educational provision, sending on its 13-year-olds to the many renowned senior schools in London, and some to boarding further afield with an excellent record of academic success and achievement, matched by a strong participation in sports, music and art.

Pupils develop a good knowledge of their own and other cultures and traditions. Visits to theatres, museums and art galleries feature prominently throughout the year. A significant strength of the school is the way pupils from a wide range of cultural backgrounds work and play together harmoniously.

One of the smaller prep schools in the area, Lyndhurst provides a structured but individually responsive education from reception at four-plus up to Common Entrance and scholarship at 13, delivered by an experienced, well-qualified, and stable staff team, and the abiding characteristics of its pupils seem to be a lively enthusiasm and sense of engagement and belonging. Lyndhurst House is a non-denominational school.

North Bridge House Preparatory School Regent's Park

North Bridge House Preparatory School

(Founded 1939)

1 Gloucester Avenue, London, NW1 7AB

Tel: 020 7428 1520

Email:

admissions@northbridgehouse.com

Website:

www.northbridgehouse.com/prep

Head: Brodie Bibby

School type: Co-educational Day

Age range of pupils: 7–13

No. of pupils enrolled as of 01/09/2016: 100

Fees per annum as of 01/09/2016:

Day: £16,290

Located in an impressive former convent on the edge of Regent's Park, North Bridge House Preparatory School provides a high quality, 'all-round' education for girls and boys.

We are continually recognised for our on-going commitment to our pupils. At our last inspection, the school was awarded *"outstanding in all areas"* by the inspectorate, receiving the following comments... *"The school is a close-knit learning community in which pupils are very well behaved, happy and high achieving. From an early age, pupils develop a strong sense of self-esteem"*

We know, support and inspire every pupil to achieve their full potential and provide a solid foundation for a successful academic career and adult life.

Thanks to our nurturing approach and thorough academic preparation, a consistently high number of children are accepted by their first choice Senior School, with many winning much sought-after academic, music, sport, drama and art scholarships. To ensure each individual flourishes and achieves their aspirations, we work closely with the pupil and parents to choose the right school for them. Both boys and girls have the option to move onto our Senior Schools in Hampstead or Islington in year 7, or stay with us until age 13. At the 13+ transition point they can continue their education with us at our Canonbury Sixth Form in Islington or go onto other leading London schools.

At North Bridge House Prep, we teach a rich and varied curriculum, tailor-made to challenge, stimulate and reward every pupil. We also endeavour to go that bit further than the norm and equip our pupils with more than just the basic understanding of a subject. What's more, our inspection report describes our *"quality of teaching as outstanding"* with staff who *"bring a lively enthusiasm*

to their teaching, which encourages and enthuses pupils in their learning."

Sport is essential to our pupils' physical and emotional wellbeing and development – with PE and games sessions held in Regent's Park or the school gym, rock-climbing at a local sports club and winter cricket in our Senior School's state-of-the-art sports hall.

In addition, our extra-curricular offering is rich, diverse and character-building with activities ranging from music, art, drama and sport (also enjoyed as part of the curriculum) – to chess, cookery, design technology, Spanish, ballet and street dance.

Our inspection also lauded the *"outstanding leadership"* of the school and recognised how pupils' behaviour *"is founded on the high levels of mutual trust and respect between pupils and staff"*. We were also praised for the excellent quality of safeguarding and the provision for the welfare, health and safety of pupils.

North Bridge House is very proud to be recognised as one of London's most prestigious Prep Schools and we welcome you and your family to visit us during one of our open days or for a private tour. Find out more at northbridgehouse.com/open.

Orchard House School

ORCHARD
HOUSE SCHOOL

(Founded 1993)
16 Newton Grove, London, W4 1LB
2 Rupert Road, London, W4 1LX

Tel: 020 8742 8544
Email: info@orchardhs.org.uk
Website: www.orchardhs.org.uk
Headmistress:
Mrs Maria Edwards BEd(Beds) PGCE(Man)
Mont Cert
Appointed: September 2015

School type: Co-educational Day
Age range of pupils: 3–11
No. of pupils enrolled as at 01/09/2017: 290
Fees per annum as at 01/09/2017:
Day: £8,205–£17,100
Average class size: 20
Teacher/pupil ratio: 1:7

At Orchard House School, children are loved first and taught second. Our Pupil Pastoral Plan monitors the well-being of each child and was recently shortlisted for a national award. This emphasis on a nurturing environment is not, however, at the cost of academic excellence. In fact, our outstanding results show how creating the right environment enables every child to thrive. We believe learning should be exciting and fun, and the children should positively want to come to Orchard House every day. And they do: we harness the exuberance and energy of every child in our care, and instill within them a lifelong love of learning.

We collaborate closely with our sister schools, Bassett House and Prospect House, sparking off new ideas to promote ever more successful teaching practices. The three schools share a common ethos but each retains its unique personality. The schools (brought together under the umbrella of House Schools Group) are proudly non-selective. True to our belief, children are not tested and judged at the tender age of 3 or 4 years. Our educational success shows all children can fulfil their potential, regardless of early learning ability.

Orchard House's varied and diverse curriculum creates a sense of adventure, developing the children's appetite for risk, which feeds into greater academic and creative achievements. Sport at Orchard House encourages a respectful, competitive attitude, teaching children the value of camaraderie and the buzz of going for gold, or goal. Similarly, music and drama build confidence and self-esteem, as well as many opportunities for every child to perform.

The Independent Schools Inspectorate recently awarded Orchard House the highest accolades of 'excellent' in all areas and 'exceptional' in achievements and learning. These are mirrored in our first-class academic results.

Prospect House School

PROSPECT HOUSE SCHOOL

(Founded 1991)

75 Putney Hill, London, SW15 3NT
76-78 Putney Hill, London, SW15 6RB
Tel: 020 8246 4897
Email: info@prospecths.org.uk
Website: www.prospecths.org.uk
Headmistress: Mrs Dianne Barratt MEd
(Newcastle-upon-Tyne)

School type: Co-educational Day
Age range of pupils: 3–11
No. of pupils enrolled as at 01/01/2017: 300
Fees per annum as at 01/01/2017:
Day: £8,205–£17,100
Average class size: 20
Teacher/pupil ratio: 1:7

At Prospect House School, we focus on making each child feel valued and secure and on making their educational experience both challenging and fun. This allows us to develop every child to their fullest potential, as our outstanding results demonstrate. Our most recent ISI inspection, in 2013, rated us 'excellent' against all the inspectors' criteria.

Prospect House's superb teachers provide a supportive and encouraging academic environment in which children excel. The sound of laughter is never far away, as children discover their aptitude for sport, music, art, computing, drama or a whole host of other opportunities both within the curriculum or before or after school. Residential trips thrill the children with the sense of adventure, encouraging risk-taking and building self-reliance.

We encourage our children to think for themselves, to be confident and to develop a sense of responsibility for the world in which they live. By the time they leave us aged 11, Prospect House children are ready to thrive at London's best senior schools.

We collaborate closely with our sister schools, Bassett House and Orchard House, sparking off new ideas to promote ever more successful teaching practices. The three schools share a common ethos but each retains its unique personality.

The schools (brought together under the umbrella of House Schools Group) are proudly non-selective. True to our belief, children are not tested and judged at the tender age of 3 or 4 years. Our stellar results repeatedly show all children can fulfil their potential, regardless of early learning ability. We encourage our high fliers to soar, whilst children who need a little extra help are given the support they need to reach their fullest potential. At Prospect House, every child is helped to achieve a personal best.

Queen's Gate School

(Founded 1891)

133 Queen's Gate, London, SW7 5LE

Tel: 020 7589 3587

Fax: 020 7584 7691

Email: registrar@queensgate.org.uk

Website: www.queensgate.org.uk

Principal: Mrs R M Kamaryc BA, MSc, PGCE

Appointed: January 2006

School type: Girls' Day

Age range of girls: 4–18

No. of pupils enrolled as at 01/01/2017: 533

Junior School: 159

Senior School: 373

Fees per annum as at 01/01/2017:

Junior School: £16,650

Senior School: £18,900

Average class size: 23

Teacher/pupil ratio: 1:10

Queen's Gate School is an independent day school for girls between the ages of 4 and 18 years. Established in 1891, the school is an Educational Trust situated in five large Victorian Houses within easy walking distance of Kensington Gardens, Hyde Park, and many of the main London museums.

We offer girls a friendly, supportive environment, where individuality is nurtured, academic standards are high and where a broad based curriculum ensures a well-rounded education.

Sport is highly valued at Queen's Gate with two compulsory sessions for all girls each week. We have many sports available at other times during the school day including netball, athletics, basketball, hockey, fencing, swimming, rowing, horse riding, cross-country running, biathlon and dance.

Admission is by test and interview in the Junior School. Girls for 4+ entry are invited for an assessment in early January of the year of entry. Parents will be invited to meet the Director of the Junior School during the preceding half term. Entrance to the Senior School is by the North London Independent Girls' Schools' Consortium entrance examination at 11+, and the school's own entrance examinations to other years in the Senior School. Applicants for the Sixth Form are expected to have passed six GCSEs with grades of A or A* (or equivalent qualifications) in the subjects they wish to pursue to A level.

In addition to the Open Events that take place in the Senior and Junior Schools throughout the year, parents are always welcome to make a private visit to see the schools at work. Appointments can be made by contacting the Registrar on 0207 594 4982 or by email registrar@ queensgate.org.uk.

Read more about Queen's Gate on our website, www.queensgate.org.uk.

St Paul's Cathedral School

ST PAUL'S CATHEDRAL SCHOOL

(Founded 12th Century or earlier)
2 New Change, London, EC4M 9AD
Tel: 020 7248 5156
Fax: 020 7329 6568

Email: admissions@spcs.london.sch.uk
Website: www.spcslondon.com
Headmaster: Mr Simon Larter-Evans BA (Hons), PGCE, FRSA
Appointed: September 2016
School type: Coeducational Pre-Prep, Day Prep & Boarding Choir School
Religious Denomination: Church of England, admits pupils of all faiths

Age range of pupils: 4–13
No. of pupils enrolled as at 01/01/2017: 250
Boys: 145 **Girls:** 105
No. of boarders: 29
Fees per annum as at 01/01/2017:
Day: £13,200–£14,211
Full Boarding: £8,057
Average class size: 15-20
Teacher/pupil ratio: 1:10

Curriculum

A broad curriculum, including the International Primary Curriculum, prepares all pupils for 11+, 13+, scholarship and Common Entrance examinations. There is a strong musical tradition and choristers' Cathedral choral training is outstanding. A wide variety of games and other activities is offered.

Entry requirements

Entry at 4+ and 7+ years: Pre-prep and day pupils interview and short test; Choristers voice trials and tests held throughout the year for boys between 6 -8 years.

St Paul's Cathedral School is a registered charity (No. 312718), which exists to provide education for the choristers of St Paul's Cathedral and for children living in the local area.

St Benedict's School

(Founded 1902)
54 Eaton Rise, Ealing, London, W5 2ES
Tel: 020 8862 2000

Fax: 020 8862 2199
Email: enquiries@stbenedicts.org.uk
Website: www.stbenedicts.org.uk
Headmaster: Mr A Johnson BA
Appointed: September 2016
School type: Coeducational Day
Age range of pupils: 3–18
No. of pupils enrolled as at 01/01/2017: 1113

Boys: 735 **Girls:** 378 **Sixth Form:** 212
Fees per annum as at 01/01/2017:
Day: £12,120–£15,300
Average class size:
Junior School: Max 23
Senior School: Max 24
Sixth Form: Max 14
Teacher/pupil ratio: 1:10

St Benedict's is London's leading independent Catholic co-educational school, in leafy Ealing. Within a caring, happy community, St Benedict's has strong academic standards, with considerable ambition for future academic success. The Junior School and Nursery offers a holistic education for children aged 3 to 11, which continues through the Senior School and Sixth Form. St Benedict's, which welcomes children of other Christian denominations and faiths, is committed to supporting all children to develop their full potential.

Inspirational teaching and exceptional pastoral care are at the heart of the education we offer.

The Junior School and Nursery provide a supportive, friendly and vibrant co-educational environment in which to learn. In the Nursery a carefully planned and child-centred programme enables and extends learning and development. The Junior School provides a broad and balanced curriculum based on a rigorous academic core. Sharing excellent facilities with the Senior School, and participating in a programme of cross-curricular activities, helps ease the transition at 11+ to the Senior School, which is on the same site.

There are extensive opportunities in music, art, sport and drama. St Benedict's has a proud sporting tradition, which promotes the highest sporting aspirations while encouraging everyone to enjoy sport, fitness and teamwork. Music is excellent, with several choirs (including the renowned Ealing Abbey Choir) and many instrumental ensembles. A wide range of co-curricular activities is offered, and an after-school club is available at the Junior School.

There has been huge investment in building and facilities at St Benedict's. Having opened our new Sixth Form Centre and Art Department in 2015, a new Nursery and Pre-Prep Department will open in September 2017, providing our youngest pupils with a first-rate learning environment.

St Benedict's School is unique. Come and visit and see what we have to offer. You can be sure of a warm Benedictine welcome.

The Hampshire School, Chelsea

The Hampshire School
C H E L S E A

(Founded 1928)
15 Manresa Road, Chelsea, London,
SW3 6NB

Tel: 020 7352 7077
Fax: 020 7351 3960
Email:
info@thehampshireschoolchelsea.co.uk
Website:
www.thehampshireschoolchelsea.co.uk
Principal: Mr Donal Brennan
Appointed: January 2014
School type: Co-educational Day

Age range of pupils: 3–13
No. of pupils enrolled as at 01/01/2017: 300
Boys: 180 *Girls:* 120
Fees per annum as at 01/01/2017:
Day: £16,155–£17,100
Average class size:
Early Years: 13
Main School: 20
Teacher/pupil ratio: 1:6.4

Founded in 1928 and located in Chelsea, The Hampshire School provides the top class education one would expect from a traditional English Preparatory School.

It is a day school providing outstanding learning in small classes, led by our highly qualified and dedicated teaching staff. The school offers a stimulating curriculum, ensuring that learning is interactive, fun and that every child is confident and valued.

The Early Years School is situated a mile away from the main school and is housed in a newly renovated classical London townhouse, providing children with the 'home away from home' secure and nurturing environment they need at this young age. The Early Years Foundation Stage curriculum is followed and the school puts emphasis on the children becoming happy, confident and polite learners who are engaged and enthusiastic in their education.

Visits to the Forest School at Holland Park Ecology Centre and exciting, original bespoke programmes occur throughout the year.

The main school's outstanding facilities include a galleried library, gymnasium, science laboratory, art and design studio, fully equipped stage and large outdoor playground.

Children excel academically at The Hampshire School, Chelsea, successfully navigating the 11+ and 13+ to gain entry to their first choice school.

Both schools have invitation only

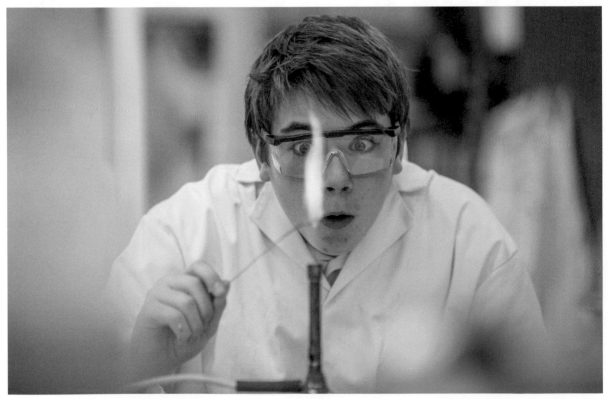

Stonyhurst St Mary's Hall

STONYHURST
ST MARY'S HALL

(Founded 1945)
Stonyhurst, Lancashire BB7 9PU

Tel: 01254 827073
Fax: 01254 827135
Email: admissions@stonyhurst.ac.uk
Website: www.stonyhurst.ac.uk
Headmaster:
Mr Ian Murphy BA (Hons), PGCE Durham
School type:
Coeducational Boarding & Day

Age range of pupils: 3–13
No. of pupils enrolled as at 01/01/2017: 262
Fees per annum as at 01/01/2017:
Day: £8,370–£15,585
Weekly Boarding: £20,325
Full Boarding: £23,985
Average class size: Max 20
Teacher/pupil ratio: 1:8

Stonyhurst St Mary's Hall is the Preparatory School of Stonyhurst College, providing the first steps in a seamless education from age 3 to 18. We are a Roman Catholic school in the Jesuit tradition offering an excellent education for boarders and day pupils alike. The Prep school is housed in its own buildings on the same site as the senior school with which it shares several facilities.

Stonyhurst St Mary's Hall is a place of enthusiastic learning, achievement and energy, with a genuine sense of family. We have a highly personalised approach to the children's learning following the International Primary Curriculum up to the age of 11. At 11+ the Stonyhurst College HODs take responsibility for the academic programme which means that the children benefit from the leadership, development and pastoral support of a Prep School system but with the academic stretch that comes with being taught by secondary subject specialists. Bringing to life their learning in class, teachers and children have access to the artefacts and curator expertise of the oldest museum in the English speaking world, the Stonyhurst Collections. The museum contains over 50,000 objects and books, including a wide and rich collection of Natural History pieces, a first folio by William Shakespeare and a prayer book that was once the property of Mary, Queen of Scots.

The school is proud of its strong sporting tradition with high levels of performance in traditional sports, cross country and swimming. This year Tennis goes under cover with the opening of our new Tennis Dome run to LTA standards. Drama is another area offering creative excellence across the school which engages, stretches and inspires young people. Investment

this year continues in the creation of a performing arts 'Drama and Music Hub'. Other excellent facilities include a new science lab, an art studio, a swimming pool, sports hall and a theatre, in which all children have their drama lessons.

Boarders

We offer an outstanding boarding experience and sense of belonging. Our boarders are cared for by houseparent's, who are supported by an enthusiastic and caring team. At Stonyhurst St Mary Hall, boarders can be as young as eight. Operating very much on a family basis, the children enjoy exciting weekend trips, many clubs and activities and love to play in the school's extensive grounds and beautiful surroundings.

Pre Prep – For children aged 3 to 7

Welcoming children from the age of three, Hodder House is our purpose built, award-winning pre-prep unit at St Mary's Hall. Set in beautiful surroundings and equipped

with exceptional facilities from the latest iPads to a unique woodland classroom, it is the ideal environment for indoor/outdoor play and learning. Children work in small classes under the care and guidance of highly skilled and experienced early years' teachers. In addition to literacy, numeracy, science and ICT, children learn modern languages, enjoy the arts, PE and swimming.

Stonyhurst St Mary's Hall is a very safe, nurturing, vibrant and warm hearted child centered environment within a beautiful and extensive rural location approx. an hour from Manchester, two hours from London by train and 40 minutes from Preston. The school prides itself on being creative and innovative with a genuine ambition for each individual. We successfully blend high performance with opportunity and engagement for the less confident by being challenging yet supporting in equal measures.

Barrow Hills School

Barrow Hills
SCHOOL
(Founded 1950)

Roke Lane, Witley, Godalming, GU8 5NY
Tel: +44 (0)1428 683639
Email: info@barrowhills.org
Website: www.barrowhills.org
Headmaster: Mr Sean Skehan
Appointed: September 2016
Chairman of Governors: Mrs Justine Voisin

School type: Coeducational Day
Age range of pupils: 2–13
No. of pupils enrolled as at 01/01/2017: 230
Fees per annum as at 01/01/2017:
Day: £14,985
Average class size: 15-19
Teacher/pupil ratio: 1:12

Barrow Hills School is committed to delivering an exceptional, all-round independent education with a strong family ethos, focusing on the whole child and the importance of developing strong core values.

Set in 33 acres of Surrey Hills countryside in Witley near Godalming, Surrey, the co-educational preparatory school for children aged two to thirteen prides itself on offering a nurturing progressive environment for children to thrive.

School life centres on a broad curriculum. Alongside academics, music, art and drama also play a major role. An outstanding range of sports aims to encourage every level and ability.

Following the School's official merger with King Edward's Witley in September 2015, Barrow Hills children now have access to facilities beyond the reach of most stand-alone preparatory schools, and parents can see their children benefit the seamless transition from prep school to senior school.

Boys and girls leave Barrow Hills, usually at 13, to join the finest independent schools, including King Edward's Witley. In 2016, the School once again celebrated when Y8 children achieved a 100% pass rate in their Common Entrance exams.

The School comprises a caring Nursery and Pre-Preparatory School providing children with the same special, caring and nurturing environment that is unique to Barrow Hills. This ensures a consistent, stable and secure learning environment as the child progresses through the School.

The School is proud to offer 11+ Scholarships to children for entry into Years 7 and 8 in the following categories: Academic, Art, Drama, Music, Sport and outstanding 'all-round' ability. Up to 30% remission of fees is awarded to exceptional candidates. This initiative enables children to enjoy two outstanding years of focused preparation for the major 13+ public scholarship exams with the added benefit of the established excellence in pastoral care that is the hallmark of a Barrow Hills School education.

For more information please visit: www.barrowhills.org.uk

Kent College Junior School

KENT COLLEGE
CANTERBURY

(Founded 1948)

Harbledown, Canterbury, Kent CT2 9AQ

Tel: 01227 762436

Email: prepenquiries@kentcollege.co.uk

Website: www.kentcollege.com/junior

Headmaster: Mr Andrew Carter

Appointed: 2000

School type:

Coeducational Day & Boarding

Age range of pupils: 3–11

No. of pupils enrolled as at 01/01/2017: 190

Boys: 101 **Girls:** 89

No. of boarders: 9

Fees per annum as at 01/01/2017:

Day: £9,939–£15,390

Full Boarding: £24,375

Teacher/pupil ratio: 1:9

Kent College is a very successful school for boys and girls aged 3-18, which is situated in the south east of England on the outskirts of the beautiful and historic city of Canterbury. Canterbury is less than one hour from the centre of London by train and very close to all of the London airports.

Our Prep School is based on its own site in idyllic countryside, just one mile out of the centre of Canterbury and close to the Senior School. This is a day and boarding school and offers a traditional British education, full of opportunities for children to grow and develop their skills and talents. We have recently introduced a range of innovative one term or one year residential courses to develop talent and excellence in English language, music or sport.

Nestling in an idyllic setting on the outskirts of Canterbury children thrive in this traditional day and boarding school where the emphasis is finding the right pace of education for each child. Boarding starts at the age of 7 with accompanied travel to and from London, on HS1, at weekends an easy option for working parents.

We believe in making the time table appropriate for each individual child. All children in the junior school take part in our Gifted, Really Enthusiastic, Able and Talented Programme which enables the children to increase their performance even further in their chosen area. These lessons are given curriculum time and are delivered by specialist teachers who develop individual programmes for each pupil based on their needs.

The areas of choice are geared towards maximising each child's chances of winning a scholarship to senior school and gaining entry to the school of their choice.

The school boasts a working farm where students can have a real hands on experience with the animals or even learn to ride.

Ludgrove

(Founded 1892)
Wokingham, Berkshire RG40 3AB

Tel: 0118 978 9881
Fax: 0118 979 2973
Email: registrar@ludgroveschool.co.uk
Website: www.ludgrove.net
Head of School: Mr Simon Barber
Appointed: Sept 2008
School type: Boys' Boarding
Religious Denomination: Church of

England
Age range of boys: 8–13
No. of pupils enrolled as at 01/01/2017: 190
Fees per term as at 01/01/2017:
Fees: £8,650 per term
Average class size: 12
Teacher/pupil ratio: 1:8

Ludgrove is a thriving full boarding school for 190 boys age 8 to 13, which sits in 130 acres of spectacular grounds. It is a magical place to spend five years of childhood, where outstanding pastoral care lies at the heart of everything and with fortnightly exeats we have a wonderful balance between school and home life.

We are a strong community where respect and kindness towards others and traditional values are paramount. Our boys relish their independence and enjoy nothing more than an hour or so of free time in which they can make the most of the extensive grounds and facilities; building camps, playing golf, digging in gardens, throwing a pot on the wheel or just kicking a ball with friends.

As a school, we are unashamedly ambitious for every boy and are proud of our strong academic record. We have a non-selective intake in year 4 and in recent years over 70% of boys have gone onto Eton, Harrow and Radley, in addition to other distinguished public schools.

The boys have a wealth of opportunities: a stimulating curriculum, exceptional facilities including a 350 seat theatre and a vibrant extra-curricular programme with exposure to music, drama, sport and art. We aim to develop the boys' confidence in a caring supportive environment, where they are valued as individuals and learn to live as a community. Friendships are made for life and the unique Ludgrove spirit allows boys to thrive in an atmosphere of happiness, good manners and kindness.

Ludgrove is conveniently placed just 50 minutes from central London, with easy access to Heathrow and Gatwick.

Bursaries are available.

Milbourne Lodge School

Arbrook Lane, Esher, Surrey KT10 9EG
Tel: 01372 462737
Email: registrar@milbournelodge.co.uk
Website: www.milbournelodge.co.uk
Head: Mrs Judy Waite
School type: Coeducational Day

Age range of pupils: 4–13
No. of pupils enrolled as at 01/01/2017: 255
Boys: 213 **Girls:** 42
Fees per annum as at 01/01/2017:
Day: £11,325–£14,085

Milbourne Lodge is a Pre-Prep and selective Prep School for boys and girls aged 4 to 13. Founded in 1912, the school has a long-standing tradition of preparing children for Common Entrance and Scholarship exams to the most prestigious and well known public schools including; Tonbridge, Eton, Charterhouse, Epsom College, Wellington, Winchester and Benenden. In the past 5 years alone over 50 academic, art, music and sports scholarships have been won by our pupils.

We strive to set the academic bar high, to value sport and extra-curricular activities, to instil a sense of responsibility and good manners and to develop children that are resilient and confident. Our academic curriculum, taught by a highly experienced and dedicated team of staff, is supported by excellent music, art & sports programmes, with games played every day. A strong emphasis is also placed on pastoral care and the school provides a warm and supportive environment in which each child feels valued and can flourish.

Milbourne Lodge is a very energetic school which provides endless opportunities and variety. Every child is encouraged to build on their own particular talents and to discover new ones. Here at Milbourne we work hard and play hard!

'Our overriding objective is to prepare your child for his or her senior school. We will prepare each child to be ready to relish the experience of their new school, to be confident in their own skin and to be eager to take the next steps', Judy Waite, Head.

Following an extensive building programme, 4 new classrooms and a specialist Science Laboratory have recently been opened and there is now 2 form entry throughout the school. Located in Esher, Surrey, the School is situated in over 8 acres of beautiful grounds within easy access of the A3 and M25. A daily bus runs from SW London.

Notre Dame School

NOTRE DAME SCHOOL

Cobham, Surrey KT11 1HA
Tel: 01932 869990
Email: admissions@notredame.co.uk
Website: www.notredame.co.uk
Head of Seniors: Mrs Anna King MEd, MA (Cantab), PGCE

Head of Prep: Ms Merinda D'Aprano BEd, MA, CTC, FRSA
School type: Girls' Day 2-18, Boys' Day 2-7
Religious Denomination: Roman Catholic
Age range of pupils: 2–18
No. of pupils enrolled as at 01/01/2017: 600

Notre Dame School with its exceptional on-site facilities provides a dynamic environment giving every pupil the opportunity to develop and excel. The talented and dedicated teaching staff ensure the girls achieve outstanding results in all areas of the academic curriculum. Set in 17 acres of Surrey parkland Notre Dame girls enjoy high levels of success in all areas of Sport while the professional, 380-seat professional theatre gives pupils a really unique opportunity to tread the boards from a very young age; in drama, singing, ballet and dance or playing their individual instrument of choice.

Notre Dame's facilities include an outstanding Nursery which welcomes boys and girls from the age of two and follows the Early Years Foundation Stage Guidance. As well as their own classrooms and outdoor play areas they can access the whole school facilities such as the indoor swimming pool, the treehouse, large indoor sports arena, and enjoy specialist teaching for music, ballet, Spanish and swimming. Our curriculum is further enhanced with our Woodland Explorers activities which take place within the 25 acres of secure parkland.

Sessions are flexible to suit the family's needs. Hot lunches and teas are available.

Early Birds opens at 8:15am and Night Owls after school club runs until 5:30pm.

Recent development has included an outstanding new all weather-pitch for hockey, football and athletics as well as six netball/tennis courts. The Early Years

Department has undergone a complete refurbishment, and new land has been acquired for the continuing development of additional sporting facilities. Notre Dame will also be offering places to boys up to age 7 from September 2017.

St Neot's School

ST NEOT'S
PREPARATORY SCHOOL

(Founded 1888)

St Neot's Road, Eversley, Hampshire RG27 0PN

Tel: 0118 9739650
Fax: 0118 9739949
Email: admissions@stneotsprep.co.uk
Website: www.stneotsprep.co.uk
Head of School: Mrs Deborah Henderson
Appointed: September 2015
School type: Co-educational Day

Age range of pupils: Nursery–13 years
No. of pupils enrolled as at 01/01/2017: 319
Fees per annum as at 01/01/2017:
Day: £2,006–£14,994
Average class size: 18
Teacher/pupil ratio: 1:8

St Neot's, founded in 1888, is a happy, vibrant community for boys and girls from Nursery to 13 years and is situated on the Hampshire/Berkshire border in 70 acres of beautiful grounds.

Our pupils develop a love of learning in a supportive and happy environment, where each individual is encouraged to achieve their full academic potential. Children are given the opportunity to embrace challenge, think creatively, develop self-confidence and foster empathy towards others, preparing them both intellectually and emotionally for success in the 21st Century. Forest School and Outdoor Education programmes encourage pupils to develop these attributes, which are so vital in the modern world. The St Neot's journey culminates in the Years 7 and 8 leadership programme, which draws together a mix of skills through the core elements of the Prep Schools Baccalaureate (PSB).

We aim to provide the highest standards in teaching and learning, within a well rounded educational experience, and St Neot's has a very strong record of success in achieving Scholarships and Awards to numerous Senior Schools.

Physical Education is a strength of the school and our sports complex, comprising sports hall, 25m indoor pool, all-weather astro, cricket nets, hard tennis and netball courts, significantly supplements extensive playing fields. After school activities cover a wide range of interests and Holiday Clubs run in all school breaks offering a wealth of opportunities, both sporting and creative.

St Neot's holds a Gold Artsmark award, recognising our achievements in art, music, drama and dance. Plays, concerts and recitals take place throughout the school year for all age groups.

Open Mornings take place termly – details can be found on the school website – www.stneotsprep.co.uk. We would also be delighted to arrange individual tours and meetings with the Head. Please contact Admissions on 0118 9739650 – e mail – admissions@stneotsprep.co.uk.

Exeter Cathedral School

UT VOCE ITA VITA

(Founded 1179)

The Chantry, Palace Gate, Exeter, EX1 1HX

Tel: 01392 255298

Email: admissions@exetercs.org

Website: www.exetercs.org

Headmaster: James Featherstone

Appointed: January 2016

School type:

Co-educational Day & Boarding

Age range of pupils: 3–13

No. of pupils enrolled as at 01/01/2017: 275

Boys: 138 **Girls:** 137

No. of boarders: 23

Fees per annum as at 01/01/2017:

Day: £6,519–£10,872

Full Boarding: £16,683–£17,658

Average class size: 17

Exeter Cathedral School is a leading independent day and boarding Prep School for girls and boys aged 2.5 – 13.

Founded in the 12th century as a choir school, ECS now educates approximately 275 pupils. 36 of these are the boy and girl Choristers of Exeter Cathedral, who continue the centuries-old pattern of leading the daily sung worship in the Cathedral. Nowadays, we offer a fully-rounded Prep School education to pupils from a variety of backgrounds and with a range of talents and interests, whether they be sporting, academic, artistic or musical.

We have an enviable location (right in the heart of the city and yet nestled safely in the lee of the Cathedral); a maximum class size of 18, allowing us to really know each and every pupil as an individual; a proven track record of securing places and scholarships (academic, art, music, performing arts, sport) to a range of leading senior schools; and a firm commitment to being a forward-thinking Prep School with traditional values. We aim to offer an outstanding Prep School experience and are proud of our commitment to educating the 'whole child': we seek to do this by providing a nurturing, purposeful, exciting and gently-Christian environment in which each child is known as an individual, and in which each child is mindful of, and grateful for, those around them, and aware of the part that they and others play in building their community.

Our purpose-built Nursery building was opened in 2015 and is housed in our Pre-Prep Department in the Cathedral Close. Run by our specialist Head of Nursery and a team of Key Workers, the ECS Nursery offers a first-rate Nursery

Education which encourages children to explore, to question, to discover and to build confidence. Children spend 2 years in our Nursery before moving across the playground into our Reception classes.

Our Pre-Prep is housed in a former Canonry in the Cathedral Close, nestled safely between the ancient city wall and the Bishop's Garden. Children transfer across the playground into Reception, before moving up to Year 1 and then Year 2. Our dedicated and highly-qualified staff, led by our Head of Pre-Prep, work with the children (c15 per class) and families to build independence, enquiry, curiosity and a genuine love of learning.

Our Prep School is located right next to the Cathedral: our main site is on Palace Gate and other departments are clustered together in the corner of the Cathedral Green. In the younger years, the core subjects are taught by Form Teachers

and our creative curriculum is delivered by in-house specialists. Our senior pupils receive Common Entrance preparation from experienced subject specialists. At 13, pupils move on to a range of leading Senior Schools, many with scholarships and awards: in 2016, 100% of Year 8 pupils secured a place/scholarship at their first-choice senior school.

We expect high standards from our pupils and our staff, and we share a commitment to rigorous academic endeavour; outstanding pastoral care and individualized attention; an exciting range of extra-curricular opportunities; a world-class musical heritage; and to working with families to help each child flourish and thrive.

Above all, we are a school where people matter, and where staff and families work in partnership to help children acquire the right habits for life.

King Henry VIII Preparatory School

KING
HENRY VIII
PREPARATORY
SCHOOL

CONFIDE RECTE AGENS

(Founded 2008)

Kenilworth Road, Coventry, West

Midlands CV3 6PT

Tel: 024 7627 1307

Fax: 024 7627 1308

Email: admissions@khps.co.uk

Website: www.khps.co.uk

Headteacher: Mrs Gillian Bowser

Appointed: 2015

School type: Coeducational Day

Age range of pupils: 3–11

No. of pupils enrolled as at 01/01/2017:

Boys: 272 **Girls:** 210

Fees per annum as at 01/01/2017:

Day: £8,334–£8,880

Average class size: 22

Teacher/pupil ratio: 1:10

King Henry VIII Preparatory School is a co-educational school serving the needs of children aged from 3 to 11. We work closely with parents ensuring the many and varied gifts of all children are given the opportunity to shine. The positive relationships between talented staff and pupils, alongside the obvious benefits of small class sizes and excellent facilities, help to ensure that each child is known as an individual and can flourish academically, socially and emotionally.

The school motto, Confide Recte Agens – Have the confidence to do what is right, is the driver for the moral compass we aim to develop in our pupils. We promise that the best interests of the child will always be at the heart of our decision making and as such our motto is equally applicable to our staff.

Rooted in a long standing history of excellence, we are able to hold fast to the many positive traditions of the British preparatory education system whilst selecting the most effective contemporary, engaging and innovative teaching methods to ensure our children are fully equipped for the next stage of their educational journey and beyond. The benefits of this approach can be seen throughout the school in the happy faces, friendly voices and enquiring minds of our pupils.

The school is based on 2 campuses Swallows and Hales. Swallows caters for children in Nursery (from the age of 3) up to the end of Year 2. Hales campus was purpose built in 1996. Children in Years 3 to 6 learn happily each day in a mix of general classrooms and specialist facilities.

On his return from the First World War Rev Kenelm Swallow M.C. wanted the school to be 'a place to inspire pupils, a place they would love when they were there and after they had left, and a place they would look upon as their second home.' In this he succeeded.

Moor Park

MOOR PARK
AD DEUM QUI LAETIFICAT JUVENTUTEM MEAM

(Founded 1963)
Ludlow, Shropshire SY8 4DZ

Tel: 01584 872342
Fax: 01584 877311
Email: head@moorpark.org.uk
Website: www.moorpark.org.uk
Headmaster: Mr Charles G O'B Minogue
Appointed: September 2015
School type: Co-educational Day, Full & Flexi Boarding

Age range of pupils: 3–13 years
No. of pupils enrolled as at 01/01/2017: 227
Boys: 120 **Girls:** 106
Fees per annum as at 01/01/2017:
Day: £7,140–£15,930
Full Boarding: £19,560–£23,475
Average class size: 14
Teacher/pupil ratio: 1:8

More than just a school – A community where individuals matter

Moor Park is a co-educational, boarding and day school accepting children from 3 months to 13 years of age.

Children often start in the Tick Tock Nursery, which provides a secure, nurturing and fun environment for our very youngest children. They transfer to the Pre-Prep Nursery and Kindergarten in the term that they turn 3. Children are then carefully prepared to start more formal schooling by a team of well-qualified and caring staff. Our Early Years provision was graded as Outstanding in All Areas by ISI in 2016.

Our children are prepared mentally, emotionally and physically to move on with confidence to the full range of schools nationally. Eton, Harrow, Cheltenham Ladies' College and Radley, as well as the more local schools such as Shrewsbury School and Moreton Hall, are regular destinations and children also develop the independence they will need to succeed in a rapidly changing world whilst making full use of the 85 acres of beautiful grounds. An impressive proportion of our leavers win scholarships in a variety of disciplines. These include academic and extra-curricular awards to some of the top senior schools in the country.

It is also worth saying that Moor Park is a school where children of all abilities thrive and where children are treated as unique individuals. All of this is underpinned by a culture of kindness founded on Catholic principles, which ensures that all children are valued for who they are. Passionate teachers and an average class size of around 14 also make a difference.

Not every child can be good at everything but every child can be good at something and finding something for every child is something that we take seriously. Moor Park's facilities and, more importantly, enthusiastic and dedicated staff ensure that the school is well placed to get the best out of every child.

Moreton First

Moreton First

(Founded 1913)

Weston Rhyn, Oswestry, Shropshire
SY11 3EW

Tel: 01691 776028
Email: moretonfirst@moretonhall.com
Website:
www.moretonhall.org/moreton-first
Head: Mrs Catherine Ford M.A., B.Sc.
School type: Coeducational Day

Age range of pupils: 6 months–11 years
No. of pupils enrolled as at 01/01/2017: 119
Fees per annum as at 01/01/2017:
Day: £9,225–£13,020
Full Boarding: £21,270
Average class size: 13

Set amidst 100 acres of beautiful Shropshire parkland at the foot of the Berwyn Hills, Moreton First is the preparatory school of Moreton Hall. Its location allows easy access from Chester, Wrexham, North Wales and Shrewsbury.

We offer boys and girls a unique start to their education, welcoming babies from six months to First Steps, our purpose built, outstanding nursery. At three years children move to Transition Class, our preschool where Early Years teachers guide the children sensitively in preparation for Reception.

Being a school within a school, we share not only extensive facilities but also a commitment to nurture and celebrate the individual talents of every child from the moment they arrive in our care.

By combining the best of traditional educational methods with exciting initiatives, we have created a distinctive school where pupils are active participants in the adventure of their education. We ensure academic rigour goes hand in hand with encouragement to achieve success in all creative and sporting fields. Furthermore we believe an important goal of preparatory education must be to develop individual character whilst cultivating a community where respect and consideration are paramount.

We place great effort and importance on everything that takes place both inside and outside the classroom by offering a wide range of clubs and extra-curricular activities catering for all interests.

Our successful formula of small class sizes, specialist teachers, a stimulating curriculum and activity options combined with outstanding facilities in a nurturing environment ensures that children are treated as individuals and guided to reach their full potential.

This can only provide a glimpse of the wealth of opportunities that await at Moreton First and so we warmly invite you to visit us.

To arrange a visit, please contact Ruth Brown on admin@moretonhall.com or 01691 776028.

Oswestry School

Oswestry School
Founded 1407

(Founded 1407)
Upper Brook Street, Oswestry, Shropshire
SY11 2TL

Tel: 01691 655711
Fax: 01691 662726
Email: admissions@oswestryschool.org.uk
Website: www.oswestryschool.org.uk
Headmaster: Mr Julian Noad BEng
Appointed: September 2014
School type:
Coeducational Boarding & Day

Age range of pupils: 4–19
Boys: 240 **Girls:** 203 **Sixth Form:** 92
No. of boarders: 134
Day: £8,160–£14,700
Weekly Boarding: £21,390–£25,920
Full Boarding: £24,570–£30,750
Average class size: 18
Teacher/pupil ratio: 1:9

Founded in 1407, Oswestry is one of England's oldest schools and stands on the edge of a safe, typically English old-fashioned market town surrounded by some of the most beautiful countryside in Britain. 'A small, traditional British school… with a personal approach. Family values and a close-knit community breeds confidence and stability for all the pupils… a home away from home.' The Good Schools Guide

We are extremely proud of the excellent academic results; A-levels over recent years have had a 97-100% pass rate and around 90% of GCSE grades were A-C.

Teaching of the highest standard takes places in classrooms benefiting from the latest technology. Our one year IGCSE programme enables students to join the mainstream school for part of the normal timetable, in order to ensure they experience a typical English boarding school environment. Pupils enjoy enormous success with their university applications with most going on to their first choice university. Destinations include Oxford, Cambridge, Durham, Warwick, London School of Economics, University College London, Manchester, Leeds, Bristol and other top universities in the UK and elsewhere.

There are three comfortable boarding houses on the School site, where boarders are cared for by attentive and dedicated house staff; wi-fi throughout the School campus makes it easy for pupils to stay in touch with home. The spacious, modern dining hall provides three hot meals a day; food is served as a buffet selection and there is plenty of choice, to ensure all diets are catered for. In addition to the academic programme, a wide range of weekend activities is arranged for the boarding pupils by members of the teaching staff.

St Winefride's Convent School

(Founded 1868)

Belmont, Shrewsbury, Shropshire SY1 1TE

Tel: 01743 369883
Fax: 01743 369883
Email: st.winefrides@btconnect.com
Website: www.stwinefrides.weebly.com
Headmistress: Sister M Felicity CertEd, BA(Hons)
School type: Coeducational Day

Age range of pupils: 3–11
No. of pupils enrolled as at 01/01/2017: 179
Boys: 89 **Girls:** 90
Fees per annum as at 01/01/2017:
Day: £4,335–£4,380
Average class size: 18-20
Teacher/pupil ratio: 1:8

St. Winefride's School is situated in Belmont close to the Town Centre and was founded by the Sisters of Mercy in 1868.

St Winefride's provides a secure and happy environment in which children thrive and achieve. The day is filled with interesting and motivating activities designed to stimulate and inspire, as well as to instil a love of learning in the child that will last a lifetime.

Teaching is led by a committed and efficient staff team and children are taught to a high standard. Since 2011 St. Winefride's has been placed in Sunday Times 'best schools guide', in the top 100 schools in the UK and this year was

placed 27th. However, the cultural and recreational activities necessary for a child's development are blended into the days' timetable.

The sound of music both vocal and instrumental can be heard daily, dance, ballet, drama, all play an important part in the life of the school. Music lessons are offered in brass, piano, wind, string and percussion. Pupils have achieved grades in music to G5.

The choir and brass ensemble combined to make an excellent CD in December 'Christmas at St. Winefride's'.

Gymnastics is taught to a high level by a highly skilled teacher. The A Team takes

part in competitions and gains top places for both team and individual entries in the ISA National championships.

The school has a multi sports programme which includes football, cricket, hockey, tennis, netball, cross country, athletics, chess and karate. The children play in tournaments and matches with other schools. This year the girls football team will play in the County Finals in May.

Swimming takes place in the Quarry Swimming Pool.

Pupils are prepared to take entrance examinations and scholarships to Independent and grammar schools. The success rate is high.

West House School

(Founded 1895)

24 St James Road, Edgbaston,
Birmingham, West Midlands B15 2NX
Tel: 0121 440 4097
Fax: 0121 440 5839
Email: secretary@westhouseprep.com
Website: www.westhouseprep.com
Headmaster:
Mr Alistair M J Lyttle BA(Hons), PGCE, NPQH

School type: Boys' Day
Age range of boys: 1–11
Age range of girls: 1–4
No. of pupils enrolled as at 01/01/2017: 320
Fees per annum as at 01/01/2017:
Day: £1,466–£3,695
Average class size: 16 (two form entry)
Teacher/pupil ratio: 1:12

Situated in the leafy oasis of the Calthorpe Estate, West House School has occupied the same site since its foundation in 1895. Since that time, the school has evolved significantly to become an independent preparatory school for boys aged 4-11 years, with a co-educational Early Years setting offering care for children aged from 12 months. West House is a member of The Independent Association of Preparatory Schools and, as such, upholds the requirement to provide a 'world class education'.

West House is a non-denominational school, guided by Christian principles. It is divided into three departments – Prep (Years 3-6), Pre-Prep (Years 1 & 2) and the Early Years Foundation Stage (Nursery – Reception).

With five acres of beautiful grounds, less than two miles from Birmingham city centre, the school lies at the heart of a thriving community. It is surrounded by many outstanding cultural and recreational facilities. These enrich the lives of all pupils and complement a broad and balanced curriculum through which boys explore and extend their talents in sport, music and performing arts.

The school continues to boast a unique family atmosphere of which founding Headmaster, Arthur Perrott Cary Field, would have been proud. However, in the spirit of combining the best of its traditions with an education that prepares pupils for life in the middle part of the twenty first century, it remains determined to be at the forefront of innovation.

Employing 45 full-time and part-time academic staff, West House has grown considerably during the last five years to accommodate approximately 310 pupils – 130 of whom attend the EYFS Department.

Pupils are prepared for a wide range of senior schools and standards at 11+ are consistently high, with most Year 6 boys transferring to local grammar schools, King Edward's School, Birmingham and Solihull School.

Further details about the school can be found at www.westhouseprep.com

Pocklington Prep School

POCKLINGTON PREP SCHOOL

Ages 3 to 11

(founded 1514)

West Green, Pocklington, York, North Yorkshire YO42 2NH

Tel: 01759 321228
Email: prep@pocklingtonschool.com
Website: www.pocklingtonschool.com
Headmaster:
Mr I D Wright BSc(Hons), PGCE, NPQH
Appointed: January 2009
School type:
Co-educational Day & Boarding
Age range of pupils: 3–11

No. of pupils enrolled as at 01/01/2017: 225
Boys: 117 **Girls:** 108
No. of boarders: 8
Fees per annum as at 01/01/2017:
Day: £7,275–£11,412
Weekly Boarding: £19,923
Full Boarding: £21,462
Average class size: 16-19
Teacher/pupil ratio: 1:11

Pocklington Prep School – a strong and caring community

Children flourish in the supportive environment of Pocklington Prep School, where an excellent all-round education inspires a lifelong enthusiasm for learning.

Our strong and caring community, for day and boarding pupils aged 3-11, includes a vibrant co-curricular life and sense of involvement in the rounded education we are renowned for. It is underpinned by a deep-rooted belief in and commitment to pastoral care, which allows staff to support children as they grow.

Innovative teaching

Specialist and innovative teachers focus on each individual and stretch and challenge them to ensure they are happy, confident learners who achieve their full potential. Pupils' natural talents and curiosity are encouraged while developing the core skills of reading, writing and numeracy. Our aim is to embed the skill of independent thought so that pupils can draw on a solid foundation of knowledge to form and apply new ideas.

Continually evolving

Pocklington Prep School lies 12 miles east of York, on the edge of Pocklington, and shares a 65-acre campus with Pocklington School, which caters for 11 to 18-year-olds. The school was founded in 1514 and has continually evolved since then to combine the best teaching methods with the latest technologies.

Extensive facilities

The school's superb classroom facilities are complemented by a 300-seat theatre, an indoor sports hall and a swimming pool, plus 21 acres of grass sports pitches and two full-sized synthetic pitches. Numerous co-curricular activities take place every day and each child is encouraged to develop their own interests.

The school has good public transport links and its own minibus pick-up service. Full, flexible and casual boarding options are available. Junior boarders live in modern single-sex houses and enjoy a dedicated programme of weekend and after-school activities, in addition to the normal school calendar.

Inspired for Life

Our aim is that when our pupils move on to their senior schools, they will be confident independent thinkers who are proud of their achievements and 'Inspired for Life'.

The Froebelian School

(Founded 1913)

Clarence Road, Horsforth, Leeds,
West Yorkshire LS18 4LB
Tel: 0113 2583047
Fax: 0113 2580173
Email: office@froebelian.co.uk
Website: www.froebelian.com
Head Teacher:
Mrs Catherine Dodds BEd (Hons), PGCE

Appointed: 2015
School type: Coeducational Day
Age range of pupils: 3–11
No. of pupils enrolled as at 01/01/2017: 181
Boys: 91 **Girls:** 90
Fees per annum as at 01/01/2017:
Day: £4,785–£7,140
Teacher/pupil ratio: 1:10

The Froebelian School is one of the leading independent preparatory schools in Leeds for boys and girls aged 3 to 11 years. Our motto of 'Giving a Flying Start to the Citizens of Tomorrow' sums up our determination to provide the best possible start to lifelong education.

Our pupils reach the highest possible standards in academic work, sport, music, technology, art and drama. We offer an excellent staff: pupil ratio (1:10), modern facilities and the support of highly dedicated, professional teachers.

We aim to provide children with a happy learning environment, one where they are challenged and supported to achieve personal excellence. Each year

approximately 24 children aged 3+ are admitted to the Lower Kindergarten (Nursery) class. Other places for an older child are sometimes available and enquires are always welcome.

Situated in Horsforth, a pleasant suburb of Leeds near to the ring road, the school is easily accessible from most areas of Leeds, Bradford and Harrogate. Our site is very secure with a wooded area offering delightful views over the Aire valley.

In 2015, the Froebelian School opened a new day nursery close to the school in a purposely-renovated building. First Steps at Froebelian, for children aged 3 months to 5 years, shares the Froebelian goals of nurturing children and allowing them to

fulfill their potential and was awarded outstanding in all areas in its first ever Ofsted inspection after only 12 months of opening.

The Froebelian School is the only school in Leeds to appear consistently in The Sunday Times Parent Power 'Top 100' Independent Preparatory Schools ranking number 23 in 2016 placing us top in Leeds and 2nd in Yorkshire. Please explore our website and arrange to visit us soon, you will receive a warm welcome. You will also be able to see at first hand why Froebelian really is the best choice of the private preparatory schools in Leeds.

Gordonstoun

(Founded 1934)
Elgin, Moray IV30 5RF

Tel: 01343 837829
Fax: 01343 837808
Email: admissions@gordonstoun.org.uk
Website: www.gordonstoun.org.uk
Principal: Mr Simon Reid BA
Appointed: April 2011
School type:
Coeducational Boarding & Day

Age range of pupils: 6-13
No. of pupils enrolled as at 01/01/2017: 570
Prep: **No. of boarders:** 35
 Fees per annum as at 01/01/2017:
Day: £13,473
Weekly Boarding: £21,912
Full Boarding: £21,912
Average class size: 12
Teacher/pupil ratio: 1:7

"Gordonstoun Junior School brings out the best in my daughter. Her self-assurance has improved and she is willing to tackle any challenge with enthusiasm." **Mother of Year 7 girl**

"The School really does focus on finding out what your child is both good at and capable of and getting it out of them!" **Father of Year 7 boy**

At Gordonstoun Junior School children can be children, living in a happy and caring environment, fulfilling their academic potential and inspired to pursue new passions. The famous Gordonstoun broader curriculum develops every child through a wide range of experiences beyond the classroom to learn more about themselves, about taking responsibility and about living and contributing to a community.

Academically we follow the English National curriculum and focus on developing the key skills needed as they progress through the school. Class sizes are small, no more than 15, so individual attention can be given to support and stretch every child.

There are few children of this age who can treasure experiences such as sailing on an 80 foot yacht, spending a week camping at the most northerly part of the Scottish Highlands, playing sport at a highly competitive level and at the same time making lifelong friendships.

"I love the school grounds because they are so big and you are free to go where you want. You can play in the woods or on the field, you can have a game of football on the pitches or you can just gossip with your friends in the sun." **Ben, Year 7**

"The School's motto is Plus est en Vous which means there is more in you and I think everyone believes and follows it." **Robbie, Year 6**

Merchiston Castle School

MERCHISTON
JUNIORS | Boys first

(Founded 1833)
294 Colinton Road, Edinburgh, EH13 0PU
Tel: 0131 312 2201

Fax: 0131 441 6060
Email: admissions@merchiston.co.uk
Website: www.merchiston.co.uk
Headmaster: Mr A R Hunter BA
Appointed: September 1998
Deputy Head: Mr Peter Hall MA
School type: Boys' Boarding & Day

Age range of boys: 7–18
No. of pupils enrolled as at 01/01/2017: 460
No. of boarders: 330
Fees per annum as at 01/01/2017:
Day: £14,100–£22,710
Full Boarding: £19,650–£30,660
Teacher/pupil ratio: 1:9

'A balanced curriculum, excellent pastoral care and a high A level pass rate make Merchiston one of the UK's leading independent schools' – www.ukboardingschools.com

Academic record:
Merchiston really does turn the 'C student' into a 'B student' and the 'B student' into an 'A student'. Our 2016 results at every level offer clear evidence of the value-added by the School, for which we are in the top 5 per cent of the UK schools.

Merchiston's exceptional performance at A Level and GCSE over a significant number of years, demonstrates that our boys, as a cohort, are consistently amongst the highest achieving boys in Scotland. Furthermore, nine of our leavers in 2016 are attending top 30 international universities in QS World University Rankings 2016-17, and 50 per cent of students have gained places to Russell Group Universities, such as Bath, Cambridge, Oxford and other top international institutions. A number of students gained admission to USA Ivy League Universities, such as Cornell and Brown.

Merchiston is committed to leading students towards 'personal excellence'. Currently, our extra-mural initiatives include entry for the Mathematics and Physics Challenges and Olympiads, English Speaking Board examinations, foreign language trips, Arkwright Scholarships (Design and Technology), and many others.

Sport for all
Merchiston prides itself on fostering the pursuit of excellence in a sport-for-all environment. In 2015-16, there were 87 different teams, of all abilities, playing competitive fixtures across 16 sports: a total of 590 fixtures. More impressive is that 87% of all pupils, from 7-18, represented the school at some stage in 2015-16. The

School is currently represented nationally and internationally in many sports, such as athletics, cricket, golf, rugby and target shooting. We have also achieved Scottish honours in tennis, rugby and clay pigeon shooting in the last three years. The Tennis Academy is ranked number three in the UK in the LTA Team Tennis Schools rankings, 2016; the Golf Academy is ranked number one Junior Golf School in the ISGA rankings 2015-16.

Co-curricular

The co-curricular programme at Merchiston delivers life skills, such as: leadership, teamwork, and mentoring through the Duke of Edinburgh's Award Scheme, Combined Cadet Force, prefectship, Koinonia and other activities.

Music and Drama are major parts of life at Merchiston. These departments collaborate regularly and pupils of all ages have the chance to be involved, either performing on stage or working behind the scenes. There is an orchestra and other instrumental groups, including pipe bands, and a choir and choral society, as well as opportunities for individual instrumental lessons. Merchiston also benefits from its strong links with local girls' schools for drama and musical performances, other cultural events and social gatherings. Our links ensure that our boys can develop their social skills and relationships soon blossom.

"Science is a great strength."
Tatler Schools Guide, 2015

"I am very happy with my son's Merchiston journey – he has turned into a thoughtful, confident, friendly, ambitious young man, eager to make his way in the world, safe in the knowledge that he has the backing of a group of fellow Merchistonians with whom he has shared his journey. He can stand in any company and speak eloquently with wit and charm and we are extremely proud of him."
Parent

Kilgraston School
Junior Years, Senior, Sixth Form

KILGRASTON
JUNIOR YEARS · SENIOR · SIXTH FORM

(Founded 1930)
Bridge of Earn, Perth, Perth & Kinross
PH2 9BQ

Tel: 01738 812257
Fax: 01738 813410
Email: headspa@kilgraston.com
Website: www.kilgraston.com
Head: Mrs Dorothy MacGinty
Appointed: April 2014
School type: Girls' Day & Boarding
Religious Denomination: Catholic

Age range of girls: 5–18
No. of pupils enrolled as at 01/01/2017: 260
No. of boarders: 86
Fees per term as at 01/01/2017:
Day: £3,385–£5,490
Full Boarding: £7,165–£9,380
Average class size: Av 15
Teacher/pupil ratio: 1:9

Kilgraston Junior Years is the junior school for Kilgraston for girls aged 5 to 12. Kilgraston is a leading boarding and day school for girls in Scotland and the top performing independent school for Advanced Highers 2016 -bestschools. Located in its own building, the Junior Years is surrounded by 54 acres of stunning parkland in Bridge of Earn, three miles from the centre of Perth, 45 minutes from Edinburgh and an hour's drive from Glasgow.

Admission to Kilgraston Junior Years is by interview. Girls are able to progress into Kilgraston Senior School, or prepare for scholarship exams for Kilgraston and Common Entrance exams for other schools. The academic standard is high with all pupils completing the Junior Years and achieving a place in their senior school of choice.

Pupils are taught by class teachers until the age of 9, with specialist teachers for PE, French, music and drama. Form teachers hold pastoral responsibility for the pupils and classes are small with provision for additional support needs. From age 10, the curriculum becomes more specialized with increasing input from specialised subject staff and use of the facilities in the Senior School. Pastoral care is the responsibility of a tutor.

The core academic curriculum is enhanced by a wide range of co-curricular subjects. While academic excellence is a priority, art, drama and music flourish and are an important feature of life at Kilgraston. Classrooms are well equipped and modern IT facilities are spread throughout the school. Opportunities are

provided throughout the year for pupils to perform in groups or as soloists and they compete successfully in local festivals and events. The girls have the opportunity to take LAMDA, Associated Board and Trinity examinations. There is an annual production involving all pupils.

Sports and recreation thrive within the superb Sports Hall, which includes a climbing wall and gym. Pupils benefit from a 25m indoor swimming pool, 9 floodlit all-weather courts, playing fields, astro-turf and athletics track. Kilgraston is the only school in Scotland with an equestrian facility on campus and also hosts the Scottish Schools Equestrian

Championships. The school's main sports are: hockey, netball, tennis, rounders, swimming and athletics, and fixtures are regularly played against other preparatory schools. The school has an excellent skiing record.

Kilgraston Junior Years has a pastoral house system. Inter-House competitions and challenges in games, music and debating provide an opportunity for friendly competition and fun. The family atmosphere in the newly refurbished boarding area, Butterstone, is enhanced by the wide range of weekend activities that make use of the superb local facilities in and around Perthshire.

Directory

Please note the following: The user will find Essex and Hertfordshire in Greater London and East of England; Kent and Surrey in Greater London and South-East. When seeking schools in any of these counties, therefore, the user is advised to check both regional sections.

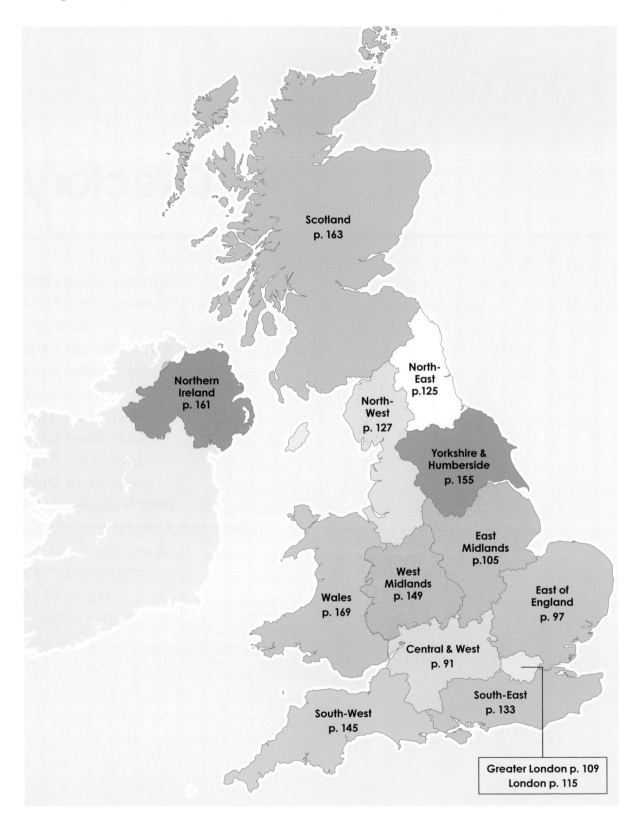

Scotland
p. 163

Northern
Ireland
p. 161

North-
East
p.125

North-
West
p. 127

Yorkshire &
Humberside
p. 155

East
Midlands
p.105

West
Midlands
p. 149

East of
England
p. 97

Wales
p. 169

Central & West
p. 91

South-East
p. 133

South-West
p. 145

Greater London p. 109
London p. 115

Channel Islands

KEY TO SYMBOLS
- Boys' school
- Girls' school
- International school
- Tutorial or sixth form college
- A levels
- Boarding accommodation
- £ Bursaries
- IB International Baccalaureate
- Learning support
- 16+ Entrance at 16+
- Vocational qualifications
- (IAPS) Independent Association of Prep Schools
- (HMC) The Headmasters' & Headmistresses' Conference
- (ISA) Independent Schools Association
- (GSA) Girls' School Association
- (BSA) Boarding Schools' Association
- (S) Society of Heads

Unless otherwise indicated, all schools are coeducational day schools. Single-sex and boarding schools will be indicated by the relevant icon.

Guernsey

The Ladies' College
Les Gravees, St Peter Port,
Guernsey GY1 1RW
Tel: 01481 721602
Principal: Mrs J Riches
Age range: G4–18
No. of pupils: 555 VIth100
Fees: Day £5,385–£5,964
(♣)(A)

Jersey

Beaulieu Convent School
Wellington Road, St
Helier, Jersey JE2 4RJ
Tel: 01534 731280
Headmaster: Mr C Beirne
Age range: G4–18
No. of pupils: 762 VIth127
Fees: Day £4,584
(♣)(A)(£)(✎)

De La Salle College
Wellington Road, St
Saviour, Jersey JE2 7TH
Tel: 01534 754100
Head of College: Mr Jason Turner
Age range: 4–18
No. of pupils: 762
Fees: Day £5,103
(A)

FCJ Primary School
Deloraine Road, St Saviour,
Jersey JE2 7XB
Tel: 01534 723063
Headmistress: Ms Maureen Doyle
Age range: 4–11
No. of pupils: 290
Fees: Day £2,820
(✎)

Helvetia House School
14 Elizabeth Place, St
Helier, Jersey JE2 3PN
Tel: 01534 724928
Headmistress:
Mrs Ann Atkinson BA, DipEd
Age range: G4–11
No. of pupils: 82
Fees: Day £4,200
(♣)

**St George's
Preparatory School**
La Hague Manor, Rue de la
Hague, St Peter, Jersey JE3 7DB
Tel: 01534 481593
Headmaster: Mr Colin Moore
Age range: 2–11
No. of pupils: 210
Fees: Day £4,890–£13,440
(£)(✎)

**St Michael's
Preparatory School**
La Rue de la Houguette, St
Saviour, Jersey JE2 7UG
Tel: 01534 856904
Head of School: Mr Mike Rees
Age range: 3–13
No. of pupils: 315
Fees: Day £9,195–£14,190
(£)(✎)

**Victoria College
Preparatory School**
Pleasant Street, St Helier,
Jersey JE2 4RR
Tel: 01534 723468
Headmaster:
Russell Price BSc, MPhil
Age range: B7–11
No. of pupils: 300
Fees: Day £1,476
(♣)(✎)

Central & West

KEY TO SYMBOLS

(♟) Boys' school
(♀) Girls' school
(🌐) International school
(16·) Tutorial or sixth form college
(A) A levels
(🏫) Boarding accommodation
(£) Bursaries
(IB) International Baccalaureate
(✐) Learning support
(16·) Entrance at 16+
(♣) Vocational qualifications
(IAPS) Independent Association of Prep Schools
(HMC) The Headmasters' & Headmistresses' Conference
(ISA) Independent Schools Association
(GSA) Girls' School Association
(BSA) Boarding Schools' Association
(S) Society of Heads

Unless otherwise indicated, all schools are coeducational day schools. Single-sex and boarding schools will be indicated by the relevant icon.

Bath & North-East Somerset

Downside School
Stratton-on-the-Fosse, Radstock, Bath, Bath & North-East Somerset BA3 4RJ
Tel: 01761 235103
Head Master: Dr J Whitehead
Age range: 11–18
No. of pupils: 350 VIth135
Fees: Day £14,937–£17,196 FB £23,559–£30,687

King Edward's Junior School
North Road, Bath, Bath & North-East Somerset BA2 6JA
Tel: 01225 464218
Head: Mr Greg Taylor
Age range: 7–11
No. of pupils: 182
Fees: Day £10,560

King Edward's Pre-Prep & Nursery School
Weston Lane, Bath, Bath & North-East Somerset BA1 4AQ
Tel: 01225 421681
Head: Ms. Jayne Gilbert
Age range: 3–7
No. of pupils: 107
Fees: Day £7,845–£9,525

Kingswood Preparatory School
College Road, Lansdown, Bath, Bath & North-East Somerset BA1 5SD
Tel: 01225 734460
Headmaster: Mr Marcus E Cornah
Age range: 3–11
No. of pupils: 335
Fees: Day £7,125–£8,250 WB £14,118 FB £16,806–£17,808

MONKTON PREP SCHOOL
For further details see p. 41
Church Road, Combe Down, Bath, Bath & North-East Somerset BA2 7ET
Tel: +44 (0)1225 837912
Email: admissions@monktonprep.org.uk
Website: www.monktonprep.com
Headmaster: Mr M Davis
Age range: 7–13 (boarding from 8)
No. of pupils: 240

The Paragon School
Lyncombe House, Lyncombe Vale, Bath, Bath & North-East Somerset BA2 4LT
Tel: 01225 310837
Headmaster: Mr Titus Mills BA
Age range: 3–11
No. of pupils: 252
Fees: Day £5,835–£6,504

The Royal High School, Bath GDST
Lansdown Road, Bath, Bath & North-East Somerset BA1 5SZ
Tel: +44 (0)1225 313877
Head: Mrs Jo Duncan BA, MA
Age range: G3–18
No. of pupils: 640
Fees: Day £4,212 WB £8,105 FB £8,105

Bristol

Badminton Junior School
Westbury-on-Trym, Bristol BS9 3BA
Tel: 0117 905 5200
Head of the Junior School: Mrs E Davies
Age range: G3–11
No. of pupils: 130
Fees: Day £8,040–£10,830 FB £20,190–£21,240

Bristol Grammar School
University Road, Bristol BS8 1SR
Tel: 0117 973 6006
Headmaster: R I Mackinnon
Age range: 4–18
No. of pupils: 1137 VIth288
Fees: Day £5,700–£10,590

Bristol Steiner School
Redland Hill House, Redland, Bristol BS6 6UX
Tel: 0117 933 9990
Age range: 3–16
No. of pupils: 213
Fees: Day £1,728–£4,800

Carmel Christian School
817A Bath Road, Brislington, Bristol BS4 5NL
Tel: 0117 977 5533
Headteacher: Mr David Owens
Age range: 5–16
No. of pupils: 28
Fees: Day £480–£720

Cleve House School
254 Wells Road, Knowle, Bristol BS4 2PN
Tel: 0117 9777218
Headmaster: Mr. Craig Wardle
Age range: 2–11
No. of pupils: 90
Fees: Day £5,985

CLIFTON COLLEGE PREPARATORY SCHOOL
For further details see p. 38
The Avenue, Clifton, Bristol BS8 3HE
Tel: +44 (0)117 405 8396
Email: prepadmissions@cliftoncollege.com
Website: www.cliftoncollege.com/prep
Head of Preparatory School: Mr John Milne
Age range: 2–13
No. of pupils: 495
Fees: Day £12,465–£16,485 WB £15,465–£19,485 FB £21,420–£27,240

Clifton High School
College Road, Clifton, Bristol BS8 3JD
Tel: 0117 973 0201
Head: Dr Alison M Neill BSc, PhD, PGCE
Age range: 4–18
No. of pupils: 527
Fees: Day £7,605–£10,905 FB £19,605

Colston's School
Stapleton, Bristol BS16 1BJ
Tel: 0117 965 5207
Headmaster: Peter Fraser
Age range: 3–18
No. of pupils: 581 VIth138
Fees: Day £5,160–£7,110 FB £15,045

Fairfield School
Fairfield Way, Backwell, Bristol BS48 3PD
Tel: 01275 462743
Headmistress: Mrs Lesley Barton
Age range: 2–11
No. of pupils: 110
Fees: Day £2,480–£2,730

Gracefield Preparatory School
266 Overndale Road, Fishponds, Bristol BS16 2RG
Tel: 0117 956 7977
Headmistress: Mrs E Morgan
Age range: 4–11
No. of pupils: 90
Fees: Day £2,725

Queen Elizabeth's Hospital
Berkeley Place, Clifton, Bristol BS8 1JX
Tel: 0117 930 3040
Head: Mr Stephen Holliday MA (Cantab)
Age range: B7–18
No. of pupils: 670
Fees: Day £8,793–£13,455

Redland High School for Girls
Redland Court, Redland, Bristol BS6 7EF
Tel: 0117 924 5796
Headmistress: Mrs Caroline Bateson BA(Hons)
Age range: G3–18
No. of pupils: 450 VIth90
Fees: Day £5,760–£9,600

Silverhill School
Swan Lane, Winterbourne, Bristol BS36 1RL
Tel: 01454 772156
Principal: Mr Julian Capper
Age range: 2–11
No. of pupils: 185
Fees: Day £4,800–£6,255

The Downs School
Wraxall, Bristol BS48 1PF
Tel: 01275 852008
Head: M A Gunn MA(Ed), BA, PGCE
Age range: 4–13
No. of pupils: 262

The Red Maids' Junior School
Grange Court Road, Westbury-on-Trym, Bristol BS9 4DP
Tel: 0117 962 9451
Headteacher: Mrs Lisa Brown BSc (Hons)
Age range: B3–7 G3–11

Tockington Manor School
Washingpool Hill Road, Tockington, Bristol BS32 4NY
Tel: 01454 613229
Headmaster: Mr Stephen Symonds
Age range: 2–14
No. of pupils: 250
Fees: Day £7,650–£12,510 FB £17,070

Torwood House School
8, 27-29 Durdham Park, Redland, Bristol BS6 6XE
Tel: 0117 9735620
Headmistress: Mrs D Seagrove
Age range: 0–11
No. of pupils: 70
Fees: Day £1,964–£2,049

Buckinghamshire

Akeley Wood School
Akeley Wood, Buckingham,
Buckinghamshire MK18 5AE
Tel: 01280 814110
Headmaster:
Dr Jerry Grundy BA, PhD
Age range: 12 months–18 years
No. of pupils: 833 VIth119
Fees: Day £7,185–£10,575
(A)(£)⌖

Ashfold School
Dorton House, Dorton, Aylesbury,
Buckinghamshire HP18 9NG
Tel: 01844 238237
Headmaster: Mr M O M Chitty BSc
Age range: 3–13
No. of pupils: 280 VIth28
Fees: Day £7,320–£12,900
WB £15,084
⌖(£)⌖

Broughton Manor Preparatory School
Newport Road, Broughton, Milton
Keynes, Buckinghamshire MK10 9AA
Tel: 01908 665234
Headmaster: Mr Ross Urquhart
Age range: 2 months–11 years
No. of pupils: 250
Fees: Day £9,600
(£)

Chesham Preparatory School
Two Dells Lane, Chesham,
Buckinghamshire HP5 3QF
Tel: 01494 782619
Headmaster:
Mr Michael Davies BA, PGCE
Age range: 3–13
No. of pupils: 392
Fees: Day £8,700–£12,300
⌖

Childfirst Day Nursery Aylesbury
Green End, off Rickford's Hill,
Aylesbury, Buckinghamshire
HP20 2SA
Tel: 01296 392516
Registrar: Mrs Carole Angood
Age range: 2 months–7 years
No. of pupils: 80
Fees: Day £6,276

Childfirst Pre School Aylesbury
35 Rickfords Hill, Aylesbury,
Buckinghamshire HP20 2RT
Tel: 01296 433224

Crown House School
19 London Road, High Wycombe,
Buckinghamshire HP11 1BJ
Tel: 01494 529927
Headmaster: Ben Kenyon
Age range: 4–11
No. of pupils: 120
Fees: Day £5,985–£6,570

Davenies School
Station Road, Beaconsfield,
Buckinghamshire HP9 1AA
Tel: 01494 685400
Headmaster: C Rycroft
Age range: B4–13
No. of pupils: 325
Fees: Day £12,180–£15,540
⌖(£)⌖

Filgrave School
Filgrave Village, Newport
Pagnell, Milton Keynes,
Buckinghamshire MK16 9ET
Tel: 01234 711534
Headteacher:
Mrs H Schofield BA(Hons), MA, PGCE
Age range: 2–7
No. of pupils: 27
Fees: Day £5,160

Gateway School
1 High Street, Great Missenden,
Buckinghamshire HP16 9AA
Tel: 01494 862407
Headteacher:
Mrs Sue LaFarge BA(Hons), PGCE
Age range: 2–11
No. of pupils: 355
Fees: Day £10,002
⌖

Godstowe Preparatory School
Shrubbery Road, High Wycombe,
Buckinghamshire HP13 6PR
Tel: 01494 529273
Headmaster: Mr David Gainer
Age range: B3–7 G3–13
No. of pupils: 409
Fees: Day £8,505–£13,245
WB £19,455 FB £19,455
(£)⌖

Griffin House School
Little Kimble, Aylesbury,
Buckinghamshire HP17 0XP
Tel: 01844 346154
Headmaster: Mr Tim Walford
Age range: 3–11
No. of pupils: 100
Fees: Day £7,395–£7,695
(£)⌖

High March School
23 Ledborough Lane, Beaconsfield,
Buckinghamshire HP9 2PZ
Tel: 01494 675186
Headmistress: Mrs S J Clifford
Age range: G3–11
No. of pupils: 292
Fees: Day £903–£12,510
⌖(£)⌖

Milton Keynes Preparatory School
Tattenhoe Lane, Milton Keynes,
Buckinghamshire MK3 7EG
Tel: 01908 642111
Heads of School: Mr C
Bates & Mr S Driver
Age range: 3 months–11 years
No. of pupils: 500
Fees: Day £12,712–£14,700
(£)

Pipers Corner School
Pipers Lane, Great
Kingshill, High Wycombe,
Buckinghamshire HP15 6LP
Tel: 01494 718 255
Headmistress:
Mrs H J Ness-Gifford BA(Hons), PGCE
Age range: G4–18
No. of pupils: VIth72
Fees: Day £7,230–£14,010
WB £18,750–£222,845 FB
£18,990–£23,085
⌖(A)⌖(£)⌖

St Teresa's Catholic School & Nursery
Aylesbury Road, Princes
Risborough, Buckinghamshire
HP27 0JW
Tel: 01844 345005
Head: Mr Simon Detre
Age range: 3–11
No. of pupils: 132
Fees: Day £5,775–£7,308
⌖

Swanbourne House School
Swanbourne, Milton Keynes,
Buckinghamshire MK17 0HZ
Tel: 01296 720264
Headmaster:
Mr Simon Hitchings MA (Oxon)
Age range: 3–13
No. of pupils: 361
Fees: Day £4,155–£15,780 FB £21,250
⌖(£)⌖

The Beacon School
Chesham Bois, Amersham,
Buckinghamshire HP6 5PF
Tel: 01494 433654
Headmaster:
P Brewster BSc(Hons), PGCE
Age range: B3–13
No. of pupils: 470
Fees: Day £4,695–£13,200
⌖(£)⌖

The Grove Independent School
Redland Drive, Loughton, Milton
Keynes, Buckinghamshire MK5 8HD
Tel: 01908 690590
Principal: Mrs Deborah Berkin
Age range: 3 months–13 years
No. of pupils: 210

The Webber Independent School
Soskin Drive, Stantonbury
Fields, Milton Keynes,
Buckinghamshire MK14 6DP
Tel: 01908 574740
Principal: Mrs Hilary Marsden
Age range: 3–18
No. of pupils: 300 VIth15
Fees: Day £3,894–£10,371
(A)(£)⌖

Thornton College
Thornton, Milton Keynes,
Buckinghamshire MK17 0HJ
Tel: 01280 812610
Headmistress: Miss Agnes T Williams
Age range: B2–4+ G2–16
No. of pupils: 370
Fees: Day £6,300–£10,095 WB
£10,500–£13,305 FB £13,305–£16,545
⌖⌖⌖(£)⌖

Walton Pre-Preparatory School & Nursery
The Old Rectory, Walton
Drive, Milton Keynes,
Buckinghamshire MK7 6BB
Tel: 01908 678403
Headmistress:
Mrs M Ramsbotham CertEd
Age range: 2 months–7 years
No. of pupils: 120
Fees: Day £8,316

Gloucestershire

Airthrie School
29 Christchurch Road, Cheltenham,
Gloucestershire GL50 2NY
Tel: 01242 512837
Principal: Mrs A E Sullivan DipEd,
DipIM, CertCounselling
Age range: 3–11
No. of pupils: 168
Fees: Day £5,280–£7,494
🖉

Beaudesert Park School
Minchinhampton, Stroud,
Gloucestershire GL6 9AF
Tel: 01453 832072
Headmaster:
Mr J P R Womersley BA, PGCE
Age range: 3–13
No. of pupils: 430
Fees: Day £2,710–£5,310 WB £6,900
🏛🖉

Berkhampstead School
Pittville Circus Road, Cheltenham,
Gloucestershire GL52 2QA
Tel: 01242 523263
Head: R P Cross BSc(Hons)
Age range: 3–11
No. of pupils: 215
Fees: Day £2,793–£7,470
£🖉

Bredon School
Pull Court, Bushley, Tewkesbury,
Gloucestershire GL20 6AH
Tel: 01684 293156
Headmaster: Mr David Ward MA
Age range: 3–18
🌐Ⓐ🏛£🖉

Cheltenham College Preparatory School
Thirlestaine Road, Cheltenham,
Gloucestershire GL53 7AB
Tel: 01242 522697
Headmaster:
Mr Jonathan Whybrow
Age range: 3–13
No. of pupils: 420
Fees: Day £2,421–£15,442
FB £5,424–£7,074
🏛£🖉

Dean Close Pre-Preparatory & Preparatory School
Lansdown Road, Cheltenham,
Gloucestershire GL51 6QS
Tel: 01242 512217
Head of School: Paddy Moss
Age range: 2+–13
No. of pupils: 292
Fees: Day £10,485–£15,852
FB £18,405–£23,310
🏛£🖉

Dormer House School
High Street, Moreton-in-Marsh,
Gloucestershire GL56 0AD
Tel: 01608 650758
Headmistress: Mrs Alison Thomas
Age range: 2–11
Fees: Day £7,425
£🖉

Hatherop Castle School
Hatherop, Cirencester,
Gloucestershire GL7 3NB
Tel: 01285 750206
Headmaster: P Easterbrook BEd
Age range: 2–13
No. of pupils: 190
Fees: Day £6,285–£10,455
FB £15,270–£16,110
🏛£🖉

Hopelands Preparatory School
38 Regent Street, Stonehouse,
Gloucestershire GL10 2AD
Tel: 01453 822164
Headmistress: Mrs S Bradburn
Age range: 3–11
No. of pupils: 59
Fees: Day £4,479–£5,322
🖉

Kitebrook House
Little Compton, Moreton-in-Marsh,
Gloucestershire GL56 0RP
Tel: 01608 674350
Headmistress: Mrs Susan McLean
Age range: 3–13
No. of pupils: 134
Fees: Day £8,790–£11,200
WB £14,940
🏛£🖉

Rendcomb College
Rendcomb, Cirencester,
Gloucestershire GL7 7HA
Tel: 01285 831213
Headmaster:
Mr R Jones BA(Hons), MEd
Age range: 3–18
No. of pupils: 371 VIth54
Fees: Day £5,205–£7,150 WB
£7,480–£9,885 FB £7,480–£9,885
🌐Ⓐ🏛£🖉

St Edward's Preparatory School
London Road, Charlton
Kings, Cheltenham,
Gloucestershire GL52 6NR
Tel: 01242 538900
Headmaster: Mr Stephen
McKernan BA(Hons) MEd NPQH
Age range: 1–11
No. of pupils: 295
Fees: Day £7,095–£11,340
🖉

The Acorn School
Church Street, Nailsworth,
Gloucestershire GL6 0BP
Tel: 01453 836508
Headmaster: Mr Graeme
E B Whiting
Age range: 3–19
No. of pupils: VIth30
Fees: Day £3,800–£6,000

The King's School
Gloucester, Gloucestershire
GL1 2BG
Tel: 01452 337337
Headmaster:
Alistair K J Macnaughton
Age range: 3–18
No. of pupils: VIth80
Fees: Day £5,985–£15,960
Ⓐ£🖉

The Richard Pate School
Southern Road, Cheltenham,
Gloucestershire GL53 9RP
Tel: 01242 522086
Headmaster:
Mr Robert MacDonald
Age range: 3–11 years
No. of pupils: 300
Fees: Day £3,000–£9,360
🖉

WESTONBIRT PREP SCHOOL
For further details see p. 43
Westonbirt, Tetbury,
Gloucestershire GL8 8QG
Tel: 01666 881400
Email: admissions@
westonbirt.org
Website: www.westonbirt.org
Headmaster: Mr Sean Price
Age range: 3–11
Fees: Day £2,800–£3,750
£🖉

Wycliffe Preparatory & Senior School
Bath Road, Stonehouse,
Gloucestershire GL10 2JQ
Tel: 01453 822432
Senior School Head: Mrs M
E Burnet Ward MA(Hons)
Age range: 2–18
No. of pupils: VIth178
Fees: Day £5,295–£15,870
FB £13,620–£25,800
🌐Ⓐ🏛£🖉

Wynstones School
Whaddon Green, Gloucester,
Gloucestershire GL4 0UF
Tel: 01452 429220
Chair of the College of Teachers:
Marianna Law-Lindberg
Age range: 3–18
No. of pupils: VIth9
Fees: Day £4,956–£7,236 FB £4,835
🌐Ⓐ🖉

North Somerset

Ashbrooke House School
9 Ellenborough Park North,
Weston-Super-Mare, North
Somerset BS23 1XH
Tel: 01934 629515
Headteacher: Karen Wallington
Age range: 3–11
Fees: Day £4,494–£5,277
£🖉

Sidcot School
Oakridge Lane, Winscombe,
North Somerset BS25 1PD
Tel: 01934 843102
Head: Iain Kilpatrick
Age range: 3–18
No. of pupils: 515 VIth170
Fees: Day £6,150–£14,250
FB £22,050–£27,750
🌐Ⓐ🏛£IB🖉

Oxfordshire

Abingdon Preparatory School
Josca's House, Frilford, Abingdon, Oxfordshire OX13 5NX
Tel: 01865 391570
Headmaster: Mr C Hyde-Dunn
Age range: B4–13
No. of pupils: B250
Fees: Day £10,770–£14,805

Carrdus School
Overthorpe Hall, Banbury, Oxfordshire OX17 2BS
Tel: 01295 263733
Head: Mr Edward Way
Age range: B3–8 G3–11
No. of pupils: 110
Fees: Day £1,278–£10,140

Chandlings
Bagley Wood, Kennington, Oxford, Oxfordshire OX1 5ND
Tel: 01865 730771
Head: Mrs Cath Burton-Green
Age range: 2–11
Fees: Day £9,540–£12,540

Childfirst Day Nursery Banbury
The Old Museum, 8 Horsefair, Banbury, Oxfordshire OX16 0AA
Tel: 01295 273743

Childfirst Day Nursery Bicester
32 Launton Road, Bicester, Oxfordshire OX26 6PY
Tel: 01869 323730
Headmistress: Miss J Fowler BA(Hons), QTS
Age range: 2 months–7 years
Fees: Day £7,500

Christ Church Cathedral School
3 Brewer Street, Oxford, Oxfordshire OX1 1QW
Tel: 01865 242561
Headmaster: Martin Bruce MA, BA, FCollP
Age range: B3–13 G3–4
No. of pupils: 159
Fees: Day £5,409–£12,123 FB £7,560

Cokethorpe School
Witney, Oxfordshire OX29 7PU
Tel: 01993 703921
Headmaster: Mr D Ettinger BA, MA, PGCE
Age range: 4–18
No. of pupils: 666 VIth133
Fees: Day £11,025–£15,974

Cothill House
Abingdon, Oxfordshire OX13 6JL
Tel: 01865 390800
Headmaster: Mr D M Bailey
Age range: B8–13
No. of pupils: 250
Fees: FB £24,300

Cranford House School
Moulsford, Wallingford, Oxfordshire OX10 9HT
Tel: 01491 651218
Head of School: Dr James Raymond
Age range: B3–11 G3–16
No. of pupils: 380
Fees: Day £10,500–£15,450

Dragon School
Bardwell Road, Oxford, Oxfordshire OX2 6SS
Tel: 01865 315400
Head: Mr John R Baugh BEd
Age range: 4–13
No. of pupils: 844
Fees: Day £10,500–£18,690 FB £26,940

Emmanuel Christian School
Sandford Road, Littlemore, Oxford, Oxfordshire OX4 4PU
Tel: 01865 395236
Principal: Mr P Bate
Age range: 3–11
No. of pupils: 73
Fees: Day £5,040

Headington Preparatory School
26 London Road, Oxford, Oxfordshire OX3 7PB
Tel: +44 (0)1865 759400
Head: Mrs Jane Crouch BA (Hons) Keele, MA London
Age range: G3–11
No. of pupils: 250

Magdalen College School
Cowley Place, Oxford, Oxfordshire OX4 1DZ
Tel: 01865 242191
Master: Dr Tim Hands
Age range: B7–18
No. of pupils: 669 VIth161
Fees: Day £8,018–£9,880

Moulsford Preparatory School
Moulsford, Wallingford, Oxfordshire OX10 9HR
Tel: 01491 651438
Headmaster: Mr B Beardmore-Gray
Age range: B4 13
Fees: Day £9,840–£14,700 WB £18,450

New College School
2 Savile Road, Oxford, Oxfordshire OX1 3UA
Tel: 01865 285 560
Headmaster: Mr N R Gullifer MA, FRSA
Age range: B4–13
No. of pupils: 160
Fees: Day £7,413–£11,985

Our Lady's Abingdon School
Radley Road, Abingdon, Oxfordshire OX14 3PS
Tel: 01235 524658
Principal: Mr Stephen Oliver
Age range: 3–18
No. of pupils: VIth81
Fees: Day £8,079–£13,683

Oxford High School GDST
Belbroughton Road, Oxford, Oxfordshire OX2 6XA
Tel: 01865 559888
Head: Mrs Judith Carlisle BA(Hons)
Age range: G4–18
No. of pupils: 900

Oxford Montessori School
Forest Farm, Elsfield, Oxford, Oxfordshire OX3 9UW
Tel: 01865 358210
Principal: Judith Walker Mont Dip, NNEB
Age range: 5–10
No. of pupils: 169

Rupert House School
90 Bell Street, Henley-on-Thames, Oxfordshire RG9 2BN
Tel: 01491 574263
Headmistress: Mrs N J Gan MA(Ed), FRSA
Age range: B4–7 G4–11
No. of pupils: 214
Fees: Day £3,810–£9,150

Rye St Antony
Pullens Lane, Oxford, Oxfordshire OX3 0BY
Tel: 01865 762802
Headmistress: Miss A M Jones BA, PGCE
Age range: B3–11 G3–18
No. of pupils: 400 VIth70
Fees: Day £9,360–£14,175 WB £18,930–£22,275 FB £20,040–£23,400

Sibford School
Sibford Ferris, Banbury, Oxfordshire OX15 5QL
Tel: 01295 781200
Head of School: Toby Spence
No. of pupils: VIth840
Fees: Day £7,758–£12,453 WB £15,555–£22,530 FB £23,718 £24,195

St Helen and St Katharine
Faringdon Road, Abingdon, Oxfordshire OX14 1BE
Tel: 01235 520173
Headmistress: Miss R Edbrooke
Age range: G9–18
No. of pupils: VIth170
Fees: Day £12,420

St Hugh's School
Carswell Manor, Faringdon, Oxfordshire SN7 8PT
Tel: 01367 870700
Headmaster: A J P Nott BA(Hons), PGCE
Age range: 3–13
Fees: Day £10,530–£17,880 WB £20,025–£21,405

St John's Priory School
St John's Road, Banbury, Oxfordshire OX16 5HX
Tel: 01295 259607
Headmaster: Paul Cawley-Wakefield
Age range: 3–11
Fees: Day £3,400–£8,130

St Mary's School
13 St Andrew's Road, Henley-on-Thames, Oxfordshire RG9 1HS
Tel: 01491 573118
Headmaster: Mr Rob Harmer (BA)Hons
Age range: 2–11
No. of pupils: 143
Fees: Day £3,320

Summer Fields
Mayfield Road, Oxford, Oxfordshire OX2 7EN
Tel: 01865 454433
Headmaster: Mr David Faber MA(Oxon)
Age range: B7–13
No. of pupils: 256
Fees: Day £17,700 FB £22,857

The King's School, Witney
New Yatt Road, Witney, Oxfordshire OX29 6TA
Tel: 01993 778463
Principal: Mr Steve Beegoo
Age range: 3–16
No. of pupils: 200
Fees: Day £4,536

The Manor Preparatory School
Faringdon Road, Abingdon, Oxfordshire OX13 6LN
Tel: 01235 858458
Headmaster: Mr Piers Heyworth MA, PGCE
Age range: B2–7 years G2–11 years
No. of pupils: 375
Fees: Day £10,800–£13,155

Windrush Valley School
The Green, London Lane, Ascott-under-Wychwood, Oxfordshire OX7 6AN
Tel: 01993 831793
Headmaster: Mr Alan Wood MEd, TCert, DipSpEd, ACP, FCollP
Age range: 3–11
No. of pupils: 125
Fees: Day £5,970

West Berkshire

Brockhurst & Marlston House Schools
Hermitage, Newbury, West Berkshire RG18 9UL
Tel: 01635 200293
Joint Heads: Mr David Fleming & Mrs Caroline Riley
Age range: G3–13
No. of pupils: 275
Fees: Day £7,410–£12,450 WB £16,530 FB £16,530

Cheam School
Headley, Newbury, West Berkshire RG19 8LD
Tel: +44 (0)1635 268242
Headmaster: Mr Martin Harris
Age range: 3–13
No. of pupils: 407
Fees: Day £3,805–£6,655 FB £8,995

Horris Hill
Newtown, Newbury, West Berkshire RG20 9DJ
Tel: 01635 40594
Headmaster: Mr G F Tollit B.A.(Hons)
Age range: B8–13
No. of pupils: 120
Fees: Day £17,250 FB £23,250

Marlston House Preparatory School
Hermitage, Newbury, West Berkshire RG18 9UL
Tel: 01635 200293
Headmistress: Mrs Caroline Riley MA, BEd
Age range: G3–13
No. of pupils: 110
Fees: Day £7,410–£12,450 WB £16,530

St Gabriel's
Sandleford Priory, Newbury, West Berkshire RG20 9BD
Tel: 01635 555680
Principal:
Alun S Jones LTCL, LWCMD
Age range: B3–7 G3–18
No. of pupils: 462 VIth59
Fees: Day £9,945–£14,205

St Michael's School
Harts Lane, Burghclere, Newbury, West Berkshire RG20 9JW
Tel: 01635 278137
Headmaster:
Rev. Fr. Patrick Summers
Age range: 5–18
No. of pupils: VIth5

The Cedars School
Church Road, Aldermaston, West Berkshire RG7 4LR
Tel: 0118 971 4251
Headteacher: Mrs Jane O'Halloran
Age range: 4–11
No. of pupils: 50
Fees: Day £8,250

Thorngrove School
The Mount, Highclere, Newbury, West Berkshire RG20 9PS
Tel: 01635 253172
Headmaster: Mr Adam King
Age range: 2–13
Fees: Day £11,070–£13,860

Wiltshire

Avondale School
High Street, Bulford, Salisbury, Wiltshire SP4 9DR
Tel: 01980 632387
Headmaster: Mr Stuart Watson
Age range: 3–11
Fees: Day £5,625–£5,685

Chafyn Grove School
33 Bourne Avenue, Salisbury, Wiltshire SP1 1LR
Tel: 01722 333423
Headmaster: Mr Simon Head
Age range: 3–13
No. of pupils: 265

Emmaus School
School Lane, Staverton, Trowbridge, Wiltshire BA14 6NZ
Tel: 01225 782684
Head: Mrs M Wiltshire
Age range: 5–16
No. of pupils: 54
Fees: Day £2,900

Godolphin Preparatory School
Laverstock Road, Salisbury, Wiltshire SP1 2RB
Tel: 01722 430 652
Headmistress:
Mrs P White BEd(Winchester)
Age range: G3–11
No. of pupils: 85
Fees: Day £5,535–£10,692

Heywood Prep
The Priory, Corsham, Wiltshire SN13 0AP
Tel: 01249 713379
Headmaster:
Mr Guy Barrett BSc(Hons)
Age range: 2–11
No. of pupils: 140
Fees: Day £6,450–£7,410

LEEHURST SWAN PREP SCHOOL
For further details see p. 40
Campbell Road, Salisbury, Wiltshire SP1 3BQ
Tel: 01722 333094
Email: registrar@leehurstswan.org.uk
Website: www.leehurstswan.org.uk
Headmaster: Mr Roger Leake BSc (Hons), PGCE, CBiol, MSB
Age range: 6 weeks–16 years
Fees: Day £8,190–£13,770

Maranatha Christian School
Queenlaines Farm, Sevenhampton, Swindon, Wiltshire SN6 7SQ
Tel: 01793 762075
Headteacher: Mr Paul Medlock
Age range: 3–18
No. of pupils: 68
Fees: Day £1,935–£7,470

Meadowpark Nursery & Pre-Preparatory
Calcutt Street, Cricklade, Wiltshire SN6 6BA
Tel: 01793 752600
Headteacher: Mrs R Kular
Age range: 0–11
Fees: Day £4,900

Pinewood School
Bourton, Swindon, Wiltshire SN6 8HZ
Tel: 01793 782205
Headmaster: Mr P J Hoyland
Age range: 3–13
No. of pupils: 313
Fees: Day £6,485–£13,410 WB £13,800–£14,670 FB £14,310–£15,210

Prior Park Preparatory School
Calcutt Street, Cricklade, Wiltshire SN6 6BB
Tel: 01793 750275
Headteacher: M A Pearce
Age range: 3–13
No. of pupils: 240
Fees: Day £10,212–£12,804 FB £15,009–£17,898

Salisbury Cathedral School
The Old Palace, 1 The Close, Salisbury, Wiltshire SP1 2EQ
Tel: 01722 555300
Head Master:
Mr Clive Marriott BEd MA
Age range: 3–13
No. of pupils: 200
Fees: Day £2,385–£4,535 FB £18,270

Sandroyd School
Rushmore, Tollard Royal, Salisbury, Wiltshire SP5 5QD
Tel: 01725 516264
Headmaster: Mr Alastair Speers
Age range: 5–13
No. of pupils: 225
Fees: Day £7,470–£17,505 FB £16,650–£20,940

South Hills School
Home Farm Road, Wilton, Salisbury, Wiltshire SP2 8PJ
Tel: 01722 744971
Principal: Mrs A Proctor
Age range: 3 months–7 Years

St Francis School
Marlborough Road, Pewsey, Wiltshire SN9 5NT
Tel: 01672 563228
Headmaster: Mr David Sibson
Age range: 2–13
Fees: Day £684–£12,216

ST MARGARET'S PREPARATORY SCHOOL
For further details see p. 42
Curzon Street, Calne, Wiltshire SN11 0DF
Tel: 01249 857220
Email: office@stmargaretsprep.org.uk
Website: www.stmargaretsprep.org.uk
Headmistress: Mrs Karen Cordon
Age range: 3–11
No. of pupils: 200
Fees: Day £4,614–£12,600

Stonar School
Cottles Park, Atworth, Melksham, Wiltshire SN12 8NT
Tel: 01225 701740
Head: Mr Toby Nutt
Age range: B2–11 G2–18
No. of pupils: 330 VIth46
Fees: Day £7,665–£14,895 WB £16,350–£19,050 FB £18,060–£26,880

Warminster School
Church Street, Warminster, Wiltshire BA12 8PJ
Tel: +44 (0)1985 210160
Headmaster:
Mr Mark Mortimer MBA BA
Age range: 3–18
No. of pupils: 550
Fees: Day £4,910 FB £10,195

East

Bedfordshire D98
Cambridgeshire D98
Essex D99
Hertfordshire D100
Norfolk D102
Suffolk D103
*See also Greater London (D109)
for schools in Essex and Hertfordshire

KEY TO SYMBOLS

- (†) *Boys' school*
- (♀) *Girls' school*
- (🌐) *International school*
- (16) *Tutorial or sixth form college*
- (A) *A levels*
- (🏛) *Boarding accommodation*
- (£) *Bursaries*
- (IB) *International Baccalaureate*
- (✎) *Learning support*
- (16) *Entrance at 16+*
- (👥) *Vocational qualifications*
- (IAPS) *Independent Association of Prep Schools*
- (HMC) *The Headmasters' & Headmistresses' Conference*
- (ISA) *Independent Schools Association*
- (GSA) *Girls' School Association*
- (BSA) *Boarding Schools' Association*
- (S) *Society of Heads*

*Unless otherwise indicated, all schools are
coeducational day schools. Single-sex and boarding
schools will be indicated by the relevant icon.*

Bedfordshire

Bedford Girls' School
Cardington Road, Bedford,
Bedfordshire MK42 0BX
Tel: 01234 361900
Headmistress:
Miss Jo MacKenzie BSc, MSc
Age range: G7–18
No. of pupils: 1000
Fees: Day £7,602–£10,683
(symbols)

Bedford Modern School
Manton Lane, Bedford,
Bedfordshire MK41 7NT
Tel: 01234 332500
Headmaster:
Mr M Hall BA(Hons) MA
Age range: 7–18
No. of pupils: 1195
Fees: Day £8,000–£11,499
(symbols)

Bedford Preparatory School
De Parys Avenue, Bedford,
Bedfordshire MK40 2TU
Tel: 01234 362271/362274
Headmaster: Mr C Godwin BSc, MA
Age range: B7–13
No. of pupils: 438
Fees: Day £9,312–£12,204 WB
£14,694–£17,586 FB £15,414–£18,306
(symbols)

Luton Pentecostal Church Christian Academy
15 Church Street, Luton,
Bedfordshire LU1 3JE
Tel: 01582 412276
Principal: Pastor Chris Oakey
Age range: 3–13
No. of pupils: 56
Fees: Day £2,640
(symbol)

Orchard School & Nursery
High Gobion Road, Barton-le-Clay,
Bedford, Bedfordshire MK45 4LT
Tel: 01582 882054
Headteacher: Mrs A Burton
Age range: 0–6
No. of pupils: 127

Pilgrims Pre-Preparatory School
Brickhill Drive, Bedford,
Bedfordshire MK41 7QZ
Tel: 01234 369555
Head:
Mrs J Webster BEd(Hons), EYPS
Age range: 3 months–8 years
No. of pupils: 385
Fees: Day £2,795–£7,590

Polam School
43-45 Lansdowne Road, Bedford,
Bedfordshire MK40 2BU
Tel: 01234 261864
Head: Mrs Jessica Harris
Age range: 1–9
No. of pupils: 100
Fees: Day £8,145

Rabia Girls School
12-16 Portland Road, Luton,
Bedfordshire LU4 8AX
Tel: 01582 493239
Headteacher: Mrs F Shaikh
Age range: G4–16
No. of pupils: 265
(symbol)

Rushmoor School
58-60 Shakespeare Road,
Bedford, Bedfordshire MK40 2DL
Tel: 01234 352031
Headteacher: Ian Daniel BA, NPQH
Age range: B3–16 G3–11
Fees: Day £4,890–£8,985
(symbols)

St Andrew's School
78 Kimbolton Road, Bedford,
Bedfordshire MK40 2PA
Tel: 01234 267272
Headmistress:
Mrs J E Marsland BPhil(Ed)
Age range: B3–9 G3–16
No. of pupils: 385
Fees: Day £5,205–£8,505
(symbols)

St George's School
28 Priory Road, Dunstable,
Bedfordshire LU5 4HR
Tel: 01582 661471
Headmistress: Mrs Plater
Age range: 3–11
No. of pupils: 120
Fees: Day £4,020–£4,560
(symbol)

Cambridgeshire

Cambridge International School
Cherry Hinton Hall, Cherry
Hinton Road, Cambridge,
Cambridgeshire CB1 8DW
Tel: +44 (0)1223 416938
Age range: 3–18 years
(symbols)

Cambridge Steiner School
Hinton Road, Fulbourn, Cambridge,
Cambridgeshire CB21 5DZ
Tel: 01223 882727
Age range: 2–11
No. of pupils: 100
Fees: Day £6,300
(symbol)

Kimbolton School
Kimbolton, Huntingdon,
Cambridgeshire PE28 0EA
Tel: 01480 860505
Headmaster: Jonathan Belbin BA
Age range: 4–18
No. of pupils: VIth170
Fees: Day £8,625–£13,425 FB £22,215
(symbols)

King's Acremont, King's Ely Nursery & Pre-Prep
30 Egremont Street, Ely,
Cambridgeshire CB6 1AE
Tel: 01353 660702
Head: Lynda Brereton
Age range: 3–7
Fees: Day £7,563–£8,136
(symbol)

King's College School
West Road, Cambridge,
Cambridgeshire CB3 9DN
Tel: 01223 365814
Headmaster: Mr Nicholas
Robinson BA, PGCE, FRSA
Age range: 4–13
No. of pupils: 418
Fees: Day £10,755–£13,680
WB £21,300
(symbols)

KING'S ELY JUNIOR
For further details see p. 44
Ely, Cambridgeshire CB7 4DB
Tel: 01353 660707
Email: admissions@kingsely.org
Website: www.kingsely.org
Head: Mr Richard Whymark
Age range: 7–13
No. of pupils: 345
Fees: Day £13,180–£14,382
FB £21,013–£22,181
(symbols)

Kirkstone House School
Main Street, Baston, Peterborough,
Cambridgeshire PE6 9PA
Tel: 01778 560350
Head: Mrs C Jones BSocSc
Age range: 5–16
No. of pupils: 234
Fees: Day £5,688–£8,493
(symbols)

Magdalene House Preparatory School
North Brink, Wisbech,
Cambridgeshire PE13 1JX
Tel: 01945 586 780
Head: Mr Chris Moxon BA, PGCE
Age range: 4–11
No. of pupils: 180
Fees: Day £8,200
(symbol)

Phoenix School Cambridge
Willow Tree, Twenty Pence
Road, Wilburton, Ely,
Cambridgeshire CB6 3PX
Tel: 01353 967581
Headteacher: Mrs Gill Cooke
Age range: 3–11
No. of pupils: 11

Sancton Wood School
2 St Paul's Road, Cambridge,
Cambridgeshire CB1 2EZ
Tel: 01223 471703
Head Teacher: Mr Richard Settle
Age range: 3–16
No. of pupils: 193
Fees: Day £3,546–£11,337
(symbols)

St Faith's
Trumpington Road, Cambridge,
Cambridgeshire CB2 8AG
Tel: 01223 352073
Headmaster: Mr N L Helliwell
Age range: 4–13
No. of pupils: 539
Fees: Day £9,735–£12,270
(symbols)

St John's College School
73 Grange Road, Cambridge,
Cambridgeshire CB3 9AB
Tel: 01223 353532
Headmaster: Mr N. Chippington
MA(Cantab), FRCO
Age range: 4–13
No. of pupils: 453
Fees: Day £11,391–£14,313
FB £22,602
(symbols)

St Mary's School
Bateman Street, Cambridge,
Cambridgeshire CB2 1LY
Tel: 01223 353253
Headmistress: Miss Charlotte Avery
Age range: G4–18
No. of pupils: 650 VIth105
Fees: Day £14,457 WB
£26,571 FB £30,867
(symbols)

Stephen Perse Foundation Junior School
St Eligius Street, Cambridge,
Cambridgeshire CB2 1HX
Tel: 01223 346 140
Head: Miss K Milne
Age range: 7–11
No. of pupils: 135
Fees: Day £11,610
(symbol)

Stephen Perse Pre-prep, Madingley
Cambridge Road,
Madingley, Cambridge,
Cambridgeshire CB23 8AH
Tel: 01954 210309
Head of Pre-prep:
Mrs Sarah Holyoake
Age range: 3–7
No. of pupils: 60
Fees: Day £10,200

The Perse Pelican Nursery and Pre-Preparatory School
Northwold House, 92
Glebe Road, Cambridge,
Cambridgeshire CB1 7TD
Tel: 01223 403940
Headmistress:
Mrs S C Waddington MA
Age range: 3–7
No. of pupils: 154
Fees: Day £11,640

The Perse Preparatory School
Trumpington Road, Cambridge,
Cambridgeshire CB2 8EX
Tel: 01223 403920
Head: James Piper
Age range: 7–11
Fees: Day £13,119

The Peterborough School
Thorpe Road, Peterborough,
Cambridgeshire PE3 6AP
Tel: 01733 343357
Headmaster:
Mr A D Meadows BSc(Hons)
Age range: 6 weeks–18 years
No. of pupils: 430
Fees: Day £9,893–£14,121

Whitehall School
117 High Street, Somersham,
Cambridgeshire PE28 3EH
Tel: 01487 840966
Principal: Rebecca Hutley
Age range: 3–11
No. of pupils: 109
Fees: Day £1,510–£1,953

Essex

Alleyn Court Preparatory School
Wakering Road, Southend-on-Sea, Essex SS3 0PW
Tel: 01702 582553
Headmaster:
Mr Gareth Davies BA(Hons), PGCE
Age range: 2–11
Fees: Day £2,607–£10,881

Braeside School for Girls
130 High Road, Buckhurst
Hill, Essex IG9 5SD
Tel: 020 8504 1133
Head Teacher:
Mrs G Haddon BA(Hons), PGCE
Age range: G3–16
No. of pupils: 199
Fees: Day £5,175–£10,875

Brentwood Preparatory School
Middleton Hall Lane,
Brentwood, Essex CM15 8EQ
Tel: 01277 243333
Headmaster: Mr Jason Whiskerd
Age range: 3–11
Fees: Day £5,889–£11,640

Brentwood Pre-Preparatory School
Shenfield Road, Brentwood,
Essex CM15 8BD
Tel: 01277 243239
Headmistress:
Mrs S E Wilson BEd, CertEd
Age range: 3–7
Fees: Day £5,130

Chigwell School
High Road, Chigwell, Essex IG7 6QF
Tel: 020 8501 5700
Headmaster: Mr M E Punt MA, MSc
Age range: 4–18
No. of pupils: 915 VIth185
Fees: Day £10,200–£16,020
FB £26,730–£26,730

Colchester High School
Wellesley Road, Colchester,
Essex CO3 3HD
Tel: 01206 573389
Principal:
David Young BA(Hons), PGCE
Age range: 2–16
No. of pupils: 486
Fees: Day £3,300–£10,000

Coopersale Hall School
Flux's Lane, off Stewards Green
Road, Epping, Essex CM16 7PE
Tel: 01992 577133
Headmistress: Miss Kaye Lovejoy
Age range: 2–11
No. of pupils: 275
Fees: Day £3,645–£7,275

Dame Bradbury's School
Ashdon Road, Saffron
Walden, Essex CB10 2AL
Tel: 01799 522348
Headmistress: Ms Tracy Handford
Age range: 3–11
No. of pupils: 254
Fees: Day £2,000–£10,950

Elm Green Preparatory School
Parsonage Lane, Little Baddow,
Chelmsford, Essex CM3 4SU
Tel: 01245 225230
Principal: Ms Ann Milner
Age range: 4–11
No. of pupils: 220
Fees: Day £7,449

Felsted Preparatory School
Felsted, Great Dunmow,
Essex CM6 3JL
Tel: 01371 822610
Headmistress: Mrs Jenny Burrett
BA(Dunelm), MEd(Cantab), PGCE
Age range: 4–13
No. of pupils: 460
Fees: Day £6,390–£13,965 FB £17,850

Gosfield School
Cut Hedge Park, Halstead Road,
Gosfield, Halstead, Essex CO9 1PF
Tel: 01787 474040
Principal: Dr Sarah Welch
Age range: 4–18
No. of pupils: VIth21
Fees: Day £4,740–£13,695 WB
£15,465–£17,310 FB £17,985–£23,130

Great Warley School
Warley Street, Great Warley,
Brentwood, Essex CM13 3LA
Tel: 01277 233288
Head: Mrs B Harding
Age range: 3–11
Fees: Day £2,250–£3,500

Guru Gobind Singh Khalsa College
Roding Lane, Chigwell, Essex IG7 6BQ
Tel: 020 8559 9160
Principal: Mr Amarjit Singh
Toor BSc(Hons), BSc, BT
Age range: 3–17
Fees: Day £3,900

Heathcote School
Eves Corner, Danbury,
Chelmsford, Essex CM3 4QB
Tel: 01245 223131
Head Teacher: Miss H Petersen
Age range: 2–11
Fees: Day £4,830–£7,245

Herington House School
1 Mount Avenue, Hutton,
Brentwood, Essex CM13 2NS
Tel: 01277 211595
Principal: Mr R Dudley-Cooke
Age range: 3–11
No. of pupils: 129
Fees: Day £4,365–£8,670

Holmwood House Preparatory School
Chitts Hill, Lexden, Colchester,
Essex CO3 9ST
Tel: 01206 574305
Headmaster: Alexander Mitchell
Age range: 4–13
No. of pupils: 302
Fees: Day £7,920–£14,079
WB £18,258

Hutton Manor School
428 Rayleigh Road, Hutton,
Brentwood, Essex CM13 1SD
Tel: 01277 245585
Head: Mr P Pryke
Age range: 3–11
Fees: Day £2,975–£3,995

LITTLEGARTH SCHOOL
For further details see p. 45
Horkesley Park, Nayland,
Colchester, Essex CO6 4JR
Tel: 01206 262332
Email:
office@littlegarth.essex.sch.uk
Website:
www.littlegarth.essex.sch.uk
Headmaster: Mr Peter H Jones
Age range: 2–11 years
No. of pupils: 318
Fees: Day £2,700–£3,140

Loyola Preparatory School
103 Palmerston Road,
Buckhurst Hill, Essex IG9 5NH
Tel: 020 8504 7372
Headmaster: Mr P G M Nicholson
CertEd, BEd(Hons)
Age range: B3–11
No. of pupils: 195
Fees: Day £8,820

Maldon Court Preparatory School
Silver Street, Maldon, Essex CM9 4QE
Tel: 01621 853529
Headteacher: Mrs L Guest
Age range: 3–11
Fees: Day £7,305

New Hall School
The Avenue, Boreham,
Chelmsford, Essex CM3 3HS
Tel: 01245 467588
Principal: Mrs Katherine Jeffrey
MA, BA, PGCE, MA(Ed Mg), NPQH
Age range: Coed 3-11,
Single 11-16, Coed 16–18
No. of pupils: 1175 VIth197
Fees: Day £8,742–£18,042 WB
£17,670–£25,815 FB £19,521–£27,099

Oaklands School
8 Albion Hill, Loughton,
Essex IG10 4RA
Tel: 020 8508 3517
Headmistress: Mrs Cheryl Macnair
Age range: B2–7 G2–11
No. of pupils: 243
Fees: Day £3,795–£7,650

Oxford House School
2-4 Lexden Road, Colchester,
Essex CO3 3NE
Tel: 01206 576686
Acting Head: Mrs Sarah Leyshon
Age range: 2–11
No. of pupils: 158

Saint Pierre School
16 Leigh Road, Leigh-on-Sea,
Southend-on-Sea, Essex SS9 1LE
Tel: 01702 474164
Headmaster: Mr Chris Perkins
Age range: 2–11+
Fees: Day £2,062–£6,186
(£)

St Anne's Preparatory School
New London Road, Chelmsford,
Essex CM2 0AW
Tel: 01245 353488
Head: Mrs S Robson
Age range: 3–11
No. of pupils: 160
Fees: Day £6,300–£6,600

ST CEDD'S SCHOOL
For further details see p. 46
178a New London Road,
Chelmsford, Essex CM2 0AR
Tel: 01245 392810
Email: hbrierley@stcedds.org.uk
Website: www.stcedds.org.uk
Head: Dr Pamela Edmonds
Age range: 3–11
No. of pupils: 400
Fees: Day £8,550–£9,720

St John's School
Stock Road, Billericay,
Essex CM12 0AR
Tel: 01277 623070
Head Teacher:
Mrs F Armour BEd(Hons)
Age range: 3–16
No. of pupils: 392
Fees: Day £4,470–£10,650

St Margaret's Preparatory School
Gosfield Hall Park, Gosfield,
Halstead, Essex CO9 1SE
Tel: 01787 472134
Headmaster: Mr. Callum Douglas
Age range: 2–11
Fees: Day £8,955–£10,755

St Mary's School
Lexden Road, Colchester,
Essex CO3 3RB
Tel: 01206 572544
Admissions: 01206 216420
Principal: Mrs H K Vipond
MEd, BSc(Hons), NPQH
Age range: B3–4 G3–16
No. of pupils: 430
Fees: Day £7,464–£11,340

St Michael's Church Of England Preparatory School
198 Hadleigh Road, Leigh-on-Sea,
Southend-on-Sea, Essex SS9 2LP
Tel: 01702 478719
Head: Steve Tompkins
BSc(Hons), PGCE, MA, NPQH
Age range: 3–11
No. of pupils: 271
Fees: Day £3,510–£6,990

St Nicholas School
Hillingdon House, Hobbs Cross
Road, Harlow, Essex CM17 0NJ
Tel: 01279 429910
Headmaster:
Mr K M Knight BEd, MA, NPQH
Age range: 4–16
No. of pupils: 400
Fees: Day £7,470–£9,660

St Philomena's Catholic School
Hadleigh Road, Frinton-on-
Sea, Essex CO13 9HQ
Tel: 01255 674492
Headmistress:
Mrs B McKeown DipEd
Age range: 3–11
Fees: Day £5,670–£6,750

The Daiglen School
68 Palmerston Road, Buckhurst
Hill, Essex IG9 5LG
Tel: 020 8504 7108
Headteacher: Mrs M Bradfield
Age range: 3–11
No. of pupils: 130
Fees: Day £6,360

Thorpe Hall School
Wakering Road, Southend-
on-Sea, Essex SS1 3RD
Tel: 01702 582340
Headmaster: Mr Andrew Hampton
Age range: 2–16 years
No. of pupils: 359
Fees: Day £7,695–£10,620

Trinity School
Brizes Park, Ongar Road, Kelvedon
Hatch, Brentwood, Essex CM15 0DG
Tel: 01277 374123
Headmaster:
Reverend M S B Reid BD
Age range: 4–18
(A)

Ursuline Preparatory School
Old Great Ropers, Great
Ropers Lane, Warley,
Brentwood, Essex CM13 3HR
Tel: 01277 227152
Headmistress: Mrs
Pauline Wilson MSc
Age range: 3–11
Fees: Day £1,835–£3,425

Walden School
Mount Pleasant Road, Saffron
Walden, Essex CB11 3EB
Tel: 01799 525351
Head: Ms Anna Chaudhri MA
Age range: 3–18
No. of pupils: 390 VIth50
Fees: Day £2,375–£5,305 WB
£6,615–£7,690 FB £7,190–£8,590

Widford Lodge School
Widford Road, Chelmsford,
Essex CM2 9AN
Tel: 01245 352581
Headmaster: Mr Simon Trowell
Age range: 2–11
Fees: Day £5,400–£7,050

Hertfordshire

Abbot's Hill School
Bunkers Lane, Hemel Hempstead,
Hertfordshire HP3 8RP
Tel: 01442 240333
Headmistress:
Mrs E Thomas BA (Hons),
PGCE, NPQH
Age range: B3–5 G3–16
Fees: Day £9,159–£16,332

Aldenham School
Elstree, Hertfordshire WD6 3AJ
Tel: 01923 858122
Headmaster:
Mr James C Fowler MA
Age range: 3–18
No. of pupils: 700
Fees: Day £15,291–£21,414
FB £21,099–£31,384

Aldwickbury School
Wheathampstead Road,
Harpenden, Hertfordshire AL5 1AD
Tel: 01582 713022
Headmaster: Mr V W Hales
Age range: B4–13
No. of pupils: 330
Fees: Day £2,002–£3,012
WB £3,800–£3,884

Beechwood Park School
Markyate, St Albans,
Hertfordshire AL3 8AW
Tel: 01582 840333
Headmaster:
Mr E Balfour BA (Hons), PGCE
Age range: 3–13
Fees: Day £10,155–£15,225
WB £18,843

Berkhamsted School
Overton House, 131 High Street,
Berkhamsted, Hertfordshire HP4 2DJ
Tel: 01442 358001
Principal:
Mr Richard Backhouse MA(Cantab)
Age range: 3–18 years
No. of pupils: 1680 VIth367
Fees: Day £10,065–£19,665
WB £26,330 FB £31,325

Bhaktivedanta Manor School
Hilfield Lane, Aldenham, Watford,
Hertfordshire WD25 8EZ
Tel: 01923 851000 Ext:241
Headteacher: Mrs. Wendy Harrison
Age range: 4–12
No. of pupils: 45
Fees: Day £1,680

Bishop's Stortford College Prep School
Maze Green Road, Bishop's
Stortford, Hertfordshire CM23 2PH
Tel: 01279 838607
Head of Prep School:
Mr Bill Toleman
Age range: 4–13
Fees: Day £8,412–£14,556 WB
£18,975–£20,604 FB £19,182–£21,675

Charlotte House Preparatory School
88 The Drive, Rickmansworth,
Hertfordshire WD3 4DU
Tel: 01923 772101
Head: Miss P Woodcock
Age range: G3–11
No. of pupils: 140
Fees: Day £6,900–£11,100

Duncombe School
4 Warren Park Road, Bengeo,
Hertford, Hertfordshire SG14 3JA
Tel: 01992 414100
Headmaster:
Mr Jeremy Phelan M.A. (Ed)
Age range: 2–11
No. of pupils: 325
Fees: Day £9,075–£12,585
£ ✎

Edge Grove School
Aldenham Village,
Hertfordshire WD25 8NL
Tel: 01923 855724
Headmaster: Mr Ben Evans
Age range: 3–13
Fees: Day £11,100–£114,835 WB
£15,870–£19,305 FB £15,870–£19,305
🏃 £ ✎

Egerton Rothesay School
Durrants Lane, Berkhamsted,
Hertfordshire HP4 3UJ
Tel: 01442 865275
Headteacher: Mr Colin Parker
BSc(Hons), Dip.Ed (Oxon),
PGCE, C.Math MIMA
Age range: 6–19
No. of pupils: 143
Fees: Day £14,310–£20,370
✎

Haberdashers' Aske's School
Butterfly Lane, Elstree,
Borehamwood,
Hertfordshire WD6 3AF
Tel: 020 8266 1700
Headmaster: Mr P B Hamilton MA
Age range: B5–18
No. of pupils: 1402 VIth310
Fees: Day £10,641–£14,103
🏃 A £

Haberdashers' Aske's School for Girls
Aldenham Road,
Elstree, Borehamwood,
Hertfordshire WD6 3BT
Tel: 020 8266 2300
Headmistress:
Miss Biddie A O'Connor MA (Oxon)
Age range: G4–18
No. of pupils: 1190
Fees: Day £14,199–£16,446
🏃 A £

Haresfoot School
Chesham Road, Berkhamsted,
Hertfordshire HP4 2SZ
Tel: 01442 872742
Principal:
Mrs Carole Hawkins BA, PGCE
Age range: 0–11
Fees: Day £1,845–£7,770
✎

Heath Mount School
Woodhall Park, Watton-at-Stone,
Hertford, Hertfordshire SG14 3NG
Tel: 01920 830230
Headmaster:
Mr R Middleton MSc, BEd(Hons)
Age range: 3–13
Fees: Day £2,715–£9,315
WB £12,630–£12,960
🏛 £ ✎

High Elms Manor School
High Elms Lane, Watford,
Hertfordshire WD25 0JX
Tel: 01923 681 103
Headmistress: Mrs Sheila O'Neill
MontDipDist, TCert, BA, AMI Dip
Age range: 2–11
No. of pupils: 100
Fees: Day £4,950–£11,400
£ ✎

Howe Green House School
Great Hallingbury, Bishop's
Stortford, Hertfordshire CM22 7UF
Tel: 01279 657706
Head of School: Mrs Deborah Mills
Age range: 2–11
Fees: Day £5,946–£9,444
£

Kingshott
St Ippolyts, Hitchin,
Hertfordshire SG4 7JX
Tel: 01462 432009
Headmaster: Mr Iain Gilmour
Age range: 3–13
No. of pupils: 372
Fees: Day £4,770–£10,350
£ ✎

Little Acorns Montessori School
Lincolnsfield Centre,
Bushey Hall Drive, Bushey,
Hertfordshire WD23 2ER
Tel: 01923 230705
Head of School:
Lola Davies BPA, AMIDip
Age range: 2–6
No. of pupils: 28
Fees: Day £2,120
✎

Lochinver House School
Heath Road, Little Heath, Potters
Bar, Hertfordshire EN6 1LW
Tel: 01707 653064
Headmaster:
Ben Walker BA(Hons), PGCE, CELTA
Age range: B4–13
No. of pupils: 349
Fees: Day £9,000–£11,826
🏃 £ ✎

Lockers Park
Lockers Park Lane, Hemel
Hempstead, Hertfordshire HP1 1TL
Tel: 01442 251712
Headmaster: Mr C R Wilson
Age range: B4–13 G4–7
No. of pupils: 150
🏃 🏛 £ ✎

Longwood School
Bushey Hall Drive, Bushey,
Hertfordshire WD23 2QG
Tel: 01923 253715
Head Teacher: Mrs Muriel Garman
Age range: 3–11
Fees: Day £4,590–£5,790
✎

Manor Lodge School
Rectory Lane, Ridge Hill, Shenley,
Hertfordshire WD7 9BG
Tel: 01707 642424
Headmaster: Mr G Dunn CertEd
Age range: 3–11
No. of pupils: 430
Fees: Day £10,275–£11,535
£

Merchant Taylors' Prep
Moor Farm, Sandy Lodge
Road, Rickmansworth,
Hertfordshire WD3 1LW
Tel: 01923 825648
Headmaster: Dr T D Lee BEd(Hons)
Age range: B4–13
No. of pupils: 300
Fees: Day £2,613–£9,414
🏃 £

Radlett Preparatory School
Kendal Hall, Watling Street,
Radlett, Hertfordshire WD7 7LY
Tel: 01923 856812
Principal: Mr G White BEd (Hons)
Age range: 4–11
Fees: Day £7,140–£7,250
✎

Rudolf Steiner School
Langley Hill, Kings Langley,
Hertfordshire WD4 9HG
Tel: 01923 262505
Age range: 3–19
No. of pupils: 405
Fees: Day £2,985–£7,800
A £ ✎

Sherrardswood School
Lockleys, Welwyn,
Hertfordshire AL6 0BJ
Tel: 01438 714282
Headmistress: Mrs L Corry
Age range: 2–18
No. of pupils: 357
Fees: Day £6,720–£12,750
A £ ✎

St Albans High School for Girls
Townsend Avenue, St Albans,
Hertfordshire AL1 3SJ
Tel: 01727 853800
Headmistress:
Mrs Jenny Brown MA (Oxon)
Age range: G4–18
No. of pupils: 940 VIth170
🏃 A £ ✎

St Christopher School
Barrington Road, Letchworth,
Hertfordshire SG6 3JZ
Tel: 01462 650 850
Head: Richard Palmer
Age range: 3–18
No. of pupils: 511 VIth78
Fees: Day £3,375–£14,505
FB £15,600–£25,470
🏃 A 🏛 £ ✎

St Columba's College Prep School
King Harry Lane, St Albans,
Hertfordshire AL3 4AW
Tel: 01727 862616
Head of Prep: Mrs Ruth Loveman
Age range: B4–11
Fees: Day £9,702 £12,087
🏃 £

St Edmund's College & Prep School
Old Hall Green, Nr Ware,
Hertfordshire SG11 1DS
Tel: 01920 824247
Head: Paulo Durán BA MA
Age range: 3–18
No. of pupils: 799 VIth135
Fees: Day £9,465–£14,955 WB
£19,830–£22,575 FB £21,855–£24,990
🏃 A 🏛 £ IB ✎

St Edmund's Prep
Old Hall Green, Ware,
Hertfordshire SG11 1DS
Tel: 01920 824239
Head:
Mr Steven Cartwright BSc (Surrey)
Age range: 3–11
No. of pupils: 185
Fees: Day £8,484–£12,252
✎

St Francis' College
Broadway, Letchworth Garden
City, Hertfordshire SG6 3PJ
Tel: 01462 670511
Headmistress: Mrs B Goulding
Age range: G3–18
No. of pupils: 460 VIth75
Fees: Day £8,670–£13,830 WB
£19,425–£22,875 FB £24,195–£27,645
🏃 🌐 A 🏛 £

St Hilda's
High Street, Bushey,
Hertfordshire WD23 3DA
Tel: 020 8950 1751
Headmistress:
Miss Sarah-Jane Styles MA
Age range: B2–4 G2–11
Fees: Day £4,635–£8,685
🏃 ✎

St Hilda's School
28 Douglas Road, Harpenden,
Hertfordshire AL5 2ES
Tel: 01582 712307
Headmaster: Mr Dan Sayers
Age range: G3–11 years
No. of pupils: 165
Fees: Day £5,715–£9,975
🏃 ✎

St John's Preparatory School
The Ridgeway, Potters Bar,
Hertfordshire EN6 5QT
Tel: 01707 657294
Headmistress:
Mrs C Tardios BA(Hons)
Age range: 4–11
No. of pupils: 184
Fees: Day £8,190–£8,730
✎

St Joseph's In The Park
St Mary's Lane, Hertingfordbury,
Hertford, Hertfordshire SG14 2LX
Tel: 01992 513810
Head of School: Mr Douglas Brown
Age range: 3–11
No. of pupils: 150
Fees: Day £5,430–£16,011
£ ✎

St Margaret's School, Bushey
Merry Hill Road, Bushey,
Hertfordshire WD23 1DT
Tel: 020 8416 4400
Head: Mrs Rose Hardy
MA(Oxon), MEd, FRSA
Age range: G4–18 years
No. of pupils: 450 VIth100
Fees: Day £14,730 WB
£20,220–£23,670 FB £27,600
🏃 🌐 A 🏛 £ ✎

Stanborough School
Stanborough Park, Garston,
Watford, Hertfordshire WD25 9JT
Tel: 01923 673268
Head Teacher: Ms Lorraine Dixon
Age range: 3–19
No. of pupils: 300 VIth20
Fees: Day £3,660–£5,500
WB £12,834–£15,846

Stormont
The Causeway, Potters Bar,
Hertfordshire EN6 5HA
Tel: 01707 654037
Head of School: Mrs Sharon Martin
Age range: G4–11
Fees: Day £10,215–£10,680

The Christian School (Takeley)
Dunmow Road, Brewers End,
Takeley, Bishop's Stortford,
Hertfordshire CM22 6QH
Tel: 01279 871182
Headmaster: M E Humphries
Age range: 5–16
Fees: Day £3,720

The King's School
Elmfield, Ambrose Lane,
Harpenden, Hertfordshire AL5 4DU
Tel: 01582 767566
Principal:
Mr Clive John Case BA, HDE
Age range: 5–16
Fees: Day £4,380

The Purcell School, London
Aldenham Road, Bushey,
Hertfordshire WD23 2TS
Tel: 01923 331100
Headteacher: Mr. Stephen Yeo
Age range: 8–18
No. of pupils: 167 VIth70
Fees: WB £22,452 FB £28,716

TRING PARK SCHOOL FOR THE PERFORMING ARTS
For further details see p. 48
Tring Park, Tring,
Hertfordshire HP23 5LX
Tel: 01442 824255
Email: info@tringpark.com
Website: www.tringpark.com
Principal: Mr Stefan Anderson
MA, ARCM, ARCT
Age range: 8–19
No. of pupils: 335 VIth217
Fees: Day £14,070–£22,410
FB £23,715–£33,540

WESTBROOK HAY PREP SCHOOL
For further details see p. 49
London Road,
Hemel Hempstead,
Hertfordshire HP1 2RF
Tel: 01442 256143
Email:
admin@westbrookhay.co.uk
Website:
www.westbrookhay.co.uk
Headmaster:
Keith D Young BEd(Hons)
Age range: 3–13
No. of pupils: 300
Fees: Day £9,780–£14,085

York House School
Redheath, Sarratt Road,
Croxley Green, Rickmansworth,
Hertfordshire WD3 4LW
Tel: 01923 772395
Headmaster: Jon Gray BA(Ed)
Age range: 3–13
No. of pupils: 240
Fees: Day £10,845

Norfolk

All Saints School
School Road, Lessingham,
Norwich, Norfolk NR12 0DJ
Tel: 01692 582083
Headmistress: J N Gardiner
Age range: 3–16
Fees: Day £2,736–£4,455

Beeston Hall School
Beeston Regis, West Runton,
Cromer, Norfolk NR27 9NQ
Tel: 01263 837324
Headmaster:
Mr R C Gainher BSc(Hons)
Age range: 7–13
Fees: Day £15,333 FB £20,709

Downham Preparatory School & Montessori Nursery
The Old Rectory, Stow Bardolph,
Kings Lynn, Norfolk PE34 3HT
Tel: 01366 388066
Headmistress:
Mrs E Laffeaty-Sharpe MontDip
Age range: 2–11
No. of pupils: 170
Fees: Day £4,959–£6,702

Glebe House School
2 Cromer Road, Hunstanton,
Norfolk PE36 6HW
Tel: 01485 532809
Headmaster: Mr Crofts
Age range: 0–13
No. of pupils: 110
Fees: Day £7,200–£10,800
WB £9,180–£12,780

Gresham's Prep School
Cromer Road, Holt,
Norfolk NR25 6EY
Tel: 01263 714600
Headmaster:
Mr J H W Quick BA, PGCE
Age range: 7–13
No. of pupils: 252
Fees: Day £13,830–£17,160
FB £24,150

Gresham's Pre-Prep School
Market Place, Holt,
Norfolk NR25 6BB
Tel: 01263 714575
Headmistress: Janette Davidson
Age range: 3–8
No. of pupils: 107
Fees: Day £9,045–£10,290

Hethersett Old Hall School
Hethersett, Norwich,
Norfolk NR9 3DW
Tel: 01603 810390
Headmaster: Mr S Crump
Age range: B3–11 G3–18
No. of pupils: 197 VIth29
Fees: Day £5,850–£12,450 WB
£13,395–£17,850 FB £15,585–£23,175

Norwich High School for Girls GDST
95 Newmarket Road,
Norwich, Norfolk NR2 2HU
Tel: 01603 453265
Headmaster:
Mr J J Morrow BA(Oxon), MA
Age range: G3–18
No. of pupils: VIth120
Fees: Day £6,906–£11,031

Norwich School
70 The Close, Norwich,
Norfolk NR1 4DD
Tel: 01603 728430
Head Master: Steffan D A Griffiths
Age range: 7–18
No. of pupils: 1065
Fees: Day £13,725–£15,060

Norwich Steiner School
Hospital Lane, Norwich,
Norfolk NR1 2HW
Tel: 01603 611175
Headteacher: Mr Andrew Vestrini
Age range: 3–18
No. of pupils: 91
Fees: Day £2,419–£6,515

Notre Dame Preparatory School
147 Dereham Road, Norwich,
Norfolk NR2 3TA
Tel: 01603 625593
Headmaster: Mr K O'Herlihy
Age range: 2–11
No. of pupils: 140
Fees: Day £810–£5,445

Riddlesworth Hall Preparatory School
Garboldisham, Diss,
Norfolk IP22 2TA
Tel: 01953 681 246
Headmaster: Paul Cochrane
Age range: 2–13
No. of pupils: 137
Fees: Day £10,470 WB
£16,500 FB £17,535

Sacred Heart School
17 Mangate Street, Swaffham,
Norfolk PE37 7QW
Tel: 01760 721330/724577
Headmistress: Sr Francis Ridler
FDC, BEd(Hons), EYPS
Age range: 3–16 years
No. of pupils: 156
Fees: Day £7,935–£11,775
WB £16,845–£18,045
FB £21,825–£21,825

St Nicholas House School
Yarmouth Road, North
Walsham, Norfolk NR28 9AT
Tel: 01692 403143
Headteacher: Mr Martin Castle
Age range: 3–11
No. of pupils: 65
Fees: Day £4,260

Stretton School
West Lodge, Albemarle Road,
Norwich, Norfolk NR2 2DF
Tel: 01603 451285
Principal: Mrs Y D Barnett
Age range: 1–8
No. of pupils: 80
Fees: Day £1,020–£7,500

Taverham Hall Preparatory School
Taverham, Norwich,
Norfolk NR8 6HU
Tel: 01603 868206
Headmaster: Mr Mike A
Crossley NPQH, BEd(Hons)
Age range: 2–13
Fees: Day £9,975–£11,400
WB £17,775 FB £17,775

Thetford Grammar School
Bridge Street, Thetford,
Norfolk IP24 3AF
Tel: 01842 752840
Headmaster: Mr G J Price MA
Age range: 4–18
No. of pupils: 298 VIth20
Fees: Day £10,191–£12,327
Ⓐ ⓔ 🖉

Thorpe House Langley Preparatory School
7 Yarmouth Road, Norwich,
Norfolk NR7 0EA
Tel: 01603 433055
Headmaster: Simon Marfleet
Age range: 2–11
No. of pupils: 144
Fees: Day £2,100–£2,540
ⓔ 🖉

Town Close House Preparatory School
14 Ipswich Road, Norwich,
Norfolk NR2 2LR
Tel: 01603 620180
Headmaster: Mr Graeme Lowe BEd
Age range: 3–13
No. of pupils: 455
Fees: Day £7,080–£11,085
ⓔ 🖉

Suffolk

Barnardiston Hall Preparatory School
Barnardiston, Nr Haverhill,
Suffolk CB9 7TG
Tel: 01440 786316
Headmaster:
Lt Col K A Boulter MA(Cantab)
Age range: 6 months–13 years
No. of pupils: 220
Fees: Day £8,325–£13,050
WB £18,045 FB £19,575
🏠 ⓔ 🖉

Brookes Cambridge
Flempton Road, Risby, Bury St
Edmunds, Suffolk IP28 6QJ
Tel: 01284 760531
Headteacher: Mrs C Beedham
Age range: 0–16
No. of pupils: 240
Fees: Day £4,800–£5,850
🖉

Culford Preparatory School
Culford, Bury St Edmunds,
Suffolk IP28 6TX
Tel: 01284 385383
Headmaster: Mr Mike Schofield
Age range: 7–13
No. of pupils: 214
Fees: Day £9,795–£13,200
FB £18,780–£20,340
🏠

Culford Pre-Preparatory School
Fieldgate House, Bury St
Edmunds, Suffolk IP28 6TX
Tel: 01284 385412
Headmistress: Mrs Sarah Preston BA
Age range: 3–7
Fees: Day £2,380–£8,745

Fairstead House School
Fordham Road, Newmarket,
Suffolk CB8 7AA
Tel: 01638 662318
Head: Lynda Brereton
Age range: 3–11
No. of pupils: 118
Fees: Day £9,210–£9,930
ⓔ 🖉

Finborough School
The Hall, Great Finborough,
Stowmarket, Suffolk IP14 3EF
Tel: 01449 773600
Principal: Mr J Sinclair
Age range: 2–18
No. of pupils: 226 VIth20
Fees: Day £5,220–£8,580 WB
£10,860–£14,280 FB £13,200–£17,010
🏠 Ⓐ 🏠 ⓔ 🖉

Framlingham College
College Road, Framlingham,
Suffolk IP13 9EY
Tel: 01728 723789
Headmaster:
Mr Paul Taylor BA(Hons)
Age range: 2–18
No. of pupils: 700
Fees: Day £8,172–£18,635 WB
£23,931–£25,495 FB £28,981
🏠 Ⓐ 🏠 ⓔ 🖉

Framlingham College Prep School
Brandeston, Suffolk IP13 7AH
Tel: 01728 685331
Headmaster:
Mr M K Myers-Allen BSc(Hons), PGCE
Age range: 2–13
No. of pupils: 254
Fees: Day £6,681–£11,625
WB £18,693 FB £18,693
🏠 ⓔ 🖉

Ipswich High School for Girls
Woolverstone, Ipswich,
Suffolk IP9 1AZ
Tel: 01473 201058
Head of School: Ms Oona Carlin
Age range: G3–18
No. of pupils: 489
Fees: Day £7,839–£13,374
🏠 Ⓐ ⓔ 🖉

Ipswich Preparatory School
3 Ivry Street, Ipswich,
Suffolk IP1 3QW
Tel: 01473 282800
Headteacher: Mrs A H Childs
Age range: 3–11
No. of pupils: 311
Fees: Day £8,358–£9,201
🖉

Moreton Hall Preparatory School
Mount Road, Bury St
Edmunds, Suffolk IP32 7BJ
Tel: 01284 753532
Headmaster:
Mr Chris Moxon BA PGCE
Age range: 4–13
No. of pupils: 100
Fees: Day £8,145–£13,320
WB £18,195 FB £20,385
🏠 ⓔ 🖉

Old Buckenham Hall School
Brettenham, Ipswich, Suffolk IP7 7PH
Tel: 01449 740252
Headmaster: Mr J A Brett MA
Age range: 3–13
No. of pupils: 228
Fees: Day £15,300 WB
£20,070 FB £20,070
🏠 ⓔ 🖉

Old School Henstead
Toad Row, Beccles,
Suffolk NR34 7LG
Tel: 01502 741150
Head: Mr W J McKinney
Age range: 4–11
No. of pupils: 123
Fees: Day £4,500–£6,300

Orwell Park School
Nacton, Ipswich, Suffolk IP10 0ER
Tel: 01473 659225
Headmaster: Mr Adrian
Brown MA(Cantab)
Age range: 2–13
No. of pupils: 293
🏠 ⓔ 🖉

Saint Felix School
Halesworth Road, Southwold,
Suffolk IP18 6SD
Tel: 01502 722175
Headmaster: Mr. James Harrison
Age range: 2–18
No. of pupils: 312 VIth65
Fees: Day £6,900–£14,970 WB
£16,440–£20,970 FB £21,630–£26,160
🏠 Ⓐ 🏠 ⓔ 🖉

South Lee Preparatory School
Nowton Road, Bury St
Edmunds, Suffolk IP33 2BT
Tel: 01284 754654
Headmaster:
Mr Mervyn Watch BEd (Hons)
Age range: 2–13
Fees: Day £7,575–£9,375
🖉

St Joseph's College
Birkfield, Belstead Road,
Ipswich, Suffolk IP2 9DR
Tel: 01473 690281
Principal: Mrs Danielle Clarke
Age range: 3–18
No. of pupils: 564
Fees: Day £5,310–£13,305 WB
£21,945–£24,000 FB £22,980–£29,685
🏠 Ⓐ 🏠 ⓔ 🖉

Stoke College
Stoke-by-Clare, Sudbury,
Suffolk CO10 8JE
Tel: 01787 278141
Head: Mr Chris Lumb
Age range: 3–16
Fees: Day £6,732–£10,482
WB £14,586–£16,926
🏠 🏠 ⓔ 🖉

Summerhill School
Leiston, Suffolk IP16 4HY
Tel: 01728 830540
Principal: Mrs Zoe Readhead
Age range: 5–17
No. of pupils: 70
Fees: Day £4,800–£10,530
FB £10,719–£17,691
🏠 ⓔ 🖉

Woodbridge School
Marryott House, Burkitt Road,
Woodbridge, Suffolk IP12 4JH
Tel: 01394 615000
Headmaster: Mr N P Tetley
MA(Cantab), PGCE
Age range: 4–18
No. of pupils: VIth200
🏠 Ⓐ 🏠 ⓔ 🖉

East Midlands

KEY TO SYMBOLS
- 👤 *Boys' school*
- 👤 *Girls' school*
- 🌐 *International school*
- 16ᵗ *Tutorial or sixth form college*
- Ⓐ *A levels*
- 🏠 *Boarding accommodation*
- £ *Bursaries*
- IB *International Baccalaureate*
- ✐ *Learning support*
- 16ᵗ *Entrance at 16+*
- 🌐 *Vocational qualifications*
- (IAPS) *Independent Association of Prep Schools*
- (HMC) *The Headmasters' & Headmistresses' Conference*
- (ISA) *Independent Schools Association*
- (GSA) *Girls' School Association*
- (BSA) *Boarding Schools' Association*
- Ⓢ *Society of Heads*

Unless otherwise indicated, all schools are coeducational day schools. Single-sex and boarding schools will be indicated by the relevant icon.

Derbyshire

Barlborough Hall School
Barlborough, Chesterfield,
Derbyshire S43 4TJ
Tel: 01246 810511
Headteacher: Mrs Nic Boys
Age range: 3–11
No. of pupils: 198
Fees: Day £6,420–£8,553
(£)🖉

Dame Catherine Harpur's School
Rose Lane, Ticknall, Derby DE73 7JW
Tel: 01332 862792
Head: Ms Whyte
Age range: 3–11
No. of pupils: 28
Fees: Day £3,375

Derby Grammar School
Rykneld Hall, Rykneld Road,
Littleover, Derby DE23 4BX
Tel: 01332 523027
Headmaster: Mr Richard D Paine
Age range: B7–18 G16–18
No. of pupils: 298 VIth66
Fees: Day £7,779–£10,779
(🏃)(A)(£)🖉

Derby High School
Hillsway, Littleover, Derby DE23 3DT
Tel: 01332 514267
Headmaster: Mr C T Callaghan
Age range: B3–11 G3–18
No. of pupils: 576 VIth74
Fees: Day £7,050–£9,510
(A)(£)🖉

Emmanuel School
Juniper Lodge, 43 Kedleston
Road, Derby DE22 1FP
Tel: 01332 340505
Headteacher: Mrs C Pearson
Age range: 3–16
No. of pupils: 65
Fees: Day £1,698–£2,706

Foremarke Hall
Milton, Derby DE65 6EJ
Tel: 01283 707100
Headmaster: Mr R Merriman
MA, BSc(Hons), FCollP
Age range: 3–13
(🏛)(£)🖉

Gateway Christian School
Moor Lane, Dale Abbey,
Ilkeston, Derbyshire DE7 4PP
Tel: 0115 9440609
Head Teacher: Mrs Corinna Walters
Age range: 3–11
No. of pupils: 31
Fees: Day £2,400
🖉

Michael House Steiner School
The Field, Shipley, Heanor,
Derbyshire DE75 7JH
Tel: 01773 718050
Age range: 3–16
No. of pupils: 150
Fees: Day £1,500–£4,200

Normanton House Primary School
Normanton House, Village
Street, Derby DE23 8DF
Tel: 01332 769333
Headteacher: Mr Nighat
Sultana Khan
Age range: 5–10
No. of pupils: 97

Ockbrook School
The Settlement, Ockbrook,
Derby DE72 3RJ
Tel: 01332 673532
Head: Mr Tom Brooksby
Age range: B2–14 G2–18
No. of pupils: 399 VIth50
Fees: Day £7,203–£10,613
WB £5,685 FB £6,174
(🌐)(A)(🏛)(£)🖉

Old Vicarage School
11 Church Lane, Darley
Abbey, Derby DE22 1EW
Tel: 01332 557130
Headmaster: Mr M J Adshead
Age range: 3–13
No. of pupils: 95
Fees: Day £6,135–£6,810
(£)🖉

S. Anselm's School
Stanedge Road, Bakewell,
Derbyshire DE45 1DP
Tel: 01629 812734
Headmaster: Peter Phillips BA
(Hons), MA, PGCE (SPLD), NPQH
Age range: 3–13
No. of pupils: 215
Fees: Day £7,680–£14,940 FB £17,550
(🏛)(£)🖉

St Peter & St Paul School
Brambling House, Hady Hill,
Chesterfield, Derbyshire S41 0EF
Tel: 01246 278522
Headmaster: Mr Jonathan Clark
Age range: 3 months–11 years
No. of pupils: 129
Fees: Day £6,132–£6,432
(£)🖉

St Wystan's School
High Street, Repton,
Derbyshire DE65 6GE
Tel: 01283 703258
Headmaster: Phillip Soutar
Age range: 3–11
(£)🖉

Treetops Nurseries
1 St. James Court, Friar
Gate, Derby DE1 1BT
Tel: 01332 223 553

Leicestershire

Al-Aqsa Schools Trust
The Wayne Way, Leicester LE5 4PP
Tel: 0116 2760953
Headteacher: Mrs Amina Wiltshire
Age range: 5–16
No. of pupils: 231
🖉

Brooke House Day School
Croft Road, Cosby,
Leicester, LE9 1SE
Tel: 0116 286 7372
Head: Mrs Joy Parker
Age range: 3–14

Darul Arqam Educational Institute
2 Overton Road, Leicester LE5 0JA
Tel: 0116 2741626
Headteacher:
Mr Ahmed Abdul Dadipatel
Age range: B5–16
No. of pupils: 75
(🏃)

Fairfield Preparatory School
Leicester Road, Loughborough,
Leicestershire LE11 2AE
Tel: 01509 215172
Headmaster:
Mr A Earnshaw BA Lancaster NPQH
Age range: 4–11
No. of pupils: 489
🖉

Grace Dieu Manor School
Grace Dieu, Thringstone,
Leicestershire LE67 5UG
Tel: 01530 222276
Headmaster: Mr Peter Fisher
Age range: 3–13
No. of pupils: 315
Fees: Day £7,935–£11,313
(£)🖉

Jameah Girls Academy
49 Rolleston Street, Leicester LE5 3SD
Tel: 0116 262 7745
Headteacher: Mrs S Patel
Age range: G6–16
No. of pupils: 142
(🏃)

Leicester Grammar Junior School
London Road, Grea Glen,
Leicester LE8 9FL
Tel: 0116 259 1950
Head of School: Mrs C Rigby
Age range: 3–11
No. of pupils: 391
🖉

Leicester High School for Girls
454 London Road, Leicester LE2 2PP
Tel: 0116 2705338
Headmaster: Mr Alan Whelpdale
Age range: G3–18
No. of pupils: 435 VIth60
Fees: Day £2,250–£3,100
(🏃)(A)(£)

Leicester International School
16-20 Beal Street, Leicester LE2 0AA
Tel: 0116 2515345
Principal: Mr N Hussein
Age range: 5–11
No. of pupils: 146
(🌐)

Leicester Islamic Academy
320 London Road, Leicester LE2 2PP
Tel: 0116 2705343
Principal: Dr M H Mukadam
FRSA, BEd(Hons), PhD
Age range: 3–16
Fees: Day £1,300–£1,400

Leicester Prep School
2 Albert Road, Leicester LE2 2AA
Tel: 0116 2707414
Headmaster: Christopher
J Cann MA(Oxon)
Age range: 3–11
No. of pupils: 130
Fees: Day £1,530–£5,820
🖉

Manor House School
South Street, Ashby-de-la-
Zouch, Leicestershire LE65 1BR
Tel: 01530 412932
Headteacher: Mrs E A Scrine
Age range: 4–16
Fees: Day £4,302–£5,700
(£)🖉

Our Lady's Convent School
Gray Street, Loughborough,
Leicestershire LE11 2DZ
Tel: 01509 263901
Headmaster: Dr Julian Murphy
Age range: B4–11 G4–18
No. of pupils: 212
Fees: Day £9,252–£11,298
(🏃)(A)(£)🖉

Ratcliffe College
Fosse Way, Ratcliffe on the
Wreake, Leicester LE7 4SG
Tel: 01509 817000
Headmaster:
Mr G Lloyd BA, MSc, FMusTCL
Age range: 3–18
No. of pupils: 689 VIth154
Fees: Day £8,226–£14,865 WB
£18,471–£20,673 FB £23,190
(🌐)(A)(🏛)(£)🖉

St Crispin's School
6 St Mary's Road, Stoneygate,
Leicester LE2 1XA
Tel: 0116 2707648
Head Master: Andrew Atkin
Age range: 2–16
(£)🖉

Stoneygate School
6 London Road, Great
Glen, Leicester LE8 9DJ
Tel: 0116 259 2282
Headmaster:
Mr John H Morris MA(Cantab)
Age range: 3–13
Fees: Day £4,800–£6,100

The Dixie Grammar School
Station Road, Market Bosworth,
Leicestershire CV13 0LE
Tel: 01455 292244
Headmaster: J Wood MA
Age range: 3–18
No. of pupils: 520 VIth71
Fees: Day £5,760–£7,920
Ⓐ£

**Tiny Tots Pre-School
& Primary**
16-20 Beal Street, Leicester LE2 0AA
Tel: 0116 2515345
Principal: Mr N Hussein
Age range: 2–11
No. of pupils: 104

Lincolnshire

Ayscoughfee Hall School
Welland Hall, London Road,
Spalding, Lincolnshire PE11 2TE
Tel: 01775 724733
Headmistress:
Mrs Clare Ogden BA(Hons), PGCE
Age range: 3–11
No. of pupils: 140
Fees: Day £4,080–£6,030

**Bicker Preparatory
School & Early Years**
School Lane, Bicker, Boston,
Lincolnshire PE20 3DW
Tel: 01775 821/86
Proprietor & Principal: Mrs S
A Page CertEdDist, SMPS
Age range: 3–11
No. of pupils: 74
Fees: Day £1,906–£5,430

**Copthill Independent
Day School**
Barnack Road, Uffington,
Stamford, Lincolnshire PE9 3AD
Tel: 01780 757506
Headmaster:
Mr J A Teesdale BA(Hons), PGCE
Age range: 2–11
No. of pupils: 309
Fees: Day £8,370–£9,180
£

Dudley House School
1 Dudley Road, Grantham,
Lincolnshire NG31 9AA
Tel: 01476 400184
Headmistress: Mrs Jenny Johnson
Age range: 3–11
No. of pupils: 50
Fees: Day £4,545

**Grantham Preparatory
International School**
Gorse Lane, Grantham,
Lincolnshire NG31 7UF
Tel: +44 (0)1476 593293
Headmistress: Mrs K A Korcz
Age range: 3–11
No. of pupils: 108
Fees: Day £6,900–£8,430
£

Greenwich House School
106 High Holme Road, Louth,
Lincolnshire LN11 0HE
Tel: 01507 609252
Headmistress: Mrs J Brindle
Age range: 9 months–11 years
No. of pupils: 50
Fees: Day £5,100

**Handel House
Preparatory School**
Northolme Road, Gainsborough,
Lincolnshire DN21 2JB
Tel: 01427 612426
Headmistress: Mrs Victoria Haigh
Age range: 2–11
Fees: Day £2,580–£3,075

Lincoln Minster School
Upper Lindum Street,
Lincoln LN2 5RW
Tel: 01522 551300
Principal: Mr Clive Rickart
Age range: 2½–18
No. of pupils: 840 VIth144
Fees: Day £6,510–£9,672
WB £14,289–£16,947
FB £15,417–£18,285
Ⓐ£

Regents Academy
Bliney House, Manby Park,
Manby, Lincolnshire LN11 8UT
Tel: 01507 327859
Headteacher: Mrs D Rusling
Age range: 3–18
No. of pupils: 30
Fees: Day £2,448

St Hugh's School
Cromwell Avenue, Woodhall
Spa, Lincolnshire LN10 6TQ
Tel: 01526 352169
Head: C Ward BEd(Hons)
Age range: 2–13
No. of pupils: 195
Fees: Day £7,452–£12,987 FB £18,381
£

Stamford Junior School
Kettering Road, Stamford,
Lincolnshire PE9 2LR
Tel: 01780 484400
Principal: Mr S C Roberts
Age range: 2–11
No. of pupils: 344
Fees: Day £8,580
WB £17,436 FB £17,544

Viking School
140 Church Road North,
Skegness, Lincolnshire PE25 2QJ
Tel: 01754 765749
Principal: Mrs S J Barker
Age range: 3–11
No. of pupils: 100
Fees: Day £1,085

**Witham Hall
Preparatory School**
Witham-on-the-Hill, Bourne,
Lincolnshire PE10 0JJ
Tel: +44(0)1778 590222
Headmaster:
Mr Charles Welch B.Ed (Hons)
Age range: 4–13
No. of pupils: 228
Fees: Day £6,645–£10,875 FB £14,850
£

Northamptonshire

Beachborough School
Westbury, Brackley,
Northamptonshire NN13 5LB
Tel: 01280 700071
Headmaster: Mr Jeremy Banks BEd
Age range: 2–13
No. of pupils: 260
Fees: Day £570–£10,485
£

Laxton Junior School
East Road, Oundle, Peterborough,
Northamptonshire PE8 4BX
Tel: 01832 277275
Head:
Mr Mark Potter MEd BEd(Hons)
Age range: 4–11
No. of pupils: 260
Fees: Day £10,185–£11,175
£

Maidwell Hall
Maidwell, Northampton NN6 9JG
Tel: 01604 686234
Headmaster:
R A Lankester MA, PGCE
Age range: 7–13
No. of pupils: 122
Fees: Day £16,500
WB £25,350 FB £25,350
£

**Northampton High
School GDST**
Newport Pagnell
Road, Hardingstone,
Northampton NN4 6UU
Tel: 01604 765765
Headmistress: Mrs S Dixon BA
Age range: G3–18
Fees: Day £9,795–£13,005
Ⓐ£

Overstone Park School
Overstone Park, Overstone,
Northampton NN6 0DT
Tel: 01604 643787
Principal: Mrs M F Brown
BA(Hons), PGCE
Age range: 0–18
No. of pupils: 85
Fees: Day £2,267–£3,013

Pitsford School
Pitsford Hall, Pitsford,
Northampton NN6 9AX
Tel: 01604 880306
Headmaster: N R Toone BSc, MInstP
Age range: 4–18
No. of pupils: VIth60
Fees: Day £7,752–£13,455
Ⓐ£

Quinton House School
Upton Hall, Upton,
Northampton NN5 4UX
Tel: 01604 752050
Headteacher: Ms C Cozens
Age range: 2–18
No. of pupils: 455
Fees: Day £8,145–£11,520
Ⓐ£

Spratton Hall
Smith Street, Spratton,
Northampton NN6 8HP
Tel: 01604 847292
Head Master: Mr Simon Clarke
Age range: 4–13
No. of pupils: 396
Fees: Day £9,450–£13,650
£

St Peter's Independent School
Lingswood Park, Blackthorn,
Northampton NN3 8TA
Tel: 01604 411745
Head: Tim Cooper
Age range: 4–18
No. of pupils: 130
Fees: Day £3,600
Ⓐ

St Peter's School
52 Headlands, Kettering,
Northamptonshire NN15 6DJ
Tel: 01536 512066
Headmistress: Mrs Maria Chapman
Age range: 2–11
No. of pupils: 161
Fees: Day £3,765–£6,795
£ 🐾

Wellingborough School
Wellingborough,
Northamptonshire NN8 2BX
Tel: 01933 222427
Headmaster: Mr G R Bowe MA
Age range: 3–18
No. of pupils: VIth145
Fees: Day £6,522–£11,004
Ⓐ £ 🐾

Winchester House School
High Street, Brackley,
Northamptonshire NN13 7AZ
Tel: 01280 702483
Head: Emma Goldsmith
Age range: 3–13
No. of pupils: 325
Fees: Day £690–£17,025
WB £17,820–£22,485
🏛 £ 🐾

Nottinghamshire

Colston Bassett Preparatory School
School Lane, Colston bassett,
Nottingham NG12 3FD
Tel: 01949 81118
Headteacher: Mrs Julie Hunt
Age range: 4–11
Fees: Day £5,925

Coteswood House School
19 Thackeray's Lane, Woodthorpe,
Nottingham NG5 4HT
Tel: 0115 9676551
Head: Mrs S M Fernley
Age range: 3–11
No. of pupils: 40
Fees: Day £4,200

Hazel Hurst School
400 Westdale Lane, Mapperley,
Nottingham NG3 6DG
Tel: 0115 9606759
Headteacher: Mrs Rosemary Eadie
Age range: 2–8
Fees: Day £5,406–£6,024

Highfields School
London Road, Newark,
Nottinghamshire NG24 3AL
Tel: 01636 704103
Headteacher:
Mrs C L Fraser BEd(Hons)
Age range: 3–11
No. of pupils: 120
Fees: Day £7,770
£ 🐾

Hollygirt School
Elm Avenue, Nottingham NG3 4GF
Tel: 0115 958 0596
Headmistress: Mrs Pam Hutley
BA(Hons), PGCE, MSc
Age range: B3–7 G3–16
No. of pupils: 240
Fees: Day £7,698–£10,224
🐾 £ 🐾

Iona School
310 Sneinton Dale,
Nottingham NG3 7DN
Tel: 01159 415295
Chair of College: Richard Moore
Age range: 3–11
Fees: Day £3,816

Jamia Al-Hudaa Residential College
Forest House, Berkeley
Avenue, Mapperley Park,
Nottingham NG3 5TT
Tel: 0115 9690800
Principal: Raza ul-Haq Siakhvy
Age range: G5–19
No. of pupils: 224
🐾 🏛

Jubilee House Christian School
226 Nottingham Road, Eastwood,
Nottinghamshire NG16 3GR
Tel: 01773 688100
Headteacher: Mrs J Marks
Age range: 3–16
No. of pupils: 70
£

Nottingham Girls' High School GDST
9 Arboretum Street,
Nottingham NG1 4JB
Tel: 0115 9417663
Headmistress: Mrs S M Gorham
Age range: G4–18
No. of pupils: 1117 VIth239
Fees: Day £6,978–£9,627
🐾 Ⓐ £

Nottingham High Infant and Junior School
Waverley Mount,
Nottingham NG7 4ED
Tel: 0115 845 2214
Headteacher: Mrs Clare Bruce
Age range: 4–11
No. of pupils: 180
Fees: Day £3,155–£3,670
🐾

Nottingham Islamia School
30 Bentinck Road, Hyson
Green, Nottingham NG7 4AF
Tel: 0115 970 5858
Head: Dr Musharraf Hussain
Age range: 5–11

Plumtree School
Church Hill, Plumtree,
Nottingham NG12 5ND
Tel: 0115 937 5859
Head Teacher: Phil Simpson
Age range: 3–11
Fees: Day £5,250
🐾

Salterford House School
Salterford Lane, Calverton,
Nottingham NG14 6NZ
Tel: 0115 9652127
Headmistress:
Mrs Marlene Venables CertEd
Age range: 2–11
No. of pupils: 124
Fees: Day £6,150

Saville House School
11 Church Street, Mansfield
Woodhouse, Mansfield,
Nottinghamshire NG19 8AH
Tel: 01623 625068
Head: Mrs S Hagues
Age range: 3–11
No. of pupils: 89
Fees: Day £4,125
🐾

St Joseph's School
33 Derby Road,
Nottingham NG1 5AW
Tel: 0115 9418356
Head Teacher: Mr
Ashley Crawshaw
Age range: 1–11
Fees: Day £7,503
🐾

The Elms, Nursery & Junior School to Trent College
Derby Road, Long Eaton,
Nottingham NG10 4AD
Tel: 0115 8494942
Head: Mr Keith Morrow BA(Hons)
QTS, PGCPS(Ed), NPQH (EMTA)
Age range: 0–11
No. of pupils: 340
Fees: Day £7,200–£7,500

The Lammas School
Lammas Road, Sutton-in-Ashfield,
Nottinghamshire NG17 2AD
Tel: 01623 516879
Head: Mrs P Sessions
Age range: 4–16
Fees: Day £5,125–£6,650
🐾

The Orchard School
South Leverton, Retford,
Nottinghamshire DN22 0DJ
Tel: 01427 880395
Principal: Mrs S M Fox BA, PGCE
Age range: 5–16
No. of pupils: 200
Fees: Day £3,795–£6,180

Wellow House School
Wellow, Newark,
Nottinghamshire NG22 0EA
Tel: 01623 861054
Headmaster: Peter Cook BEd(Hons)
Age range: 3–13
No. of pupils: 152
Fees: Day £7,500–£11,985
WB £13,845
🏛 £ 🐾

Worksop College Preparatory School, Ranby House
Retford, Nottinghamshire DN22 8HX
Tel: 01777 714387
(Admissions)
Headmaster:
C S J Pritchard MA, BA(Hons), QTS
Age range: 3–13 years
No. of pupils: 240
Fees: Day £4,064–£4,274
🏛 £ 🐾

Rutland

Brooke Priory School
Station Approach, Oakham,
Rutland LE15 6QW
Tel: 01572 724778
Headmistress: Mrs E Bell BEd
Age range: 2–11
No. of pupils: 180
Fees: Day £8,655
£ 🐾

Greater London

*See also East (D97) for schools in Essex and Hertfordshire; South-East (D133) for schools in Kent and Surrey

KEY TO SYMBOLS
- Boys' school
- Girls' school
- International school
- Tutorial or sixth form college
- A levels
- Boarding accommodation
- Bursaries
- International Baccalaureate
- Learning support
- Entrance at 16+
- Vocational qualifications
- Independent Association of Prep Schools
- The Headmasters' & Headmistresses' Conference
- Independent Schools Association
- Girls' School Association
- Boarding Schools' Association
- Society of Heads

Unless otherwise indicated, all schools are coeducational day schools. Single-sex and boarding schools will be indicated by the relevant icon.

Essex

Al-Noor Primary School
Newton Industrial Estate, Eastern Avenue, Chadwell Health, Romford, Essex RM6 5SD
Tel: 020 8597 7576
Head: Mrs Someera Butt
Age range: 4–10
No. of pupils: 175
Fees: Day £2,550–£2,750

Avon House Preparatory School
490 High Road, Woodford Green, Essex IG8 0PN
Tel: 020 8504 1749
Headteacher:
Mrs Amanda Campbell
Age range: 3–11
No. of pupils: 200
Fees: Day £8,985–£9,795

Bancroft's School
High Road, Woodford Green, Essex IG8 0RF
Tel: 020 8505 4821
Head: Mr Simon Marshall MA, PGCE (Cantab), MA, MPhil (Oxon)
Age range: 7–18
No. of pupils: 1123 VIth240
Fees: Day £13,290–£16,323

Beehive Preparatory School
233 Beehive Lane, Redbridge, Ilford, Essex IG4 5ED
Tel: 020 8550 3224
Headmaster: Mr C J Beasant BEd
Age range: 4–11
Fees: Day £4,900

Cranbrook College
Mansfield Road, Ilford, Essex IG1 3BD
Tel: 020 8554 1757
Executive Principal:
Mr. David Morrison
Age range: B4–16
No. of pupils: 200
Fees: Day £6,405–£8,235

Eastcourt Independent School
1 Eastwood Road, Goodmayes, Ilford, Essex IG3 8UW
Tel: 020 8590 5472
Headmistress: Mrs Christine Redgrave BSc(Hons), DipEd, MEd
Age range: 3–11
Fees: Day £6,300

Gidea Park College
2 Balgores Lane, Gidea Park, Romford, Essex RM2 5JR
Tel: 01708 740381
Headmistress:
Mrs Susan-Jayne Gooding BA
Age range: 3–11
No. of pupils: 177
Fees: Day £1,275–£2,500

Goodrington School
17 Walden Road, Hornchurch, Essex RM11 2JT
Tel: 01708 448349
Head Teacher: Mrs J R Ellenby
Age range: 3–11
Fees: Day £6,150

Ilford Grammar School
785 High Road, Seven Kings, Ilford, Essex IG3 8RW
Tel: 020 8599 8822
Headmistress: B P M Wiggs BSc(Hons), PGCE
Age range: 3–16
Fees: Day £5,250–£7,200

Immanuel School
Havering Grange Centre, Havering Road North, Romford, Essex RM1 4HR
Tel: 01708 764449
Principal: Miss Norcross
Age range: 3–16

Maytime Montessori Nursery - Cranbrook Road
341 Cranbrook Road, Ilford, Essex IG1 4UF
Tel: 020 8554 3079

Maytime Montessori Nursery - Eastwood Road
2 Eastwood Road, Goodmayes, Essex IG3 8XB
Tel: 020 8599 3744

Maytime Montessori Nursery - York Road
87 York Road, Ilford, Essex IG1 3AF
Tel: 020 8553 1524
Age range: 0–6

Oakfields Montessori School
Harwood Hall, Harwood Hall Lane, Corbets Tey, Essex RM14 2YG
Tel: 01708 220117
Headmistress: Mrs K Malandreniotis
Age range: 2–11
Fees: Day £2,508–£4,260

Park School for Girls
20 Park Avenue, Ilford, Essex IG1 4RS
Tel: 020 8554 2466
Headmistress: Mrs N O'Brien BA
Age range: G7–18
No. of pupils: 230 VIth19
Fees: Day £4,755–£6,285

Raphael Independent School
Park Lane, Hornchurch, Essex RM11 1XY
Tel: 01708 744735
Head of School: Mr Jack Luis
Age range: 4–16
No. of pupils: 135
Fees: Day £5,200–£7,800

St Aubyn's School
Bunces Lane, Woodford Green, Essex IG8 9DU
Tel: 020 8504 1577
Headmaster: Mr Leonard Blom BEd(Hons) BA NPQH
Age range: 3–13
No. of pupils: 525
Fees: Day £4,995–£11,166

St Mary's Hare Park School & Nursery
South Drive, Gidea Park, Romford, Essex RM2 6HH
Tel: 01708 761220
Head Teacher: Mrs K Karwacinski
Age range: 2–11
No. of pupils: 180
Fees: Day £4,485

The Ursuline Preparatory School Ilford
2-8 Coventry Road, Ilford, Essex IG1 4QR
Tel: 020 8518 4050
Headteacher: Mrs Lisa McCoy
Age range: G3–11
No. of pupils: 159
Fees: Day £5,697

WOODFORD GREEN PREPARATORY SCHOOL
For further details see p. 54
Glengall Road, Woodford Green, Essex IG8 0BZ
Tel: 020 8504 5045
Email: admissions@wgprep.co.uk
Website: www.wgprep.co.uk
Headmaster: Mr J P Wadge
Age range: 3–11
No. of pupils: 381
Fees: Day £3,140

Hertfordshire

Lyonsdown School
3 Richmond Road, New Barnet, Barnet, Hertfordshire EN5 1SA
Tel: 020 8449 0225
Head: Mrs L Maggs-Wellings BEd
Age range: B3–7 G3–11
No. of pupils: 205
Fees: Day £3,612–£9,186

Norfolk Lodge Montessori Nursery & Pre-Prep School
Dancers Hill Road, Barnet, Hertfordshire EN5 4RP
Tel: 020 8447 1565
Head Teacher: Mrs Mary Wales
Age range: 6 months–7 years
No. of pupils: 140
Fees: Day £2,200–£2,400

The Royal Masonic School for Girls
Rickmansworth Park, Rickmansworth, Hertfordshire WD3 4HF
Tel: 01923 725337
Headmistress: Miss Linda Beckett BEd(Hons)
Age range: 4–11

Kent

Ashgrove School
116 Widmore Road,
Bromley, Kent BR1 3BE
Tel: 020 8460 4143
Principal: Patricia Ash CertEd,
BSc(Hons), PhD, CMath, FIMA
Age range: 4–11
Fees: Day £8,460

Babington House School
Grange Drive, Chislehurst,
Kent BR7 5ES
Tel: 020 8467 5537
Headmaster: Mr Tim Lello
MA, FRSA, NPQH
Age range: B3-11 & 16–18 G3–18
No. of pupils: 354

Benedict House
Preparatory School
1-5 Victoria Road, Sidcup,
Kent DA15 7HD
Tel: 020 8300 7206
Headmistress: Mrs Gemma Chikola
Age range: 3–11
Fees: Day £2,145–£2,395

Bickley Park School
24 Page Heath Lane, Bickley,
Bromley, Kent BR1 2DS
Tel: 020 8467 2195
Headmaster: Mr Paul Ashley
Age range: B3–13 G3–4
No. of pupils: 370
Fees: Day £6,525–£11,925

Bishop Challoner School
228 Bromley Road, Shortlands,
Bromley, Kent BR2 0BS
Tel: 020 8460 3546
Headteacher: Ms Paula Anderson
Age range: 3–18
No. of pupils: 412 VIth32
Fees: Day £6,441–£9,036

Breaside Preparatory
School
41-43 Orchard Road,
Bromley, Kent BR1 2PR
Tel: 020 8460 0916
Executive Principal: Mrs Karen A
Nicholson B.Ed, NPQH, Dip EYs
Age range: 2½–11
No. of pupils: 353
Fees: Day £9,948–£11,628

BROMLEY HIGH
SCHOOL GDST
For further details see p. 50
Blackbrook Lane, Bickley,
Bromley, Kent BR1 2TW
Tel: 020 8781 7000/1
Email: bhs@bro.gdst.net
Website:
www.bromleyhigh.gdst.net
Head: Mrs A M Drew
BA(Hons), MBA (Dunelm)
Age range: G4–18
No. of pupils: 912 VIth125
Fees: Day £12,855–£15,942

Farringtons Junior School
Perry Street, Chislehurst,
Kent BR7 6LR
Tel: 020 8467 0256
Head: Mrs C E James MA
Age range: 3–11
No. of pupils: 287
Fees: Day £8,760

Merton Court
Preparatory School
38 Knoll Road, Sidcup,
Kent DA14 4QU
Tel: 020 8300 2112
Headmaster: Mr Dominic
Price BEd, MBA
Age range: 3–11
Fees: Day £8,115–£8,910

St Christopher's
The Hall School
49 Bromley Road,
Beckenham, Kent BR3 5PA
Tel: 020 8650 2200
Headmaster: Mr A Velasco
MEd, BH(Hons), PGCE
Age range: 3–11
No. of pupils: 305
Fees: Day £2,250–£6,630

St David's College
Beckenham Road, West
Wickham, Kent BR4 0QS
Tel: 020 8777 5852
Principal: Mrs J Foulger
Age range: 4–11
No. of pupils: 155
Fees: Day £6,015–£6,165

West Lodge School
36 Station Road, Sidcup,
Kent DA15 7DU
Tel: 020 8300 2489
Head Teacher: Mrs Susan Webb
Age range: 3–11
No. of pupils: 163
Fees: Day £5,205–£8,700

Wickham Court School
Schiller International,
Layhams Road, West
Wickham, Kent BR4 9HW
Tel: 020 8777 2942
Head: Mrs Barbara Hunter
Age range: 2–16
No. of pupils: 121
Fees: Day £4,481–£6,900

Middlesex

ACS Hillingdon
International School
Hillingdon Court, 108 Vine
Lane, Hillingdon, Uxbridge,
Middlesex UB10 0BE
Tel: +44 (0) 1895 259 771
Head of School: Linda LaPine
Age range: 4–18
No. of pupils: 520
Fees: Day £17,260–£23,110

Alpha Preparatory School
21 Hindes Road, Harrow,
Middlesex HA1 1SH
Tel: 020 8427 1471
Head:
C.J.W Trinidad BSc(Hons), PGCE
Age range: 3–11
No. of pupils: 170
Fees: Day £3,150–£9,900

Ashton House School
50-52 Eversley Crescent,
Isleworth, Middlesex TW7 4LW
Tel: 020 8560 3902
Headteacher:
Mrs M Grundberg MA, PGCE
Age range: 3–11
Fees: Day £9,300–£10,200

Athelstan House School
36 Percy Road, Hampton,
Middlesex TW12 2LA
Tel: 020 8979 1045
Headmistress: Elsa Woolf
Age range: 3–7

Buckingham
Preparatory School
458 Rayners Lane, Pinner,
Middlesex HA5 5DT
Tel: 020 8866 2737
Headmaster: Mr L S Smith BA(Hons),
MSc, LCP, PGDE, CertEd
Age range: B4–11
Fees: Day £7,560–£9,900

Buxlow Preparatory School
5/6 Castleton Gardens,
Wembley, Middlesex HA9 7QJ
Tel: 020 8904 3615
Headmistress: Mrs Ann Baines
Age range: 4–11
Fees: Day £6,885

Hampton Prep and
Pre-Prep School
Gloucester Road, Hampton,
Middlesex TW12 2UQ
Tel: 020 8979 1844
Headmaster: Mr Tim Smith
Age range: 3–11
Fees: Day £4,995–£11,580

Holland House School
1 Broadhurst Avenue, Edgware,
Middlesex HA8 8TP
Tel: 020 8958 6979
Headmistress: Mrs Irinia
Tyk BA(Hons)
Age range: 4–11
Fees: Day £7,308

Jack and Jill School
30 Nightingale Road, Hampton,
Middlesex TW12 3HX
Tel: 020 8979 3195
Principal: Miss K Papirnik BEd(Hons)
Age range: B2–5 G2–7
No. of pupils: 155
Fees: Day £2,409–£9,597

Newland House School
Waldegrave Park, Twickenham,
Middlesex TW1 4TQ
Tel: 020 8865 1305
Headmaster: Mr D A Alexander
Age range: B4–13 G4–11
No. of pupils: 425
Fees: Day £3,625–£4,055

North London
Collegiate School
Canons, Canons Drive,
Edgware, Middlesex HA8 7RJ
Tel: +44 (0)20 8952 0912
Headmistress: Mrs Bernice McCabe
Age range: G4–18
No. of pupils: 1080
Fees: Day £5,370–£6,354

Northwood College
for Girls GDST
Maxwell Road, Northwood,
Middlesex HA6 2YE
Tel: 01923 825446
Head Mistress: Miss Jacqualyn
Pain MA, MA, MBA
Age range: G3–18
No. of pupils: 840 VIth100

Orley Farm School
South Hill Avenue, Harrow,
Middlesex HA1 3NU
Tel: 020 8869 7600
Headmaster: Tim Calvey
Age range: 4–13
No. of pupils: 496
Fees: Day £13,284–£15,324
🧍£🖊

**Quainton Hall
School & Nursery**
91 Hindes Road, Harrow,
Middlesex HA1 1RX
Tel: 020 8861 8861
Headmaster:
S Ford BEd (Hons), UWE Bristol
Age range: B2–13 G2–11
Fees: Day £9,075–£9,975
£

Radnor House
Pope's Villa, Cross Deep,
Twickenham, Middlesex TW1 4QG
Tel: 020 8891 6264
Head of School: Mr.
David Paton MA

Reddiford School
36-38 Cecil Park, Pinner,
Middlesex HA5 5HH
Tel: 020 8866 0660
Headteacher:
Mrs J Batt CertEd, NPQH
Age range: 3–11
No. of pupils: 320
Fees: Day £3,480–£8,340
£

Roxeth Mead School
Buckholt House, 25 Middle Road,
Harrow, Middlesex HA2 0HW
Tel: 020 8422 2092
Headmistress: Mrs A Isaacs
Age range: 3–7
No. of pupils: 54
Fees: Day £9,450

St Catherine's School
Cross Deep, Twickenham,
Middlesex TW1 4QJ
Tel: 020 8891 2898
Headmistress: Sister Paula
Thomas BEd(Hons), MA
Age range: G3–18
No. of pupils: 430
Fees: Day £10,115–£14,022
🧍🌐Ⓐ£🖊

St Christopher's School
71 Wembley Park Drive,
Wembley, Middlesex HA9 8HE
Tel: 020 8902 5069
Headteacher: Mr G. P. Musetti
Age range: 4–11
Fees: Day £8,400–£9,225

St Helen's College
Parkway, Hillingdon, Uxbridge,
Middlesex UB10 9JX
Tel: 01895 234371
Joint Headteachers: Mr D A
Crehan & Mrs G R Crehan
Age range: 3–11
No. of pupils: 351
Fees: Day £5,850–£10,695
🖊

St Helen's School
Eastbury Road, Northwood,
Middlesex HA6 3AS
Tel: +44 (0)1923 843210
Headmistress:
Dr Mary Short BA, PhD
Age range: G3–18
No. of pupils: VIth165
🧍🌐Ⓐ£

St John's School
Potter Street Hill, Northwood,
Middlesex HA6 3QY
Tel: 020 8866 0067
Headmaster: Mr M S Robinson BSc
Age range: B3–13 years
No. of pupils: 350
Fees: Day £9,000–£13,250
🧍£

St Martin's School
40 Moor Park Road, Northwood,
Middlesex HA6 2DJ
Tel: 01923 825740
Headmaster:
Mr D T Tidmarsh BSc(Wales)
Age range: B3–13
No. of pupils: 400
Fees: Day £1,450–£4,066
🧍£🖊

**STAINES PREPARATORY
SCHOOL**
For further details see p. 52
3 Gresham Road, Staines upon
Thames, Middlesex TW18 2BT
Tel: 01784 450909
Email:
admissions@stainesprep.co.uk
Website: www.stainesprep.co.uk
Head of School: Ms Samantha
Sawyer B.Ed (Hons), M.Ed, NPQH
Age range: 3–11
No. of pupils: 377
Fees: Day £9,270–£10,680
£🖊

Tashbar of Edgeware
47-49 Mowbray Road, Edgware,
Middlesex HA8 8JL
Tel: 020 8958 5162
Headteacher: Mr N Jaffe
Age range: B3–11
No. of pupils: 88
🧍

**The Falcons Preparatory
School for Boys**
41 Few Foot Road, Richmond,
Middlesex TW9 2SS
Tel: 0844 225 2211
Headmaster: Mr Gordon Milne
Age range: B7–13
No. of pupils: 100
Fees: Day £12,660
🧍🖊

**The Hall Pre-Preparatory
School & Nursery**
The Grange Country House,
Rickmansworth Road,
Northwood, Middlesex HA6 2RB
Tel: 01923 822807
Headmistress: Mrs S M Goodwin
Age range: 1–7
Fees: Day £3,120–£10,350
🖊

**The Lady Eleanor
Holles School (Junior
Department)**
177 Uxbridge Road, Hampton
Hill, Middlesex TW12 1BD
Tel: 020 8979 2173
Head of School: Mrs Paula Mortimer
Age range: G7–11
No. of pupils: 190
Fees: Day £15,639
🧍🖊

The Mall School
185 Hampton Road, Twickenham,
Middlesex TW2 5NQ
Tel: 0208 977 2523
Headmaster: Mr D C Price BSc, MA
Age range: B4–13
No. of pupils: 320
Fees: Day £10,281–£11,934
🧍£🖊

The Noam Primary School
8-10 Forty Avenue, Wembley,
Middlesex HA9 8JW
Tel: 020 8908 9491
Headteacher: Mrs Sarah Simmonds
Age range: 3–11
No. of pupils: 154

**The St Michael
Steiner School**
Park Road, Hanworth Park,
London, Middlesex TW13 6PN
Tel: 0208 893 1299
Age range: 3–16 (17 from Jul 2014)
No. of pupils: 101
Fees: Day £5,800–£8,900
£🖊

**Twickenham
Preparatory School**
Beveree, 43 High Street,
Hampton, Middlesex TW12 2SA
Tel: 020 8979 6216
Head: Mr D Malam BA(Hons)
(Southampton), PGCE(Winchester)
Age range: B4–13 G4–11
No. of pupils: 272
Fees: Day £9,345–£10,110
£🖊

Surrey

Al-Khair School
109-117 Cherry Orchard Road,
Croydon, Surrey CR0 6BE
Tel: 020 8662 8664
Headteacher: Mr Usman Qureshi
Age range: 5–16
No. of pupils: 126

Broomfield House School
Broomfield Road, Kew Gardens,
Richmond, Surrey TW9 3HS
Tel: 020 8940 3884
Headteacher: Mr N O York
BA(Hons), MA, MPhil, FRSA
Age range: 3–11
No. of pupils: 160
Fees: Day £5,054–£11,787
🖊

Collingwood School
3 Springfield Road, Wallington,
Surrey SM6 0BD
Tel: 020 8647 4607
Headmaster: Mr Chris Fenwick
Age range: 3–11
No. of pupils: 120
Fees: Day £3,600–£6,750
🖊

**CROYDON HIGH
SCHOOL GDST**
For further details see p. 51
Old Farleigh Road, Selsdon,
South Croydon, Surrey CR2 8YB
Tel: 020 8260 7500
Email: admissions@cry.gdst.net
Website:
www.croydonhigh.gdst.net
Head of Junior School:
Mrs Sophie Bradshaw
Age range: G3–18
No. of pupils: 580 VIth110
🧍Ⓐ£🖊

Cumnor House School
168 Pampisford Road, South
Croydon, Surrey CR2 6DA
Tel: 020 8660 3445
Head Master:
Mr P J Clare-Hunt MA(Ed) Cert Ed
Age range: B2–13
No. of pupils: 440
Fees: Day £2,945–£3,735

Cumnor House School – Treetops Nursery
91 Pampisford Road, South
Croydon, Surrey CR2 6DH
Tel: +44 (0)20 8660 3445
Manager:
Mrs Charlotte Figueira BEd(Hons)
Age range: 2–4
No. of pupils: 200
Fees: Day £1,370–£2,945

Cumnor House School for Girls
1 Woodcote Lane, Purley,
Surrey CR8 3HB
Tel: 020 8660 3445
Headmaster: Mr Peter Kelly
Age range: G2–11
No. of pupils: 180
Fees: Day £2,945–£3,735

Educare Small School
12 Cowleaze Road, Kingston
upon Thames, Surrey KT2 6DZ
Tel: 020 8547 0144
Head Teacher: Mrs E Steinthal
Age range: 3–11
No. of pupils: 46
Fees: Day £5,040

Elmhurst School
44-48 South Park Hill Rd, South
Croydon, Surrey CR2 7DW
Tel: 020 8688 0661
Headmaster: Mr M J Apsley
BA(Hons), PGCE
Age range: B4–11
No. of pupils: 207
Fees: Day £6,300–£7,545

Folly's End Christian School
Folly's End Church, 5-9 Surrey
Street, Croydon, Surrey CR0 1RG
Tel: 020 8649 9121
Senior Leaders: Dave & Ze Markee
Age range: 3–11
Fees: Day £4,740

Holy Cross Preparatory School
George Road, Kingston upon
Thames, Surrey KT2 7NU
Tel: 020 8942 0729
Headteacher: Mrs S Hair BEd(Hons)
Age range: G4–11
No. of pupils: 250
Fees: Day £9,960

Homefield Preparatory School
Western Road, Sutton,
Surrey SM1 2TE
Tel: 0208 642 0965
Headmaster: Mr John Towers
Age range: B3–13
No. of pupils: 350
Fees: Day £2,785–£4,275

Kew College
24-26 Cumberland Road,
Kew, Surrey TW9 3HQ
Tel: 020 8940 2039
Headteacher: Mrs Marianne Austin
BSc(Hons) MA(Hons) ACA PGCE
Age range: 3–11
No. of pupils: 296

Kew Green Preparatory School
Layton House, Ferry Lane, Kew
Green, Richmond, Surrey TW9 3AF
Tel: 020 8948 5999
Headmaster: Mr J Peck
Age range: 4–11
No. of pupils: 260
Fees: Day £15,606

King's House School
68 King's Road, Richmond,
Surrey TW10 6ES
Tel: 020 8940 1878
Head:
Mr Mark Turner BA, PGCE, NPQH
Age range: B3–13 G3–4
No. of pupils: 460
Fees: Day £2,165–£5,120

Laleham Lea School
29 Peaks Hill, Purley, Surrey CR8 3JJ
Tel: 020 8660 3351
Headteacher: Mrs J Staunton
Age range: 3–11
Fees: Day £2,128–£6,405

Oakwood Independent School
Godstone Road, Purley,
Surrey CR8 2AN
Tel: 020 8668 8080
Headmaster:
Mr Ciro Candia BA(Hons), PGCE
Age range: 3–11
No. of pupils: 176
Fees: Day £5,280–£7,644

Old Palace of John Whitgift School
Old Palace Road, Croydon,
Surrey CR0 1AX
Tel: 020 8686 7347
Head: Mrs. C Jewell
Age range: B3 months–4
years G3 months–19 years
No. of pupils: 740 VIth120
Fees: Day £10,086–£13,497

Old Vicarage School
48 Richmond Hill, Richmond,
Surrey TW10 6QX
Tel: 020 8940 0922
Headmistress: Mrs G D Linthwaite
Age range: G4–11
No. of pupils: 200
Fees: Day £4,380

Park Hill School
8 Queens Road, Kingston upon
Thames, Surrey KT2 7SH
Tel: 020 8546 5496
Principal: Mrs Marie Christie
Age range: 2–7
No. of pupils: 100
Fees: Day £4,320–£8,130

Reedham Park School
71A Old Lodge Lane,
Purley, Surrey CR8 4DN
Tel: 020 8660 6357
Headteacher: Mrs Katie Shah
Age range: 4–11
No. of pupils: 122
Fees: Day £3,540–£4,110

Rokeby School
George Road, Kingston upon
Thames, Surrey K12 7PB
Tel: 020 8942 2247
Head: Mr J R Peck
Age range: B4–13
No. of pupils: 370
Fees: Day £3,974–£4,948

Royal Russell Junior School
Coombe Lane, Croydon,
Surrey CR9 5BX
Tel: 020 8651 5884
Junior School Headmaster:
Mr James C Thompson
Age range: 3–11
No. of pupils: 300
Fees: Day £3,660–£10,155

Seaton House School
67 Banstead Road South,
Sutton, Surrey SM2 5LH
Tel: 020 8642 2332
Headmistress: Mrs Debbie Morrison
Higher Diploma in Education (RSA)
Age range: B3–5 G3–11
No. of pupils: 164
Fees: Day £2,187–£8,955

Shrewsbury House School
107 Ditton Road, Surbiton,
Surrey KT6 6RL
Tel: 020 8399 3066
Headmaster:
Mr K Doble BA, PDM, PGCE
Age range: B7–13
No. of pupils: 320
Fees: Day £13,680

St David's School
23/25 Woodcote Valley Road,
Purley, Surrey CR8 3AL
Tel: 020 8660 0723
Headmistress:
Mrs Lindsay Nash BEd(Hons)
Age range: 3–11
No. of pupils: 167
Fees: Day £2,985–£5,940

Surbiton High School
13-15 Surbiton Crescent, Kingston
upon Thames, Surrey KT1 2JT
Tel: 020 8546 5245
Principal: Ann Haydon BSc(Hons)
Age range: G4–18
No. of pupils: 1210 VIth186
Fees: Day £6,390–£10,857

The Study School
57 Thetford Road, New
Malden, Surrey KT3 5DP
Tel: 020 8942 0754
Head of School:
Ms Donna Brackstone-Drake
Age range: 3–11
No. of pupils: 134
Fees: Day £3,984–£8,973

Unicorn School
238 Kew Road, Richmond,
Surrey TW9 3JX
Tel: 020 8948 3926
Headmaster: Mr Kit Thompson
Age range: 3–11
No. of pupils: 370
Fees: Day £6,000–£11,010

Westbury House
80 Westbury Road, New
Malden, Surrey KT3 5AS
Tel: 020 8942 5885
Head of School: Rosalyn Holiday
Age range: 3–11
Fees: Day £1,045–£2,507

London

KEY TO SYMBOLS

- (†) *Boys' school*
- (♀) *Girls' school*
- (🌐) *International school*
- (16⁻) *Tutorial or sixth form college*
- (A) *A levels*
- (🏛) *Boarding accommodation*
- (£) *Bursaries*
- (IB) *International Baccalaureate*
- (✎) *Learning support*
- (16⁺) *Entrance at 16+*
- (⚙) *Vocational qualifications*
- (IAPS) *Independent Association of Prep Schools*
- (HMC) *The Headmasters' & Headmistresses' Conference*
- (ISA) *Independent Schools Association*
- (GSA) *Girls' School Association*
- (BSA) *Boarding Schools' Association*
- (S) *Society of Heads*

Unless otherwise indicated, all schools are coeducational day schools. Single-sex and boarding schools will be indicated by the relevant icon.

London

Central London

Charterhouse Square School
40 Charterhouse Square,
London EC1M 6EA
Tel: 020 7600 3805
Head of School:
Mrs Caroline Lloyd BEd (Hons)
Age range: 3–11
No. of pupils: 196
Fees: Day £4,575

City of London School for Girls
St Giles' Terrace, Barbican,
London EC2Y 8BB
Tel: 020 7847 5500
Headmistress: Mrs E Harrop
Age range: G7–18
Fees: Day £14,409
👤Ⓐ£🖋

Dallington School
8 Dallington Street, Islington,
London EC1V 0BW
Tel: 020 7251 2284
Headteacher: Mrs M C Hercules
Age range: 3–11
No. of pupils: 130
Fees: Day £9,978–£12,630

**ST PAUL'S CATHEDRAL
SCHOOL**
For further details see p. 63
2 New Change,
London EC4M 9AD
Tel: 020 7248 5156
Email:
admissions@spcs.london.sch.uk
Website: www.spcslondon.com
Headmaster: Mr Simon Larter-
Evans BA (Hons), PGCE, FRSA
Age range: 4–13
No. of pupils: 250
Fees: Day £13,200–
£14,211 FB £8,057
🏫£🖋

The Lyceum
6 Paul Street, London EC2A 4JH
Tel: 020 7247 1588
Joint Headteachers: Mr Jeremy
Rowe & Mrs Lynn Hannay
Age range: 4–11
No. of pupils: 100
Fees: Day £8,700–£13,800

East London

Al-Falah Primary School
48 Kenninghall Road,
Clapton, London E5 8BY
Tel: 020 8985 1059
Headteacher: Mr M A Hussain
Age range: 5–11
No. of pupils: 83
Fees: Day £1,600

Al-Mizan School
46 Whitechapel Road,
London E1 1JX
Tel: 020 7650 3070
Head: Mr Ziaurr Ahman
Age range: B7–18
No. of pupils: 200 VIth13
Fees: Day £2,400
👤Ⓐ

Beis Trana Girls' School
186 Upper Clapton Road,
London E5 9DH
Tel: 020 8815 8003
Age range: G3–16
No. of pupils: 270
👤

Faraday School
Old Gate House, 7 Trinity Buoy
Wharf, London E14 0JW
Tel: 020 8965 7374
Head Teacher: Miss S Stark
Age range: 4–11
No. of pupils: 100
Fees: Day £2,930
£

Forest School
College Place, Snaresbrook,
London E17 3PY
Tel: 020 8520 1744
Warden: Mr Anthony Faccinello
Age range: 4–18
No. of pupils: 1355 VIth260
Fees: Day £11,049–£16,335
Ⓐ£🖋

Gatehouse School
Sewardstone Road, Victoria
Park, London E2 9JG
Tel: 020 8980 2978
Headmistress: Mrs Belinda Canham
JP, BA(Hons), PGCE(Froebel)
Age range: 3–11
No. of pupils: 320
Fees: Day £6,920–£8,502
£🖋

Grangewood Independent School
Chester Road, Forest
Gate, London E7 8QT
Tel: 020 8472 3552
Headteacher: Mrs B A Roberts
Age range: 3–11
No. of pupils: 61
🖋

Green Gables Montessori School
St George in the East Crypt
West, 14 Cannon Street
Road, London E1 0BH
Tel: 020 7488 2374
Head: Mrs V Hunt
Age range: 0–8
No. of pupils: 45
Fees: Day £740–£10,480

Hyland House School
Holcombe Road, Tottenham,
London N17 9AD
Tel: 020 8520 4186
Head Teacher:
Mrs Gina Abbequaye
Age range: 3–11
Fees: Day £2,520

Lubavitch House School (Junior Boys)
135 Clapton Common,
London E5 9AE
Tel: 020 8800 1044
Head: Rabbi D Golomb
Age range: B5–11
No. of pupils: 101
Fees: Day £520–£3,100
👤

Monty's Montessori School
10–11 Charterhouse Square,
Hargrave Road, London EC1M 6EH
Tel: +44 (0)20 7281 3889
Principal: Carole Montana
Age range: 2.6–6

Normanhurst School
68–74 Station Road,
Chingford, London E4 7BA
Tel: 020 8529 4307
Headmistress: Mrs Claire Osborn
Age range: 2 –16
No. of pupils: 250
Fees: Day £7,470–£11,235
🖋

Paragon Christian Academy
233–241 Glyn Road, London E5 0JP
Tel: 020 8985 1119
Headteacher: Mrs J A Lynch
Age range: 5–16
No. of pupils: 34

Pillar Box Montessori Nursery & Pre-Prep School
107 Bow Road, London E3 2AN
Tel: 020 8980 0700
Age range: 0–7
Fees: Day £250–£500

Promised Land Academy
St Cedds Hall, Webb Gardens,
Plaistow, London E13 8SR
Tel: 0207 473 3229
Head: Mr A Coote
Age range: 4–16

Quwwat-ul Islam Girls School
16 Chaucer Road, Forest
Gate, London E7 9NB
Tel: 020 8548 4736
Headteacher: Mrs B Khan
Age range: G4–11
No. of pupils: 150
👤

River House Montessori School
3-4 Shadwell Pierhead, Glamis
Road, London E1W 3TD
Tel: 020 7538 9886
Headmistress: Miss S Greenwood
Age range: 3–12
Fees: Day £2,700–£9,000
🖋

Snaresbrook Preparatory School
75 Woodford Road, South
Woodford, London E18 2EA
Tel: 020 8989 2394
Head of School: Mr Christopher Curl
Age range: 3–11
No. of pupils: 164
Fees: Day £6,696–£8,952
🖋

St Joseph's Convent School For Girls
59 Cambridge Park,
Wanstead, London E11 2PR
Tel: 020 8989 4700
Headteacher: Ms C Glover
Age range: G3–11
No. of pupils: 171
Fees: Day £5,355
👤🖋

Talmud Torah Machikei Hadass School
96-98 Clapton Common,
London E5 9AL
Tel: 020 8800 6599
Headteacher: Rabbi C Silbiger
Age range: B4–11
No. of pupils: 271
👤

Winston House Preparatory School
140 High Road, London E18 2QS
Tel: 020 8505 6565
Head Teacher: Mrs Marian Kemp
Age range: 3–11
Fees: Day £5,850–£7,050

North London

Annemount School
18 Holne Chase, Hampstead
Garden Suburb, London N2 0QN
Tel: 020 8455 2132
Principal: Mrs G Maidment
BA(Hons), MontDip
Age range: 2–7
No. of pupils: 100
Fees: Day £2,500–£4,500

Avenue Nursery & Pre-Preparatory School
2 Highgate Avenue, London N6 5RX
Tel: 020 8348 6815
Principal: Mrs. Mary Fysh
Age range: 3 1/2–7 1/2
No. of pupils: 79
🖋

Beis Aharon School
97-99 Bethune Road,
London N16 5ED
Tel: 020 88007 368
Head: Y Pomerantz
Age range: B2–12
No. of pupils: 177

**Beis Chinuch Lebonos
Girls School**
Woodberry Down Centre,
Woodberry Down, London N4 2SH
Tel: 020 88097 737
Headmistress: Mrs Bertha Schneck
Age range: G2–16
No. of pupils: 421

Beis Malka Girls School
93 Alkham Road, London N16 6XD
Tel: 020 8806 2070
Headmaster: M Dresdner
Age range: G5–16
No. of pupils: 339

**Beis Rochel D'Satmar
Girls School**
51-57 Amhurst Park, London N16 5DL
Tel: 020 8800 9060
Headmistress: Mrs A Scher
Age range: G2–17
No. of pupils: 788

Bnois Jerusalem School
79-81 Amhurst Park,
London N16 5DL
Tel: 020 8802 7470
Head: Mrs Sonnenschein
Age range: G3–16

Channing School
The Bank, Highgate, London N6 5HF
Tel: 020 8340 2328
Head: Mrs B M Elliott
Age range: G4–18
No. of pupils: 746 VIth108
Fees: Day £14,085–£15,255

Dwight School London
6 Friern Barnet Lane,
London N11 3LX
Tel: +44 (0)20 8920 0637
Head: Mrs Alison Cobbin
BA, Dip Ed, MBA
Age range: 3–18

**Finchley & Acton
Yochien School**
6 Hendon Avenue, Finchley,
London N3 1UE
Tel: 020 8343 2191
Headteacher:
Mr Katsumasa Kitagaki
Age range: 2–6
No. of pupils: 145

Getters Talmud Torah
86 Amhurst Park, London N16 5AR
Tel: 020 8802 2512
Headteacher: Mr David Kahana
Age range: B4–11
No. of pupils: 171

**Grange Park
Preparatory School**
13 The Chine, Grange Park,
Winchmore Hill, London N21 2EA
Tel: 020 8360 1469
Headteacher: Mrs B McLaughlin
Age range: G4–11
No. of pupils: 90
Fees: Day £9,900

Highgate
North Road, Highgate,
London N6 4AY
Tel: 020 8340 1524
Head Master: Mr A S Pettitt MA
Age range: 3–18
No. of pupils: 1541 VIth312
Fees: Day £15,135–£17,475

Highgate Junior School
Cholmeley House, 3 Bishopswood
Road, London N6 4PL
Tel: 020 8340 9193
Principal: Mr S M James BA
Age range: 7–11
Fees: Day £10,695–£11,955

**Highgate Pre-
Preparatory School**
7 Bishopswood Road,
London N6 4PH
Tel: 020 8340 9196
Principal: Mrs Diane Hecht
Age range: 3–7
No. of pupils: 150
Fees: Day £16,965

Keble Prep
Wades Hill, Winchmore
Hill, London N21 1BG
Tel: 020 8360 3359
Headmaster: Mr G. P. McCarthy
Age range: B4–13
Fees: Day £3,760–£4,670

Kerem School
Norrice Lea, London N2 0RE
Tel: 020 8455 0909
Acting Head Teacher:
Miss Alyson Burns
Age range: 3–11
Fees: Day £8,250–£6,675

Montessori House
5 Princes Avenue, Muswell
Hill, London N10 3LS
Tel: 020 8444 4399
Head: Ms Lisa Christoforou
Age range: 6 months–7 years
No. of pupils: 100
Fees: Day £5,355–£9,450

Norfolk House School
10 Muswell Avenue, Muswell
Hill, London N10 2EG
Tel: 020 8883 4584
Head Teacher: Ms Sam Habgood
Age range: 4–11
No. of pupils: 130
Fees: Day £9,855

**North London
Muslim School**
131-133 Fore Street, Edmonton,
London N18 2XF
Tel: 020 8345 7008
Headteacher: Mr W Abdulla
Age range: 4–10
No. of pupils: 21

**North London Rudolf
Steiner School**
1-3 The Campsbourne,
London N8 7PN
Tel: 020 8341 3770
Age range: 21/2–7
No. of pupils: 40

Palmers Green High School
Hoppers Road, Winchmore
Hill, London N21 3LJ
Tel: 020 8886 1135
Headmistress: Mrs Christine
Edmundson BMus(Hons),
MBA, PGCE, LRAM, ARCM
Age range: G3–16
No. of pupils: 300
Fees: Day £5,985–£10,785

**Rosemary Works
Independent School**
1 Branch Place, London N1 5PH
Tel: 020 7739 3950
Head: Dorothy Davey
Age range: 3–11
No. of pupils: 104
Fees: Day £6,195

**Salcombe Preparatory
School**
224-226 Chase Side,
Southgate, London N14 4PL
Tel: 020 8441 5356
Headmistress: Mrs Sarah-Jane
Davies BA(Hons) QTS MEd
Age range: 4–11
No. of pupils: 236
Fees: Day £7,890

St Paul's Steiner School
1 St Paul's Road, Islington,
London N1 2QH
Tel: 020 7226 4454
College of Teachers:
College of Teachers
Age range: 2–14
No. of pupils: 136

**Sunrise Nursery,
Stoke Newington**
1 Cazenove Road, Stoke
Newington, Hackney,
London N16 6PA
Tel: 020 8806 6279
Principal: Didi Ananda Manika

Sunrise Primary School
55 Coniston Road, Tottenham,
London N17 0EX
Tel: 020 8806 6279 (Office); 020
8885 3354 (School)
Head: Mrs Mary-Anne
Lovage MontDipEd, BA
Age range: 2–11
No. of pupils: 30
Fees: Day £5,343

**Talmud Torah Bobov
Primary School**
87 Egerton Road, London N16 6UE
Tel: 020 8809 1025
Headmaster: Mr Eisen
Age range: B3–13
No. of pupils: 320

**Talmud Torah Chaim
Meirim School**
26 Lampard Grove, London N16 6XB
Tel: 020 8806 0017
Principal: Rabbi S Hoffman
Age range: B6–13

**Talmud Torah Yetev
Lev School**
111-115 Cazenove Road,
London N16 6AX
Tel: 020 8806 3834
Headteacher: Mr J Stauber
Age range: B2–11
No. of pupils: 567

Tayyibah Girls School
88 Filey Avenue, Stamford
Hill, London N16 6JJ
Tel: 020 8880 0085
Headmistress: Mrs N B Qureishi MSc
Age range: G5–15
No. of pupils: 270
Fees: Day £1,630

**The Children's House
Upper School**
King Henry's Walk, London N1 4PB
Tel: 020 7249 6273
Headteacher: Mrs J Rothwell
Age range: 4–7
No. of pupils: 60
Fees: Day £3,250

**The Gower School
Montessori Nursery**
18 North Road, Islington,
London N7 9EY
Tel: 020 7700 2445
Principal: Miss Emma Gowers
Age range: 3 months–5 years
No. of pupils: 237

**The Gower School
Montessori Primary**
10 Cynthia Street, Barnsbury,
London N1 9JF
Tel: 020 7278 2020
Principal: Miss Emma Gowers
Age range: 4–11
No. of pupils: 237
Fees: Day £4,680–£19,129

TTTYY School
14 Heathland Road,
London N16 5NH
Tel: 020 8802 1348
Headmaster: Mr S B Gluck
Age range: B2–13
No. of pupils: 187

Vita et Pax School
Priory Close, Southgate,
London N14 4AT
Tel: 020 8449 8336
Headmistress:
Mrs M O'Connor BEd(Hons)
Age range: 3–11
Fees: Day £6,150

Yesodey Hatorah School
2-4 Amhurst Park, London N16 5AE
Tel: 020 8826 5500
Headteacher: Rabbi Pinter
Age range: 3–16
No. of pupils: 920

North-West London

Abercorn School
Infant Department, 28 Abercorn
Place, London NW8 9XP
Tel: 020 7286 4785
High Mistress: Mrs Andrea
Greystoke BA(Hons)
Age range: 2–13
No. of pupils: 360
Fees: Day £7,245–£13,425

Al-Sadiq & Al-Zahra Schools
134 Salusbury Road,
London NW6 6PF
Tel: 020 7372 7706
Headteacher: Dr M Movahedi
Age range: 4–16
No. of pupils: 389

Arnold House School
1 Loudoun Road, St John's
Wood, London NW8 0LH
Tel: 020 7266 4840
Headmaster: Mr Vivian Thomas
Age range: B5–13
No. of pupils: 270
Fees: Day £5,878

Beis Soroh Schneirer
Arbiter House, Wilberforce
Road, London NW9 6AT
Tel: 020 8343 1190
Head: Mrs R Weiss
Age range: G2–11
No. of pupils: 150

Belmont, Mill Hill Preparatory School
The Ridgeway, London NW7 4ED
Tel: 020 8906 7270
Headmaster: Mr Leon Roberts MA
Age range: 7–13
No. of pupils: 472
Fees: Day £15,500

Chalcot Montessori School AMI
9 Chalcot Gardens,
London NW3 4YB
Tel: 020 7722 1386
Principal:
Ms Joanna Morfey AMI Dip
Age range: 2–6
No. of pupils: 28
Fees: Day £7,026–£7,332

DEVONSHIRE HOUSE PREPARATORY SCHOOL
For further details see p. 56
2 Arkwright Road, Hampstead,
London NW3 6AE
Tel: 020 7435 1916
Email: enquiries@devonshire
houseprepschool.co.uk
Website: www.devonshire
houseschool.co.uk
Headmistress: Mrs S.
Piper BA(Hons)
Age range: B2 1/2–13 G2 1/2–11
No. of pupils: 650
Fees: Day £9,405–£17,220

Golders Hill School
666 Finchley Road,
London NW11 7NT
Tel: 020 8455 2589
Headmistress: Mrs A T
Eglash BA(Hons)
Age range: 2–7
No. of pupils: 180
Fees: Day £831–£6,870

Goodwyn School
Hammers Lane, Mill Hill,
London NW7 4DB
Tel: 020 8959 3756
Principal: Struan Robertson
Age range: 3–11
No. of pupils: 223
Fees: Day £3,645–£7,673.40

Grimsdell, Mill Hill Pre-Preparatory School
Winterstoke House, Wills Grove,
Mill Hill, London NW7 1QR
Tel: 020 8959 6884
Head: Mrs Kate Simon BA, PGCE
Age range: 3–7
No. of pupils: 182
Fees: Day £1,971–£4,285

Hampstead Hill Pre-Prep & Nursery School
St Stephen's Hall, Pond Street,
Hampstead, London NW3 2PP
Tel: 020 7435 6262
Principal: Mrs Andrea Taylor
Age range: B2–7+ G2–7+
Fees: Day £11,000–£14,000

Heathside Preparatory School
16 New End, Hampstead,
London NW3 1JA
Tel: +44 (0)20 7794 5857
Headteacher:
Ms Melissa Remus Elliot MSc
Age range: 2–13
No. of pupils: 370
Fees: Day £9,300–£14,250

Hendon Preparatory School
20 Tenterden Grove, Hendon,
London NW4 1TD
Tel: 020 8203 7727
Head of School:
Mr M. Lloyd-Williams
Age range: 2–13 years
No. of pupils: 165
Fees: Day £6,030–£13,455

Hereward House School
14 Strathray Gardens,
London NW3 4NY
Tel: 020 7794 4820
Headmaster: Mr T W Burden
Age range: B4–13
No. of pupils: 170
Fees: Day £13,065–£14,205

International Community School
4 York Terrace East, Regents
Park, London NW1 4PT
Tel: +44 20 7935 1206
Head of School: Ms Rose Threlfall
Age range: 3–18
No. of pupils: 260
Fees: Day £16,650–£22,100

L'Ile Aux Enfants
22 Vicar's Road, London NW5 4NL
Tel: 020 7267 7119
Headmistress: Mrs Chailleux
Age range: 3–11
No. of pupils: 192
Fees: Day £3,270

LYNDHURST HOUSE PREP SCHOOL
For further details see p. 58
24 Lyndhurst Gardens,
Hampstead, London NW3 5NW
Tel: 020 7435 4936
Email: office@
lyndhursthouse.co.uk
Website:
www.lyndhursthouse.co.uk
Headmaster: Andrew
Reid MA(Oxon)
Age range: B4–13
No. of pupils: 165
Fees: Day £5,735–£6,410

Maple Walk School
62A Crownhill Road,
London NW10 4EB
Tel: 020 8963 3890
Head Teacher: Mrs S Gillam
Age range: 4–11
No. of pupils: 200
Fees: Day £2,846

Maria Montessori School – Hampstead
26 Lyndhurst Gardens,
Hampstead, London NW3 5NW
Tel: +44 (0)20 7435 3646
Director of School: Mrs L Lawrence
Age range: 2–11
No. of pupils: 60
Fees: Day £5,400

Naima Jewish Preparatory School
21 Andover Place, London NW6 5ED
Tel: 020 7328 2802
Headteacher:
Mr Michael Cohen MA, NPQH
Age range: 3–11
Fees: Day £5,997–£7,470

Nancy Reuben Primary School
Finchley Lane, Hendon,
London NW4 1DJ
Tel: 020 82025646
Head: D A David
Age range: 3–11
No. of pupils: 207

NORTH BRIDGE HOUSE PREPARATORY SCHOOL REGENT'S PARK
For further details see p. 59
1 Gloucester Avenue,
London NW1 7AB
Tel: 020 7428 1520
Email: admissions@
northbridgehouse.com
Website: www.northbridge
house.com/prep
Head: Brodie Bibby
Age range: 7–13
No. of pupils: 100
Fees: Day £16,290

North Bridge House Pre-Preparatory School Hampstead
8 Netherhall Gardens,
London NW3 5RR
Tel: 0207 267 6266
Head Teacher: Mrs J Hockley
Age range: 5–6
No. of pupils: 208
Fees: Day £14,700

OYH Primary School
Finchley Lane, Hendon,
London NW4 1DJ
Tel: 020 8202 5646
Headteacher: D A David
Age range: 3–11
No. of pupils: 180

Rainbow Montessori School
13 Woodchurch Road,
Hampstead, London NW6 3PL
Tel: 020 7328 8986
Head Mistress:
Maggy Miller MontDip
Age range: 5–12
Fees: Day £3,250–£3,297

Saint Christina's R C Preparatory School
25 St Edmunds Terrace, Regent's
Park, London NW8 7PY
Tel: 020 7722 8784
Headteacher: Mrs P Mortimer
Age range: B3–7 G3–11
No. of pupils: 224
Fees: Day £11,076

Sarum Hall
15 Eton Avenue, London NW3 3EL
Tel: 020 7794 2261
Headmistress: Mrs Christine Smith
Age range: G3–11
No. of pupils: 170
Fees: Day £6,048–£10,065

South Hampstead High School GDST
3 Maresfield Gardens, London NW3 5SS
Tel: 020 7435 2899
Headmistress: Mrs J E Stephen BSc
Age range: G4–18
No. of pupils: 852 VIth162
Fees: Day £9,342–£12,006

Southbank International School – Hampstead
16 Netherhall Gardens, London NW3 5TH
Tel: 020 7243 3803
Principal: Shirley Harwood
Age range: 3–11

St Anthony's School for Boys
90 Fitzjohn's Avenue, Hampstead, London NW3 6NP
Tel: 020 7431 1066
Headmaster: Mr Paul Keyte
Age range: B4–13
No. of pupils: 310

St Christopher's School
32 Belsize Lane, Hampstead, London NW3 5AE
Tel: 020 7435 1521
Head:
Mrs S A West BA(Hons), PGCE, MA
Age range: G4–11
No. of pupils: 235
Fees: Day £12,450

St Johns Wood Pre-Preparatory School
St Johns Hall, Lords Roundabout, Prince Albert Road, London NW8 7NE
Tel: 020 7722 7149
Headmistress: Ms D Louskas
Age range: 3–7
No. of pupils: 70
Fees: Day £7,620–£12,090

St Margaret's School
18 Kidderpore Gardens, Hampstead, London NW3 7SR
Tel: 020 7435 2439
Principal: Mr M Webster BSc, PGCE
Age range: G4–16
No. of pupils: 156
Fees: Day £10,410–£12,060

St Martin's School
22 Goodwyn Avenue, Mill Hill, London NW7 3RG
Tel: 020 8959 1965
Head: Mrs Angela Wilson DipEd
Age range: 3–11
No. of pupils: 125
Fees: Day £6,500

St Mary's School Hampstead
47 Fitzjohn's Avenue, Hampstead, London NW3 6PG
Tel: 020 7435 1868
Head Teacher:
Mrs Harriet Connor-Earl
Age range: B2 years 9 months–7 years G2 years 9 months–11 years
No. of pupils: 300
Fees: Day £7,305–£13,500

St Nicholas School
22 Salmon Street, London NW9 8PN
Tel: 020 8205 7153
Headmistress:
Mrs Alyce Gregory CertEd
Age range: 5–11
No. of pupils: 80
Fees: Day £5,760

Swaminarayan School
260 Brentfield Road, Neasden, London NW10 8HE
Tel: 020 8965 8381
Headteacher: Nilesh Manani
Age range: 2–18
No. of pupils: 452 VIth36
Fees: Day £7,818–£10,707

The Academy School
3 Pilgrims Place, Rosslyn Hill, Hampstead, London NW3 1NG
Tel: 020 7435 6621
Headteacher: Mr Garth Evans
Age range: 6–14

The American School in London
One Waverley Place, London NW8 0NP
Tel: 020 7449 1221
Head: Mrs Coreen Hester
Age range: 4–18
No. of pupils: 1350
Fees: Day £21,950–£25,650

The Cavendish School
31 Inverness Street, Camden Town, London NW1 7HB
Tel: 020 7485 1958
Headmistress: Mrs T Dunbar BSc(Hons), PGCE, NPQH
Age range: G3–11
No. of pupils: 218
Fees: Day £11,550

The Hall School
23 Crossfield Road, Hampstead, London NW3 4NU
Tel: 020 7722 1700
Headmaster: P Lough MA
Age range: B4–13
No. of pupils: 440
Fees: Day £9,300–£11,400

The King Alfred School
Manor Wood, North End Road, London NW11 7HY
Tel: 020 8457 5200
Head:
Mrs Dawn Moore MA(London)
Age range: 4–18
No. of pupils: 615 VIth70
Fees: Day £12,624–£15,219

The Mulberry House School
7 Minster Road, West Hampstead, London NW2 3SD
Tel: 020 8452 7340
Headteacher: Ms Julie Kirwan
Age range: 2–8
No. of pupils: 184
Fees: Day £8,460–£15,698

The Phoenix School
36 College Crescent, London NW3 5LF
Tel: 020 7722 4433
Headmistress: Dr Zoe Dunn
Age range: 3–7
No. of pupils: 130
Fees: Day £2,585–£3,795

The School of the Islamic Republic of Iran
100 Carlton Vale, London NW6 5HE
Tel: 020 7372 8051
Headteacher: Mr Farzad Farzan
Age range: 6–16
No. of pupils: 53

The Village School
2 Parkhill Road, Belsize Park, London NW3 2YN
Tel: 020 7485 4673
Headmistress:
Miss C E F Gay BSc(Hons), PGCE
Age range: G3–11
No. of pupils: 100
Fees: Day £15,525

Torah Vodaas
Julian Headon House, West Hendon Broadway, London NW9 7AL
Tel: 02036704670
Head of School: Mr Mark Shelton
Age range: B2–11

Trevor-Roberts School
55-57 Eton Avenue, London NW3 3ET
Tel: 020 7586 1444
Headmaster:
Simon Trevor-Roberts BA
Age range: 5–13
Fees: Day £12,270–£14,070

University College School (Junior)
11 Holly Hill, London NW3 6QN
Tel: 020 7435 3068
Headmaster: Mr Lewis Hayward MA (Oxon Lit. Hum), MA (OU, ED. Management), PGCE
Age range: B7–11
No. of pupils: 250
Fees: Day £5,105

South-East London

Alleyn's School
Townley Road, Dulwich, London SE22 8SU
Tel: 020 8557 1500
Headmaster: Dr G Savage MA, PhD, FRSA
Age range: 4–18
No. of pupils: 1223 VIth291
Fees: Day £14,139–£16,587

Blackheath High School GDST
Vanbrugh Park, Blackheath, London SE3 7AG
Tel: 020 8853 2929
Head: Mrs Carol Chandler-Thompson BA (Hons) Exeter, PGCE Exeter
Age range: G3–18
No. of pupils: 780

Blackheath Nursery & Preparatory School
4 St Germans Place, Blackheath, London SE3 0NJ
Tel: 020 8858 0692
Headmistress: Mrs P J Thompson
Age range: 3–11
Fees: Day £8,130–£11,190

Colfe's Preparatory School
Horn Park Lane, Lee, London SE12 8AW
Tel: 020 8463 8240
Head: Mrs Sarah Marsh
Age range: 3–11
No. of pupils: 355
Fees: Day £8,730–£10,134

Dulwich College
London SE21 7LD
Tel: 020 8693 3601
Master: Dr J A F Spence
Age range: B7–18
No. of pupils: 1589 VIth470
Fees: Day £18,231 WB £35,679 FB £38,052

Dulwich College Kindergarten & Infants School
Eller Bank, 87 College Road, London SE21 7HH
Tel: 020 8693 1538
Head: Mrs H M Friell
Age range: 3 months–7 years
No. of pupils: 251

Dulwich College Preparatory School
42 Alleyn Park, Dulwich, London SE21 7AA
Tel: 020 8766 5500
Headmaster:
Mr M W Roulston MBE, MEd
Age range: B3–13 G3–5
No. of pupils: 817
Fees: Day £4,350–£13,542 WB £18,213–£19,662

Eltham College
Grove Park Road, Mottingham,
London SE9 4QF
Tel: 0208 857 1455
Headmaster:
Mr P J Henderson BA, FRSA
Age range: B7–18 G16–18
No. of pupils: 830 VIth220
Fees: Day £10,800–£12,525

Eltham College Junior School
Grove Park Road, London SE9 4QF
Tel: 020 8857 1455
Headmaster: Keith John BSc, PGCE
Age range: B7–11
No. of pupils: 213
Fees: Day £10,320

Greenwich Steiner School
Woodlands, 90 Mycenae Road,
Blackheath, London SE3 7SE
Tel: 020 8858 4404
Age range: 3–14
No. of pupils: 180
Fees: Day £5,310–£8,004

Heath House Preparatory School
37 Wemyss Road, Blackheath,
London SE3 0TG
Tel: 020 8297 1900
Head Teacher:
Mrs Sophia Laslett CertEd PGDE
Age range: 3–11
No. of pupils: 115
Fees: Day £10,185–£13,785

Henriette Le Forestier Preparatory School
147 Central Hill, Upper
Norwood, London SE19 1RS
Tel: +44 (0)20 8653 2169
Head Teacher: Mrs L Pollard
Age range: 2–11
Fees: Day £3,739–£9,003

Herne Hill School
The Old Vicarage, 127 Herne
Hill, London SE24 9LY
Tel: 020 7274 6336
Headteacher: Mrs Ngaire Telford
Age range: 2–7
No. of pupils: 275
Fees: Day £1,850–£4,585

James Allen's Girls' School
144 East Dulwich Grove,
Dulwich, London SE22 8TE
Tel: 020 8693 1181
Head of School: Mrs
Sally-Anne Huang
Age range: G4–18
No. of pupils: 1075
Fees: Day £14,955–£16,515

Kings Kids Christian School
New Testament Church of
God, Bawtree Road, New
Cross, London SE14 6ET
Tel: 020 8691 5813
Headteacher: Mrs M Okenwa
Age range: 5–11
No. of pupils: 36

London Christian School
40 Tabard Street, London SE1 4JU
Tel: 020 3130 6430
Headmistress: Miss Georgina Hale
Age range: 3–11
No. of pupils: 105
Fees: Day £7,725

Oakfield Preparatory School
125-128 Thurlow Park Road, West
Dulwich, London SE21 8HP
Tel: 020 8670 4206
Head of School: Ms. Jane Stevens
Age range: 2–11 years
No. of pupils: 420
Fees: Day £9,750

Octavia House School, Vauxhall
Vauxhall Primary School, Vauxhall
Street, London SE11 5LG
Tel: 02036 514396 (Option:1)
Executive Head: Mr James Waite
Age range: 5–14
No. of pupils: 65

Octavia House School, Walworth
Larcom House, Larcom
Street, London SE17 1RT
Tel: 02036 514396 (Option:2)
Executive Head: Mr James Waite

Riverston School
63-69 Eltham Road, Lee
Green, London SE12 8UF
Tel: 020 8318 4327
Headmistress: Mrs S E Salathiel
Age range: 9 months–19 years
No. of pupils: 215

Rosemead Preparatory School, Dulwich
70 Thurlow Park Road,
London SE21 8HZ
Tel: 020 8670 5865
Headmaster: Arthur Bray CertEd
Age range: 3–11
No. of pupils: 349
Fees: Day £10,272–£11,286

St Dunstan's College
Stanstead Road, London SE6 4TY
Tel: 020 8516 7200
Headmistress: Mrs J D Davies BSc
Age range: 3–18
No. of pupils: 870

St Olave's Preparatory School
106 Southwood Road, New
Eltham, London SE9 3QS
Tel: 020 8294 8930
Head: Mr J Tilly
Age range: 3–11
No. of pupils: 220
Fees: Day £5,414–£8,700

Sydenham High School GDST
19 Westwood Hill, London SE26 6BL
Tel: 020 8557 7000
Headteacher: Kathryn Pullen MA
Age range: G4–18
No. of pupils: 630 VIth70
Fees: Day £11,466–£14,592

The Pointer School
19 Stratheden Road,
Blackheath, London SE3 7TH
Tel: 020 8293 1331
Headmaster: Mr R J S Higgins
MA, BEd, CertEd, FCollP
Age range: 3–11
No. of pupils: 370
Fees: Day £6,912–£13,782

The Villa Pre-Preparatory School & Nursery
54 Lyndhurst Grove, Peckham,
London SE15 5AH
Tel: 020 7703 6216
Head Teacher: Emma Bryant
Age range: 2–7
No. of pupils: 210

South-West London

Al-Muntada Islamic School
7 Bridges Place, Parsons
Green, London SW6 4HW
Tel: 020 7471 8283
Headteacher: Salma Ullah
Age range: 4–11
No. of pupils: 165
Fees: Day £2,500

Al-Risalah Secondary School
145 Upper Tooting Road,
London SW17 7TJ
Tel: 020 8767 6057
Headmaster: Nasir Qurashi
Age range: 3–16
No. of pupils: 250

Beechwood School
55 Leigham Court Road,
Streatham, London SW16 2NJ
Tel: 020 8677 8778
Headmistress: Mrs M Marshall
Age range: 0–11
No. of pupils: 100
Fees: Day £6,726–£7,875

Bertrum House School
290 Balham High Road,
London SW17 7AL
Tel: 020 8767 4051
Principal: Miss. Kirsty Pirrie
Age range: 2–7
No. of pupils: 94
Fees: Day £1,630–£4,090

Broomwood Hall School
68-74 Nightingale Lane,
London SW12 8NR
Tel: 020 8682 8830
Head of School:
Mrs Carole Jenkinson
Age range: B4–8 G4–13
No. of pupils: 670
Fees: Day £13,680–£16,815

Cameron House
4 The Vale, Chelsea,
London SW3 6AH
Tel: 020 7352 4040
Headmaster:
Mr Pádraic Fahy BA (Hons), PGCE
Age range: 4–11
No. of pupils: 119
Fees: Day £17,535

Dolphin School
106 Northcote Road,
London SW11 6QW
Tel: 020 7924 3472
Principal:
Mr J Schmidt BA(Hons), BEd, BPE
Age range: 2–11
No. of pupils: 317
Fees: Day £10,785–£11,895

Donhead
33 Edge Hill, London SW19 4NP
Tel: 020 8946 7000
Headmaster: Mr G C McGrath
BA(Hons), PGCE, MBA(Ed)
Age range: B4–11
No. of pupils: 280
Fees: Day £7,800–£8,325

Eaton House Belgravia
3-5 Eaton Gate, London SW1W 9BA
Tel: 020 7730 9343
Head of School:
Mrs Annabel Abbott
Age range: B4–8
Fees: Day £15,390

Eaton House The Manor Girls School
58 Clapham Common
Northside, London SW4 9RU
Tel: 020 7924 6000
Head: Mrs Sarah Segrave
Age range: G4–11
Fees: Day £14,244

Eaton House The Manor Pre Prep School
58 Clapham Common
Northside, London SW4 9RU
Tel: 020 7924 6000
Head of School: Mr Huw May
Age range: B4–8
No. of pupils: 220
Fees: Day £14,244

Eaton House The Manor Prep School
58 Clapham Common
Northside, London SW4 9RU
Tel: 020 7924 6000
Head: Mrs Sarah Segrave
Age range: B8–13
No. of pupils: 215
Fees: Day £18,090

Eaton House The Vale
2 Elvaston Place, London SW7 5QH
Tel: 020 7924 6000
Head: Mr Robin Greenwood
Age range: 3–11
Fees: Day £7,416–£14,670

Eaton Square School
79 Eccleston Square,
London SW1V 1PP
Tel: 020 7931 9469
Headmaster:
Mr Sebastian Hepher BEd(Hons)
Age range: 2–13
No. of pupils: 529
Fees: Day £4,080–£19,785

**Eveline Day &
Nursery Schools**
14 Trinity Crescent, Upper
Tooting, London SW17 7AE
Tel: 020 8672 4673
Headmistress: Ms Eveline Drut
Age range: 3 months–11 years
No. of pupils: 80
Fees: Day £11,059

Falkner House
19 Brechin Place, South
Kensington, London SW7 4QB
Tel: 020 7373 4501
Headteacher:
Mrs Anita Griggs BA(Hons), PGCE
Age range: B3–4 G3–11
Fees: Day £8,025–£16,050

Finton House School
171 Trinity Road, London SW17 7HL
Tel: 020 8682 0921
Head of School: Mr Ben Freeman
Age range: 4–11
No. of pupils: 321
Fees: Day £4,630–£4,850

**Francis Holland School,
Sloane Square, SW1**
39 Graham Terrace,
London SW1W 8JF
Tel: 020 7730 2971
Head:
Mrs Lucy Elphinstone MA(Cantab)
Age range: G4–18
No. of pupils: 520 VIth70
Fees: Day £16,950–£19,170

Garden House School
Boys' School & Girls' School,
Turk's Row, London SW3 4TW
Tel: 020 7730 1652
Boys Head: C Warland BA(Hons)
Age range: B3–8 G3–11
No. of pupils: 449
Fees: Day £9,300–£15,885

Glendower School
86/87 Queen's Gate,
London SW7 5JX
Tel: 020 7370 1927
Headmistress:
Mrs Sarah Knollys BA, PGCE
Age range: G4–11+
No. of pupils: 206
Fees: Day £14,280

Hall School Wimbledon
Beavers Holt, Stroud Crescent,
Putney Vale, London SW15 3EQ
Tel: 020 8788 2370
Headmaster: Timothy J Hobbs MA
Age range: 4–16
No. of pupils: 520
Fees: Day £9,999–£13,224

**Hill House International
Junior School**
17 Hans Place, Chelsea,
London SW1X 0EP
Tel: 020 7584 1331
Headmaster:
Richard Townend FLSM(Chm)
Age range: 4–13
No. of pupils: 980
Fees: Day £10,350–£14,100

Hornsby House School
Hearnville Road, Balham,
London SW12 8RS
Tel: 020 8673 7573
Headmaster: Mr Edward Rees
Age range: 4–11
Fees: Day £12,375–£13,305

Hurlingham School
122 Putney Bridge Road,
Putney, London SW15 2NQ
Tel: 020 8874 7186
Headteacher: Mr Jonathan Brough
Age range: 4–11
No. of pupils: 320
Fees: Day £14,400–£15,030

Ibstock Place School
Clarence Lane, London SW15 5PY
Tel: 020 8876 9991
Head: Mrs Anna Sylvester-
Johnson BA(Hons), PGCE
Age range: 4–18
No. of pupils: 970
Fees: Day £4,995–£6,400

**Kensington Prep
School GDST**
596 Fulham Road, London SW6 5PA
Tel: 0207 731 9300
Head: Mrs P Lynch MA
(St Andrews) PGCE
Age range: G4–11
No. of pupils: 289
Fees: Day £11,103

**King's College
Junior School**
Southside, Wimbledon
Common, London SW19 4TT
Tel: 020 8255 5335
Headmaster: Dr. G A Silverlock
Age range: B7–13
No. of pupils: 460

Knightsbridge School
67 Pont Street, Knightsbridge,
London SW1X 0BD
Tel: 020 7590 5900
Head: Ms Shona Colaco
MA, PGCE, MSB, CBiol
Age range: 3–13
No. of pupils: 400
Fees: Day £16,224–£17,265

L'Ecole de Battersea
Trott Street, Battersea,
London SW11 3DS
Tel: 020 7371 8350
Director: Mrs F Brisset
Age range: 3–11
No. of pupils: 252
Fees: Day £10,550–£10,800

L'Ecole des Petits
2 Hazlebury Road, Fulham,
London SW6 2NB
Tel: 020 7371 8350
Director: Mrs F Brisset
Age range: 3–6
No. of pupils: 136
Fees: Day £10,400–£10,700

Lion House School
The Old Methodist Hall, Gwendolen
Avenue, London SW15 6EH
Tel: 020 8780 9446
Head: Miss H J Luard MontDip
Age range: 2–7
No. of pupils: 115

**Lycée Français
Charles de Gaulle**
35 Cromwell Road,
London SW7 2DG
Tel: 020 7584 6322
Head of School: Mr Olivier Rauch
Age range: 5–19
No. of pupils: 4000

Newton Prep
149 Battersea Park Road,
London SW8 4BX
Tel: 020 7720 4091
Headmistress: Mrs Alison
Fleming BA, MA Ed, PGCE
Age range: 3–13
No. of pupils: 661
Fees: Day £8,310–£17,625

Northcote Lodge School
26 Bolingbroke Grove,
London SW11 6EL
Tel: 020 8682 8888
Headmaster: Mr Mark Smith
Age range: B8–13
No. of pupils: 220
Fees: Day £17,430

**Oliver House
Preparatory School**
7 Nightingale Lane,
London SW4 9AH
Tel: 020 8772 1911
Headteacher: Ms Maureen Fields
Age range: 2–13
No. of pupils: 144
Fees: Day £4,200–£9,300

Parkgate House School
80 Clapham Common North
Side, London SW4 9SD
Tel: +44 (0)20 7350 2461
Principal: Miss Catherine Shanley
Age range: 2½–11 years
No. of pupils: 220
Fees: Day £5,550–£14,550

Parsons Green Prep School
1 Fulham Park Road,
Fulham, London SW6 4LJ
Tel: 020 7371 9000
Headteacher: Ms. Helen Stavert
Age range: 4–11
No. of pupils: 200
Fees: Day £4,995–£5,395

**PROSPECT HOUSE
SCHOOL**
For further details see p. 61
For further details see p. 61
75 Putney Hill, London SW15 3NT
Tel: 020 8246 4897
Email: info@prospecths.org.uk
Website: www.prospecths.org.uk
Headmistress:
Mrs Dianne Barratt MEd
(Newcastle-upon-Tyne)
Age range: 3–11
No. of pupils: 300
Fees: Day £8,205–£17,100

Putney High School GDST
35 Putney Hill, London SW15 6BH
Tel: 020 8788 4886
Headmistress:
Dr Denise Lodge BSc, MSc, PhD
Age range: G4–18
No. of pupils: VIth150

QUEEN'S GATE SCHOOL
For further details see p. 62
For further details see p. 62
133 Queen's Gate,
London SW7 5LE
Tel: 020 7589 3587
Email:
registrar@queensgate.org.uk
Website:
www.queensgate.org.uk
Principal: Mrs R M Kamaryc
BA, MSc, PGCE
Age range: G4–18
No. of pupils: 533

**Ravenstone
Preparatory School**
24 Elvaston Place, South
Kensington, London SW7 5NL
Tel: 020 7225 3131
Head of School: Dr Ronald Pritchard
Age range: 2–11
No. of pupils: 110
Fees: Day £11,280–£16,875

Redcliffe School Trust Ltd
47 Redcliffe Gardens,
Chelsea, London SW10 9JH
Tel: 020 7352 9247
Head: Mrs Susan Bourne BSc, PGCE
Age range: B3–8 G3–11
Fees: Day £14,610–£14,610
(£)

**Sinclair House
Montessori Nursery**
159 & 196 Munster Road,
Fulham, London SW6 6AU
Tel: 0207 736 9182
Principal:
Mrs Carlotta T M O'Sullivan

**Sinclair House
Preparatory School**
59 Fulham High Street,
Fulham, London SW6 3JJ
Tel: 0207 736 9182
Principal:
Mrs Carlotta T M O'Sullivan
Age range: 2–13
No. of pupils: 120
Fees: Day £10,950

**St Nicholas
Preparatory School**
23 Princes Gate, Kensington,
London SW7 1PT
Tel: 020 7225 1277
Headmaster: Mr Tony Lewis
Age range: 3–11
No. of pupils: 280
Fees: Day £11,475–£13,110
(✎)

St Paul's Juniors
St Paul's School, Lonsdale
Road, London SW13 9JT
Tel: 020 8748 3461
Head of School: Maxine Shaw
Age range: B7–13
No. of pupils: 436
Fees: Day £18,771
(♦)(£)(✎)

St Philip's School
6 Wetherby Place, London SW7 4NE
Tel: 020 7373 3944
Headmaster:
H J Biggs-Davison MA(Cantab)
Age range: B7–13
No. of pupils: 110
Fees: Day £12,750
(♦)(£)(✎)

**Streatham & Clapham
High School GDST**
42 Abbotswood Road,
London SW16 1AW
Tel: 020 8677 8400
Headmaster: Dr Millan Sachania
Age range: B3–5 G3–18
No. of pupils: 603 VIth70
Fees: Day £5,886–£9,810
(♦)(A)(£)(✎)

Sussex House School
68 Cadogan Square,
Knightsbridge, London SW1X 0EA
Tel: 020 7584 1741
Headmaster: Mr N P Kaye
MA(Cantab), ACP, FRSA
Age range: B8–13
No. of pupils: 182
Fees: Day £16,200
(♦)

Swedish School
82 Lonsdale Road, London SW13 9JS
Tel: 020 8741 1751
Head of School:
Ms. Annika Simonsson Bergqvist
Age range: 3–18
No. of pupils: 242
Fees: Day £6,600

**THE HAMPSHIRE
SCHOOL, CHELSEA**
For further details see p. 66
15 Manresa Road, Chelsea,
London SW3 6NB
Tel: 020 7352 7077
Email: info@thehampshire
schoolchelsea.co.uk
Website: www.thehampshire
schoolchelsea.co.uk
Principal: Mr Donal Brennan
Age range: 3–13
No. of pupils: 300
Fees: Day £16,155–£17,100
(£)(✎)

The Harrodian School
Lonsdale Road, London SW13 9QN
Tel: 020 8748 6117
Headmaster: James R Hooke
Age range: 5–18
No. of pupils: 890 VIth95
Fees: Day £10,407–£15,219
(A)(✎)

The Merlin School
4 Carlton Drive, Putney
Hill, London SW15 2BZ
Tel: 020 8788 2769
Principal: Mrs Kate Prest
Age range: 4–8
No. of pupils: 170

**The Montessori Pavilion –
The Kindergarten School**
Vine Road, Barnes,
London SW13 0NE
Tel: 020 8878 9695
Age range: 3–8
No. of pupils: 50
Fees: Day £1,950–£3,600
(✎)

The Norwegian School
28 Arterberry Road, Wimbledon,
London SW20 8AH
Tel: 020 8947 6617
Head: Mr Geir Johansen
Age range: 3–16

The Roche School
11 Frogmore, London SW18 1HW
Tel: 020 8877 0823
Headmistress:
Mrs V Adams BA(Hons), PGCE, MA
Age range: 2–11 years
No. of pupils: 239
Fees: Day £12,090–£13,050
(£)(✎)

The Rowans School
19 Drax Avenue, Wimbledon,
London SW20 0EG
Tel: 020 8946 8220
Head Teacher: Mrs S Wingrove
Age range: 3–8
Fees: Day £5,460–£10,725

**The Study Preparatory
School**
Wilberforce House, Camp
Road, Wimbledon Common,
London SW19 4UN
Tel: 020 8947 6969
Headmistress:
Mrs Susan Pepper MA Oxon, PGCE
Age range: G4–11
No. of pupils: 315
(♦)(£)(✎)

**The Waldorf School of
South West London**
PO Box 8541, London SW16 1ZB
Tel: 0208 772 3504
Age range: 3–14
No. of pupils: 80
Fees: Day £4,515–£6,217
(£)

**The White House
Preparatory School &
Woodentops Kindergarten**
24 Thornton Road, London SW12 0LF
Tel: 020 8674 9514
Principal: Mrs Mary McCahery
Age range: 2–11
Fees: Day £9,800–£12,300
(£)

**Thomas's Preparatory
School – Battersea**
28-40 Battersea High Street,
London SW11 3JB
Tel: 020 7978 0900
Head: Ben V R Thomas MA
Age range: 4–13
No. of pupils: 547
Fees: Day £12,510–£18,330
(✎)

**Thomas's Preparatory
School – Clapham**
Broomwood Road,
London SW11 6JZ
Tel: 020 7326 9300
Headmaster:
Mr Philip Ward BEd(Hons)
Age range: 4–13
Fees: Day £10,365–£11,730
(£)(✎)

**Thomas's Preparatory
School – Fulham**
Hugon Road, London SW6 3ES
Tel: 020 7751 8200
Head: Miss Annette Dobson
BEd(Hons), PGCertDys
Age range: 4–11

Tower House School
188 Sheen Lane, London SW14 8LF
Tel: 020 8876 3323
Head: Mr Gregory Evans
Age range: B4–13
No. of pupils: 180
Fees: Day £11,073–£12,558
(♦)(✎)

**Ursuline Preparatory
School**
18 The Downs, London SW20 8HR
Tel: 020 8947 0859
Headmistress: Mrs Anne Farnish
BA (Hons) MA, NPQH, PGCE
Age range: B3–4 G3–11
Fees: Day £5,886–£9,600
(£)(✎)

**Wandsworth
Preparatory School**
The Old Library, 2 Allfarthing
Lane, London SW18 2PQ
Tel: 0208 870 4133
Head of School: Miss Bridget Saul
Fees: Day £4,265
(♦)(£)

**Westminster Abbey
Choir School**
Dean's Yard, London SW1P 3NY
Tel: 0207 654 4918
Headmaster: Jonathan Milton BEd
Age range: B8–13
No. of pupils: 35
Fees: FB £7,404
(♦)(♬)(✎)

**Westminster Cathedral
Choir School**
Ambrosden Avenue,
London SW1P 1QH
Tel: 020 7798 9081
Headmaster: Mr Neil McLaughlan
Age range: B8–13
No. of pupils: 150
Fees: Day £13,656 FB £6,945
(♦)(♬)(£)(✎)

Westminster Under School
Adrian House, 27 Vincent
Square, London SW1P 2NN
Tel: 020 7821 5788
Headteacher: Mrs E A Hill MA
Age range: B7–13
No. of pupils: 265
Fees: Day £14,676
(♦)(£)(✎)

Willington School
Worcester Road, Wimbledon,
London SW19 7QQ
Tel: 020 8944 7020
Head: Mr Michael Chanter
Age range: B4–13
No. of pupils: 250
Fees: Day £9,345–£11,385
(♦)(£)

**Wimbledon Common
Preparatory**
113 Ridgway, Wimbledon,
London SW19 4TA
Tel: 020 8946 1001
Head Teacher: Mrs Tracey Buck
Age range: B4–8
No. of pupils: 160
Fees: Day £10,725
(♦)

**Wimbledon High
School GDST**
Mansel Road, Wimbledon,
London SW19 4AB
Tel: 020 8971 0900
Headmistress: Mrs H Hanbury
Age range: G4–18
No. of pupils: 900 VIth155
Fees: Day £11,445–£15,024
(♦)(A)(£)(✎)

West London

Avenue House School
70 The Avenue, Ealing,
London W13 8LS
Tel: 020 8998 9981
Headteacher: Mr Sheppard
Age range: 3–11
No. of pupils: 135
Fees: Day £5,070–£8,670

Barbara Speake Stage School
East Acton Lane, East
Acton, London W3 7EG
Tel: 020 8743 1306
Principal: Mr David
Speake BA (Hons)
Age range: 3–16
Fees: Day £8,700–£9,000

BASSETT HOUSE SCHOOL
For further details see p. 55
60 Bassett Road,
London W10 6JP
Tel: 020 8969 0313
Email: info@bassetths.org.uk
Website: www.bassetths.org.uk
Headmistress: Mrs Philippa
Cawthorne MA (Soton)
PGCE Mont Cert
Age range: 3–11
No. of pupils: 190
Fees: Day £8,205–£17,100

Bute House Preparatory School for Girls
Bute House, Luxemburg
Gardens, London W6 7EA
Tel: 020 7603 7381
Head: Mrs Helen Lowe
Age range: G4–11
No. of pupils: 306
Fees: Day £13,317

Chepstow House School
19 Pembridge Villas,
London W11 3EP
Tel: 0207 243 0243
Headteacher: Angela Barr
Age range: 4–7

Chiswick & Bedford Park Prep School
Priory House, Priory Avenue,
London W4 1TX
Tel: 020 8994 1804
Headmistress: Mrs C A Sunderland
Age range: B4–7+ G4–11
No. of pupils: 180
Fees: Day £8,850

Clifton Lodge
8 Mattock Lane, Ealing,
London W5 5BG
Tel: 020 8579 3662
Head: Mr. Floyd Steadman
Age range: 3–13
No. of pupils: 146
Fees: Day £11,340–£12,405

Connaught House School
47 Connaught Square,
London W2 2HL
Tel: 020 7262 8830
Principals: Mrs J A Hampton
& Mr F Hampton MA, RCA
Age range: B4–8 G4–11
No. of pupils: 75
Fees: Day £13,200–£14,700

Durston House
12-14 Castlebar Road,
Ealing, London W5 2DR
Tel: 020 8991 6530
Headmaster:
Mr Ian Kendrick MA, BEd(Hons)
Age range: B4–13
No. of pupils: 415
Fees: Day £9,810–£12,570

Ecole Francaise Jacques Prevert
59 Brook Green, London W6 7BE
Tel: 020 7602 6871
Principal: P Possenti
Age range: 4–11

Fulham Prep School
200 Greyhound Road,
London W14 9SD
Tel: 020 7386 2448
Principal: Mrs J Emmett
Age range: 4–13
No. of pupils: 596
Fees: Day £14,400–£15,975

Great Beginnings Montessori School
The Welsh Church Hall, 82a
Chiltern Street, Marylebone,
London W1H 5JE
Tel: 020 7486 2276
Age range: 2–6
Fees: Day £1,095–£1,650

Greek Primary School of London
3 Pierrepoint Road, Acton,
London W3 9JR
Tel: 020 8992 6156
Age range: 1–11

Harvington School
20 Castlebar Road, Ealing,
London W5 2DS
Tel: 020 8997 1583
Headmistress: Mrs Anna Evans
Age range: B3–4 G3–11
No. of pupils: 140
Fees: Day £9,300–£12,120

HAWKESDOWN HOUSE SCHOOL KENSINGTON
For further details see p. 57
27 Edge Street, Kensington,
London W8 7PN
Tel: 020 7727 9090
Email:
admin@hawkesdown.co.uk
Website:
www.hawkesdown.co.uk
Acting Head: Mrs L Quilter B.Ed
Age range: B3–8
No. of pupils: 141
Fees: Day £15,270–£17,565

Heathfield House School
Turnham Green Church
Hall, Heathfield Gardens,
Chiswick, London W4 4JU
Tel: 020 8994 3385
Headteacher: Mrs Goodsman
Age range: 4–11
Fees: Day £6,300–£6,900

Holland Park Pre Prep School and Day Nursery
5 & 9 Holland Road, Kensington,
London W14 8HJ
Tel: 020 7602 9066/020
7602 9266
Principal: Mrs Kitty Mason
Age range: 3 months–8 years
No. of pupils: 128
Fees: Day £4,650–£10,935

House Schools Group
42 Hartington Road, London W4 3TX
Tel: 020 8580 9626

Instituto Español Vicente Cañada Blanch
317 Portobello Road,
London W10 5SZ
Tel: +44 (0) 20 8969 2664
Principal: Mr A Vitria
Age range: 4–19
No. of pupils: 405

International School of London (ISL) London
139 Gunnersbury Avenue,
Ealing, London W3 8LG
Tel: +44 (0)20 8992 5823
Middle & Lower School Principal:
Andrew Mitchell
Age range: 3–18 years
No. of pupils: 480
Fees: Day £18,000–£24,600

King Fahad Academy
Bromyard Avenue, Acton,
London W3 7HD
Tel: 020 8743 0131
Director: Dr Othman Alzamil
Age range: 3–19
No. of pupils: 510
Fees: Day £2,500–£4,500

La Petite Ecole Francais
73 Saint Charles Square,
London W10 6EJ
Tel: +44 208 960 1278
Principal: Ms A Stones
Age range: 2–6

Latymer Prep School
36 Upper Mall, Hammersmith,
London W6 9TA
Tel: 020 7993 0061
Principal:
Mr Stuart Dorrian BA(Hons), PGCE
Age range: 7–11
No. of pupils: 168
Fees: Day £16,860

Le Herisson
River Court Methodist
Church, Rover Court Road,
Hammersmith, London W6 9JT
Tel: 020 8563 7664
Head Teacher: C Behroozi
Age range: 2–6
Fees: Day £8,730–£8,970

L'Ecole Bilingue
St David's Welsh Church, St
Mary's Terrace, London W2 1SJ
Tel: 020 7224 8427
Headteacher:
Ms Veronique Ferreira
Age range: 3–11
No. of pupils: 68
Fees: Day £6,000–£6,600

Norland Place School
162-166 Holland Park Avenue,
London W11 4UH
Tel: 020 7603 9103
Headmaster: Mr Patrick Mattar MA
Age range: B4–8 years G4–11 years
Fees: Day £13,590–£16,389

Notting Hill & Ealing High School GDST
2 Cleveland Road, West
Ealing, London W13 8AX
Tel: 020 8991 2165
Headmistress: Ms Lucinda Hunt
Age range: G4–18
No. of pupils: 903 VIth150
Fees: Day £12,849–£16,521

Notting Hill Preparatory School
95 Lancaster Road,
London W11 1QQ
Tel: 020 7221 0727
Headmistress: Mrs Jane Cameron
Age range: 4–13
No. of pupils: 325
Fees: Day £6,100

One World Montessori Nursery & Pre-Prep
69-71 Brock Green, Hammersmith,
London W6 7BE
Tel: 020 7603 6065
Headteacher: Ms N Greer
Age range: 2–8
No. of pupils: 21

One World Preparatory School
10 Stanley Gardens,
Acton, London W3 7SZ
Tel: 020 87433300
Head: Ms Lisa Manser
Age range: 3–11
No. of pupils: 52
Fees: Day £3,000

ORCHARD HOUSE SCHOOL
For further details see p. 60
16 Newton Grove, Bedford Park, London W4 1LB
Tel: 020 8742 8544
Email: info@orchardhs.org.uk
Website: www.orchardhs.org.uk
Headmistress: Mrs Maria Edwards BEd(Beds) PGCE(Man) Mont Cert
Age range: 3–11
No. of pupils: 290
Fees: Day £8,205–£17,100

Pembridge Hall
18 Pembridge Square, London W2 4EH
Tel: 020 7229 0121
Headteacher: Mr Henry Keighley-Elstub
Age range: G4–11
No. of pupils: 413

Ravenscourt Park Preparatory School
16 Ravenscourt Avenue, London W6 0SL
Tel: 020 8846 9153
Headmaster: Mr Carl Howes
Age range: 4–11
No. of pupils: 312
Fees: Day £15,606

Ravenstone Pre-Preparatory School
The Long Garden, St George's Fields, Albion Street, London W2 2AX
Tel: 020 7262 1190
Head of School: Mrs Karen Dapson
Age range: 2–7
No. of pupils: 74
Fees: Day £11,280–£16,875

Southbank International School – Kensington
36-38 Kensington Park Road, London W11 3BU
Tel: 020 7243 3803
Principal: Siobhan McGrath
Age range: 3–11

St Augustine's Priory
Hillcrest Road, Ealing, London W5 2JL
Tel: 020 8997 2022
Headteacher: Mrs. Sarah Raffray MA
Age range: G3–18
No. of pupils: 470
Fees: Day £3,180–£13,572

ST BENEDICT'S JUNIOR SCHOOL AND NURSERY
For further details see p. 64
5 Montpelier Avenue, Ealing, London W5 2XP
Tel: 020 8862 2254
Email: enquiries@stbenedicts.org.uk
Website: www.stbenedicts.org.uk
Headmaster: Mr R G Simmons
Age range: 3–11
No. of pupils: 286
Fees: Day £10,560–£11,760

St James Junior School
Earsby Street, London W14 8SH
Tel: 020 7348 1777
Headmistress: Mrs Catherine Thomlinson BA(Hons)
Age range: B4–11 G4–10
Fees: Day £10,650

Tabernacle School
32 St Anns Villas, Holland Park, London W11 4RS
Tel: 020 7602 6232
Headteacher: Mrs P Wilson
Age range: 3–16
Fees: Day £4,500

The Falcons School for Boys
2 Burnaby Gardens, Chiswick, London W4 3DT
Tel: 020 8747 8393
Headmaster: Mr Gordon Milne
Age range: B3–7
No. of pupils: 225
Fees: Day £3,875–£11,625

The Falcons School for Girls
15 Gunnersbury Avenue, Ealing, London W5 3XD
Tel: 020 8992 5189
Headteacher: Miss Joan McGillewie
Age range: G4–11
No. of pupils: 102
Fees: Day £3,625

The Japanese School
87 Creffield Road, Acton, London W3 9PU
Tel: 020 8993 7145
Headteacher: Mrs Kiyoe Tsuruoka
Age range: 6–16
No. of pupils: 500

The Lloyd Williamson School
12 Telford Road, London W10 5SH
Tel: 020 8962 0345
Co-Principals: Ms Lucy Meyer & Mr Aaron Williams
Age range: 4 months–14 years
Fees: Day £13,050

Thomas's Preparatory School – Kensington
17-19 Cottesmore Gardens, London W8 5PR
Tel: 020 7361 6500
Headmistress: Miss Joanna Ebner MA, BEd(Hons)(Cantab), NPQH
Age range: 4–11
Fees: Day £14,505–£15,795

Wetherby Preparatory School
48 Bryanston Square, London W1H 2EA
Tel: 020 7535 3520
Headteacher: Mr Nick Baker
Age range: B8–13
No. of pupils: 192
Fees: Day £4,665

Wetherby Pre-Preparatory School
11 Pembridge Square, London W2 4ED
Tel: 020 7727 9581
Headmaster: Mr Mark Snell
Age range: B2 1/2–8
No. of pupils: 340
Fees: Day £19,620

Ysgol Gymraeg Llundain London Welsh School
Hanwell Community Centre, Westcott Crescent, London W7 1PD
Tel: 020 8575 0237
Leadteacher: Miss Rachel Rawlins
Age range: 3–11
No. of pupils: 30
Fees: Day £1,950

North-East

KEY TO SYMBOLS

- (†) Boys' school
- (♀) Girls' school
- (🌐) International school
- (16) Tutorial or sixth form college
- (A) A levels
- (🏛) Boarding accommodation
- (£) Bursaries
- (IB) International Baccalaureate
- (✐) Learning support
- (16+) Entrance at 16+
- (💐) Vocational qualifications
- (IAPS) Independent Association of Prep Schools
- (HMC) The Headmasters' & Headmistresses' Conference
- (ISA) Independent Schools Association
- (GSA) Girls' School Association
- (BSA) Boarding Schools' Association
- (S) Society of Heads

Unless otherwise indicated, all schools are coeducational day schools. Single-sex and boarding schools will be indicated by the relevant icon.

Durham

Barnard Castle Preparatory School
Westwick Road, Barnard Castle, Durham DL12 8UW
Tel: 01833 696032
Headmaster: C F Rycroft
Age range: 4–11
No. of pupils: 180
Fees: Day £7,671 FB £14,832
🏫✏️

Bow, Durham School
South Road, Durham DH1 3LS
Tel: 0191 384 8233
Headmaster:
R N Baird BA(Hons), PGCE
Age range: 3–11
No. of pupils: 150
Fees: Day £5,370–£7,938
£✏️

Durham High School for Girls
Farewell Hall, Durham DH1 3TB
Tel: 0191 384 3226
Headmistress: Mrs Lynne Renwick
Age range: G3–18
No. of pupils: 421
🚶Ⓐ£✏️

Polam Hall School
Grange Road, Darlington, Durham DL1 5PA
Tel: 01325 463383
Headmaster: Mr J R Moreland MA (Oxon), PGCE (Oxford), NPQH
Age range: 4–19
No. of pupils: 182
Fees: Day £6,150–£8,550 WB £16,755–£16,755 FB £17,355–£17,355
🏫£✏️

The Chorister School
The College, Durham DH1 3EL
Tel: 0191 384 2935
Headmistress: Mrs Y F S Day
Age range: 3–13 years
No. of pupils: 214
Fees: Day £8,340–£11,235 WB £17,460 FB £10,170–£19,440
🏫£✏️

Northumberland

Longridge Towers School
Longridge Towers, Berwick-upon-Tweed, Northumberland TD15 2XH
Tel: 01289 307584
Headmaster: Mr T M Manning BSc
Age range: 3–18
No. of pupils: VIth46
Fees: Day £7,896–£12,336 WB £18,153–£19,506 FB £23,811–£25,128
🌐Ⓐ🏫£✏️

Mowden Hall School
Newton, Stocksfield, Northumberland NE43 7TP
Tel: 01661 842147
Headmaster:
Mr Ben Beardmore-Gray
Age range: 3–13
Fees: Day £7,920–£13,770 FB £17,790
🏫£✏️

Stockton-on-Tees

Red House School
36 The Green, Norton, Stockton-on-Tees TS20 1DX
Tel: 01642 553370
Headmaster: Mr A R W Taylor BSc, MSc, PGCE, CBiol, MSB
Age range: 3–16
No. of pupils: 382
Fees: Day £7,230–£10,320
£✏️

Teesside High School
The Avenue, Eaglescliffe, Stockton-on-Tees TS16 9AT
Tel: 01642 782095
Headmaster:
Mr Thomas Packer BSc, MSc, FInstP
Age range: G3–18
No. of pupils: 390 VIth70
🚶Ⓐ£✏️

Yarm Preparatory School
Grammar School Lane, Yarm, Stockton-on-Tees TS15 9ES
Tel: 01642 781447
Headteacher: Mr Bill Sawyer
Age range: 3–11
No. of pupils: 360
Fees: Day £4,308–£8,859
✏️

Tyne & Wear

Argyle House School
19/20 Thornhill Park, Tunstall Road, Sunderland, Tyne & Wear SR2 7LA
Tel: 0191 510 0726
Headmaster: Mr C Johnson
Age range: 3–16
Fees: Day £6,360–£7,530
✏️

Dame Allan Junior School
Hunters Road, Spital Tongues, Newcastle upon Tyne, Tyne & Wear NE2 4NG
Tel: 0191 275 0608
Head: Mr A J Edge
Age range: 3–11
No. of pupils: 140
Fees: Day £6,345–£8,310

Gateshead Jewish Primary School
18-20 Gladstone Terrace, Gateshead, Tyne & Wear NE8 4EA
Tel: 0191 477 2154 / 0191 478 5841
Headmasters:
A Hammond & Y Spitzer
Age range: 5–11
No. of pupils: 446
Fees: Day £2,392–£3,016
✏️

Newcastle High School for Girls GDST
Eskdale Terrace, Jesmond, Newcastle upon Tyne, Tyne & Wear NE2 4DS
Tel: 0191 281 1768
Head: Mrs H J French MA, MEd, NPQH
Age range: G3–18
No. of pupils: G960 VIth200
Fees: Day £7,695–£12,036
🚶Ⓐ£✏️

Newcastle Preparatory School
6 Eslington Road, Jesmond, Newcastle upon Tyne, Tyne & Wear NE2 4RH
Tel: 0191 281 1769
Head Teacher:
Mrs Margaret Coates
Age range: 3–11
No. of pupils: 273
Fees: Day £7,779–£8,742
£✏️

Newcastle School for Boys
30 West Avenue, Gosforth, Newcastle upon Tyne, Tyne & Wear NE3 4ES
Tel: 0191 255 9300
Headmaster: Mr D J Tickner
Age range: B3–18
No. of pupils: 400
Fees: Day £6,900–£9,270
🚶Ⓐ£✏️

Royal Grammar School
Eskdale Terrace, Newcastle upon Tyne, Tyne & Wear NE2 4DX
Tel: 0191 281 5711
Headmaster:
Dr Bernard St J Trafford
Age range: 7–18
No. of pupils: 1275 VIth334
Fees: Day £9,810–£11,643
Ⓐ£✏️

Westfield School
Oakfield Road, Gosforth, Newcastle upon Tyne, Tyne & Wear NE3 4HS
Tel: 0191 255 3980
Headmistress: Mrs M Farndale BA(Hons)(Lon), PGCE(Oxon), FRSA
Age range: G3–18
No. of pupils: 315 VIth50
Fees: Day £1,372–£3,688
🚶🌐Ⓐ

North-West

KEY TO SYMBOLS

- ⚥ *Boys' school*
- ⚥ *Girls' school*
- 🌐 *International school*
- 16² *Tutorial or sixth form college*
- Ⓐ *A levels*
- 🏫 *Boarding accommodation*
- £ *Bursaries*
- ⒾⒷ *International Baccalaureate*
- ✍ *Learning support*
- 16⁺ *Entrance at 16+*
- 💼 *Vocational qualifications*
- ⒾⒶⓅⓈ *Independent Association of Prep Schools*
- ⒽⓂⒸ *The Headmasters' & Headmistresses' Conference*
- ⒾⓈⒶ *Independent Schools Association*
- ⒼⓈⒶ *Girls' School Association*
- ⒷⓈⒶ *Boarding Schools' Association*
- ⓈⒿ *Society of Heads*

Unless otherwise indicated, all schools are coeducational day schools. Single-sex and boarding schools will be indicated by the relevant icon.

Cheshire

Abbey Gate College
Saighton Grange, Saighton,
Chester, Cheshire CH3 6EN
Tel: 01244 332077
Head: Mrs Tracy Pollard
Age range: 4–18
No. of pupils: 514 VIth92
Fees: Day £7,440–£10,875
Ⓐ Ⓔ ✎

Abbey Gate Prep School
Clare Avenue, Hoole, Chester,
Cheshire CH2 3HR
Tel: 01244 319649
Headteacher: Mrs Sally
Ann Rhodes-Leader
Age range: 3–11
No. of pupils: 50
Ⓔ ✎

Alderley Edge School for Girls
Wilmslow Road, Alderley
Edge, Cheshire SK9 7QE
Tel: 01625 583028
Headmistress: Mrs Susan Goff
Age range: G2–18
No. of pupils: 500 VIth60
Fees: Day £5,070–£9,201
🏃 Ⓐ Ⓔ ⒾⒷ ✎

Beech Hall School
Beech Hall Drive, Tytherington,
Macclesfield, Cheshire SK10 2EG
Tel: 01625 422192
Headmistress: Mrs G Yandell BA
Age range: 6 months–16 years
No. of pupils: 230
Fees: Day £6,285–£8,940
Ⓔ ✎

Bowdon Preparatory School for Girls
Ashley Road, Altrincham,
Cheshire WA14 2LT
Tel: 0161 928 0678
Headmistress: Mrs J H Tan BA, DipEd
Age range: G3–11
No. of pupils: 200
Fees: Day £4,986
🏃

Brabyns Preparatory School
34-36 Arkwright Road, Marple,
Stockport, Cheshire SK6 7DB
Tel: 0161 427 2395
Headteacher: Mr Lee Sanders
Age range: 2–11
No. of pupils: 134
Fees: Day £1,313–£1,779
Ⓔ ✎

Cransley School
Belmont Hall, Great Budworth,
Northwich, Cheshire CW9 6HN
Tel: 01606 891747
Head of School: Richard Pollock
Age range: 4–16
No. of pupils: 150
Fees: Day £2,440–£3,440
Ⓔ ✎

Greater Grace School of Christian Education
Church Lane, Backford,
Chester, Cheshire CH2 4BE
Tel: 01244 851 797
Head Teacher: Mrs A Mulligan
Age range: 5–18
Fees: Day £1,900

Green Meadow Independent Primary School
Robson Way, Lowton, Warrington,
Cheshire WA3 2RD
Tel: 01942 671138
Head: Mrs S Green
Age range: 4–11
Fees: Day £6,390

Hale Preparatory School
Broomfield Lane, Hale,
Cheshire WA15 9AS
Tel: 0161 928 2386
Headmaster: Mr J F Connor
Age range: 4–11
No. of pupils: 202
Fees: Day £7,110

Lady Barn House School
Schools Hill, Cheadle,
Cheshire SK7 1JE
Tel: 0161 428 2912
Head of School: Mr M Turner
Age range: 3–11
No. of pupils: 483
Fees: Day £7,782
Ⓔ ✎

Pownall Hall School
Carrwood Road, Pownall Park,
Wilmslow, Cheshire SK9 5DW
Tel: 01625 523141
Headmaster: Mr David Goulbourn
Age range: 2–11
Fees: Day £2,475–£5,385
✎

Terra Nova School
Jodrell Bank, Holmes Chapel,
Crewe, Cheshire CW4 8BT
Tel: 01477 571251
Headmaster: Mr M Mitchell
Age range: 3–13
No. of pupils: 295
Fees: Day £4,050–£12,990
🏫 Ⓔ ✎

The Firs School
Newton Lane, Upton, Chester,
Cheshire CH2 2HJ
Tel: 01244 322443
Head Teacher: Mrs L Davies
Age range: 3–11
No. of pupils: 172
Fees: Day £8,160
Ⓔ ✎

The Grange School
Bradburns Lane, Hartford,
Northwich, Cheshire CW8 1LU
Tel: 01606 74007 or 77447
Headmaster:
Mr C P Jeffery BA, FRSA
Age range: 4–18
No. of pupils: 1185 VIth193
Fees: Day £7,080–£9,480
Ⓐ Ⓔ ✎

The Hammond School
Mannings Lane, Chester,
Cheshire CH2 4ES
Tel: 01244 305350
Principal: Ms Maggie Evans BA
(Hons) MA, PGCE, NPQH, FRSA
Age range: 4–19
No. of pupils: 280
Fees: Day £10,875–£17,745
FB £18,840–£25,710
🎭 Ⓐ 🏫 Ⓔ ✎

The King's School
Wrexham Road, Chester,
Cheshire CH4 7QL
Tel: 01244 689500
Headmaster: C D Ramsey MA
Age range: 4–18
No. of pupils: 1045 VIth214
Fees: Day £8,490–£12,888
Ⓐ Ⓔ ✎

The King's School
Cumberland Street, Macclesfield,
Cheshire SK10 1DA
Tel: 01625 260000
Headmaster: Dr Simon Hyde
Age range: 3–18
No. of pupils: 1200 VIth250
Fees: Day £7,740–£10,770
Ⓐ Ⓔ ✎

The Queen's School
City Walls Road, Chester,
Cheshire CH1 2NN
Tel: 01244 312078
Headmistress: Mrs E S Clark
Age range: G4–18
No. of pupils: 610 VIth100
Fees: Day £7,455–£10,650
🏫 Ⓐ Ⓔ

The Ryleys School
Ryleys Lane, Alderley Edge,
Cheshire SK9 7UY
Tel: 01625 583241
Headteacher:
Claire Hamilton BSc(Hons), PGCE
Age range: 3–13
No. of pupils: 251
Fees: Day £9,261–£10,752
Ⓔ ✎

Wilmslow Preparatory School
Grove Avenue, Wilmslow,
Cheshire SK9 5EG
Tel: 01625 524246
Headteacher: Mrs Helen Rigby
Age range: 2–11
No. of pupils: 110
Fees: Day £1,375–£9,240
Ⓔ ✎

Yorston Lodge School
18 St John's Road, Knutsford,
Cheshire WA16 0DP
Tel: 01565 633177
Headmistress:
Mrs J Dallimore BEd(Hons)
Age range: 3–11
Fees: Day £5,160

Cumbria

Austin Friars School
Etterby Scaur, Carlisle,
Cumbria CA3 9PB
Tel: 01228 528042
Headmaster:
Mr Christopher Lumb BSc, MEd
Age range: 3–18
No. of pupils: 507 VIth70
Fees: Day £4,470–£9,210
Ⓐ Ⓔ ✎

Casterton, Sedbergh Preparatory School
Casterton, Carnforth,
Cumbria LA6 2SG
Tel: 01524 279200
Headmaster:
Mr Scott Carnochan BEd
Age range: 3–13
No. of pupils: 210
🏫 Ⓔ ✎

Hunter Hall School
Frenchfield, Penrith,
Cumbria CA11 8UA
Tel: 01768 891291
Head Teacher: Mrs Donna Vinsome
Age range: 3–11
No. of pupils: 133
Fees: Day £6,534
Ⓔ ✎

Lime House School
Holm Hill, Dalston, Carlisle,
Cumbria CA5 7BX
Tel: 01228 710225
Headmaster: Mr N A Rice
BA, CertEd, MA(EdMem)
Age range: 3–18+
No. of pupils: 138 VIth38
Fees: Day £4,500–£10,350
WB £21,000–£24,000 FB
£21,000–£25,500
🎭 Ⓐ 🏫 Ⓔ ✎

Windermere Preparatory School
Ambleside Road, Windermere,
Cumbria LA23 1AP
Tel: 015394 43308
Head:
Mr Ben Freeman BEd(Hons), PG Dip
Age range: 2–11
No. of pupils: 120
Fees: Day £6,459–£13,617 WB
£20,271–£23,166 FB £21,414–£24,378

Greater Manchester

Abbotsford Preparatory School
211 Flixton Road, Urmston,
Manchester M41 5PR
Tel: 0161 748 3261
Head Teacher: Mrs Pamela Shiels
Age range: 3–11
No. of pupils: 106
Fees: Day £5,065–£5,469

Altrincham Preparatory School
Marlborough Road, Bowdon,
Altrincham, Greater
Manchester WA14 2RR
Tel: 0161 928 3366
Headmaster: Mr Andrew C Potts
Age range: B3–11
No. of pupils: 310
Fees: Day £6,180–£6,840

Beech House School
184 Manchester Road, Rochdale,
Greater Manchester OL11 4JQ
Tel: 01706 646309
Headmaster: K Sartain BSc(Hons),
PGCE, DipSp, CBiol, FIBiol
Age range: 2–16
Fees: Day £3,945–£4,938

Beis Rochel School
1-7 Seymour Road, Crumpsall,
Manchester M8 5BQ
Tel: 0161 795 1830
Headmistress: Mrs E Krausz
Age range: G3–16
No. of pupils: 200

Bnos Yisroel School
Foigel Esther Shine House, Leicester
Road, Manchester M7 4DA
Tel: 0161 792 3896
Headmaster: Rabbi R Spitzer
Age range: G2–16
No. of pupils: 489

Bolton School (Boys' Division)
Chorley New Road, Bolton,
Greater Manchester BL1 4PA
Tel: 01204 840201
Headmaster: Philip J Britton MBE
Age range: B7–18
No. of pupils: VIth210
Fees: Day £9,024–£11,280

Bolton School (Girls' Division)
Chorley New Road, Bolton,
Greater Manchester BL1 4PB
Tel: 01204 840201
Headmistress:
Miss Sue Hincks MA(Oxon)
Age range: B0–7 G0–18
No. of pupils: VIth210
Fees: Day £9,024–£11,280

Branwood Preparatory School
Stafford Road, Monton, Eccles,
Manchester M30 9HN
Tel: 0161 789 1054
Head: Mrs C Follett NPQSL,
MA, BEd(Hons), Dip
Age range: 3–11
No. of pupils: 156
Fees: Day £5,925

Bridgewater School
Drywood Hall, Worsley Road,
Worsley, Manchester M28 2WQ
Tel: 0161 794 1463
Head Teacher:
Mrs J A T Nairn CertEd(Distinction)
Age range: 3–18
No. of pupils: 467
Fees: Day £6,750–£9,000

Bury Catholic Preparatory School
Arden House, Manchester Road,
Bury, Greater Manchester BL9 9BH
Tel: 0161 764 2346
Headteacher: Mrs A C Dean
Age range: 3–11
Fees: Day £4,500

Bury Grammar School Boys
Tenterden Street, Bury, Greater
Manchester BL9 0HN
Tel: 0161 797 2700
Headmaster: Mr R N Marshall MSc
Age range: B7–18
No. of pupils: 602 VIth92
Fees: Day £6,750–£9,084

Bury Grammar School for Girls
Bridge Road, Bury, Greater
Manchester BL9 0HH
Tel: 0161 696 8600
Headmistress: Mrs R S Georghiou
Age range: B4–7 G4–18
No. of pupils: VIth120
Fees: Day £6,750–£9,084

Cheadle Hulme School
Claremont Road, Cheadle
Hulme, Cheadle, Greater
Manchester SK8 6EF
Tel: 0161 488 3345
Head:
Miss Lucy Pearson B.A. (Oxon)
Age range: 4–18
No. of pupils: 1400
Fees: Day £8,244–£11,412

Chetham's School of Music
Long Millgate, Manchester M3 1SB
Tel: 0161 834 9644
Head of School: Mr Alun Jones
Age range: 8–18
No. of pupils: 304
Fees: Day £24,573 FB £31,713

Clarendon Cottage School
Ivy Bank House, Half Edge Lane,
Eccles, Manchester M30 9BJ
Tel: 0161 950 7868
Headteacher: Mrs E L Howard
Age range: 3–11
No. of pupils: 81
Fees: Day £3,210–£3,840

Clevelands Preparatory School
425 Chorley New Road, Bolton,
Greater Manchester BL1 5DH
Tel: 01204 843898
Headteacher: Mrs Lesley Parlane
Age range: 2–11
No. of pupils: 141
Fees: Day £6,240

Covenant Christian School
The Hawthorns, 48 Heaton
Moor Road, Stockport, Greater
Manchester SK4 4NX
Tel: 0161 432 3782
Head: Dr Roger Slack
Age range: 5–16
No. of pupils: 32

Farrowdale House Preparatory School
Farrow Street, Shaw, Oldham,
Greater Manchester OL2 7AD
Tel: 01706 844533
Headteacher: Miss K Brook
BSc(Mathematics), QTS
Age range: 3–11
No. of pupils: 140
Fees: Day £4,995

Firwood Manor Preparatory School
Broadway, Chadderton, Oldham,
Greater Manchester OL9 0AD
Tel: 0161 6206570
Headteacher: Mrs P M Wild
Age range: 2–11
Fees: Day £5,400

Forest Park School
Lauriston House, 27 Oakfield, Sale,
Greater Manchester M33 6NB
Tel: 0161 973 4835
Headteacher:
Mrs Helen Gee BEd(Hons)
Age range: 3–11
No. of pupils: 145
Fees: Day £4,515–£4,950

Forest Preparatory School
Moss Lane, Timperley, Altrincham,
Greater Manchester WA15 6LJ
Tel: 0161 980 4075
Headmaster: Rick Hyde
Age range: 2–11
No. of pupils: 197
Fees: Day £1,940–£2,190

Grafton House Preparatory School
1 Warrington Street, Ashton-under-
Lyne, Greater Manchester OL6 6XB
Tel: 0161 343 3015
Head: Mrs Pamela Oaks
Age range: 2–11
No. of pupils: 110

Greenbank Preparatory School
Heathbank Road, Cheadle
Hulme, Cheadle, Greater
Manchester SK8 6HU
Tel: 0161 485 3724
Headmistress: Mrs J L Lowe
Age range: 3–11
Fees: Day £7,095

Hulme Hall Grammar School
75 Hulme Hall Road, Cheadle
Hulme, Cheadle, Greater
Manchester SK8 6LA
Tel: 0161 485 3524
Headteacher: Miss Rachael Allen
Age range: 2–16
No. of pupils: 272
Fees: Day £2,600–£3,020

King of Kings School
142 Dantzic Street,
Manchester M4 4DN
Tel: 0161 834 4214
Head Teacher: Mrs B Lewis
Age range: 3–18
No. of pupils: 29

Lighthouse Christian School
193 Ashley Lane, Moston,
Manchester M9 4NQ
Tel: 0161 205 0957
Head: Mr A I Akinyele
Age range: 3–11
No. of pupils: 18
Fees: Day £2,880

Loreto Preparatory School
Dunham Road, Altrincham,
Greater Manchester WA14 4GZ
Tel: 0161 928 8310
Headteacher: Mrs R A Hedger
Age range: B3–7 G3–11
No. of pupils: 163
Fees: Day £4,650

Manchester High School for Girls
Grangethorpe Road,
Manchester M14 6HS
Tel: 0161 224 0447
Head Mistress: Mrs A C Hewitt
Age range: G4–18
No. of pupils: 923 VIth193
Fees: Day £7,053–£9,900

Manchester Junior Girls School
64 Upper Park Road, Salford,
Greater Manchester M7 4JA
Tel: 0161 740 0566
Headmistress: Mrs Lieberman
Age range: G3–11
No. of pupils: 200

Manchester Muslim Preparatory School
551 Wilmslow Road, Withington,
Manchester M20 4BA
Tel: 0161 445 5452
Head Teacher: Mrs A Ali
Age range: 3–11
No. of pupils: 186
Fees: Day £5,000–£5,225

Monton Village School
Francis Street, Monton, Eccles,
Manchester M30 9PR
Tel: 0161 789 0472
Head: Mrs K S McWilliams
Age range: 1–7
No. of pupils: 109

Moor Allerton School
131 Barlow Moor Road, West
Didsbury, Manchester M20 2PW
Tel: 0161 445 4521
Head of School: Ruth Adams
Age range: 3–11
Fees: Day £6,660–£7,185

Oldham Hulme Grammar School
Chamber Road, Oldham,
Greater Manchester OL8 4BX
Tel: 0161 630 6104
Principal: Mr CJD Mairs
Age range: 3–18
No. of pupils: 840 VIth160
Fees: Day £7,335–£10,035

OYY Lubavitch Girls School
Beis Menachem, Park Lane, Salford,
Greater Manchester M7 4JD
Tel: 0161 795 0002
Headmistress: Mrs J Hanson
Age range: 2–16
No. of pupils: 82

Prestwich Preparatory School
St Margaret's Building, 400
Bury Old Road, Prestwich,
Manchester M25 1PZ
Tel: 0161 773 1223
Headmistress: Miss P Shiels
Age range: 2–11
No. of pupils: 122
Fees: Day £3,336

Ramillies Hall School
Cheadle Hulme, Cheadle,
Greater Manchester SK8 7AJ
Tel: 0161 485 3804
Principal: Miss D M Patterson
BA, PGCE & Mrs A L Poole
Age range: 0–16
No. of pupils: 166
Fees: Day £6,000–£8,550

Saddleworth School
High Street, Uppermill, Oldham,
Greater Manchester OL3 6BU
Tel: 01457 872072
Headmistress: Mrs L K Hirst
Age range: 3–7

St Ambrose Preparatory School
Hale Barns, Altrincham, Greater
Manchester WA15 0HE
Tel: 0161 903 9193
Headmaster: F J Driscoll
Age range: B3–11 G3–4
No. of pupils: 150
Fees: Day £6,195

Staleydene Preparatory School
Wellington Parade, Dukinfield,
Greater Manchester SK16 4LE
Tel: 07904 693660
Head of School: Miss Kirsty Best
Age range: 3–11
No. of pupils: 23

Stella Maris Junior School
St Johns Road, Heaton
Mersey, Stockport, Greater
Manchester SK4 3BR
Tel: 0161 432 0532
Headteacher: Mrs N Johnson
Age range: 3–11
No. of pupils: 60
Fees: Day £7,488

Stockport Grammar School
Buxton Road, Stockport,
Greater Manchester SK2 7AF
Tel: 0161 456 9000
Headmaster:
Mr A H Chicken BA, MEd, FRSA
Age range: 3–18
No. of pupils: 1456 VIth240
Fees: Day £8,262–£10,710

Tashbar School
20 Upper Park Road, Salford,
Greater Manchester M7 4HL
Tel: 0161 7208254
Headteacher: Mr Pinczewski
Age range: B5–11
No. of pupils: 325

The Manchester Grammar School
Old Hall Lane, Fallowfield,
Manchester M13 0XT
Tel: 0161 224 7201
High Master: Dr Martin Boulton
Age range: B7–18
Fees: Day £11,400

Trinity Christian School
Birbeck Street, Stalybridge,
Greater Manchester SK15 1SH
Tel: 0161 303 0674
Headteacher: Mr W Ross Evans
Age range: 3–16
Fees: Day £2,964–£4,146

Withington Girls' School
Wellington Road, Fallowfield,
Manchester M14 6BL
Tel: 0161 224 1077
Headmistress: Mrs S E Marks MA
Age range: G7–18
No. of pupils: 650 VIth167
Fees: Day £9,300

Isle of Man

The Buchan School
West Hill, Castletown,
Isle of Man IM9 1RD
Tel: 01624 820481
Headteacher:
Mrs Alison Hope Hedley
Age range: 4–11
No. of pupils: 195
Fees: Day £2,849–£3,716

Lancashire

Arnold KEQMS (AKS)
Clifton Drive South, Lytham St
Annes, Lancashire FY8 1DT
Tel: 01253 784100
Headmaster: Mr. Mike Walton
BA, MA (Ed), PGCE, NPQH
Age range: 2–18
No. of pupils: 800 VIth165
Fees: Day £6,537–£8,541
(A)(£)🖉

Ashbridge Independent School
Lindle Lane, Hutton, Preston,
Lancashire PR4 4AQ
Tel: 01772 619900
Headteacher: Mrs H Sharples
Age range: 0–11
No. of pupils: 315
Fees: Day £6,318
🖉

Heathland School
Broadoak, Sandy Lane,
Accrington, Lancashire BB5 2AN
Tel: 01254 234284
Principal: Mrs J Harrison
BA(Hons), CertEd, FRSA
Age range: 4–16
Fees: Day £4,515

Highfield Priory School
58 Fulwood Row, Preston,
Lancashire PR2 5RW
Tel: 01772 709624
Headmaster:
Mr Jeremy Duke BSc (Hons)
Age range: 6 months–11 years
No. of pupils: 276
Fees: Day £7,096
(£)

Kingsfold Christian School
Moss Lane, Hesketh Bank,
Preston, Lancashire PR4 6AA
Tel: 01772 813824
Age range: 4–16

Kirkham Grammar School
Ribby Road, Kirkham, Preston,
Lancashire PR4 2BH
Tel: 01772 684264
Head of School: Mr. Daniel Berry
Age range: 3–18
No. of pupils: 850 VIth180
🌐(A)(🏛)(£)🖉

Lancaster Steiner School
Lune Road, Lancaster,
Lancashire LA1 5QU
Tel: 01524 841351
Headteacher: Mrs Denise Randal
Age range: 0–14

Moorland School
Ribblesdale Avenue, Clitheroe,
Lancashire BB7 2JA
Tel: 01200 423833
Principal:
Mr T Smith BSc(Hons), PGCE
Age range: 3 months–16 years
Fees: Day £4,650–£5,190 WB
£10,800–£12,750 FB £11,250–£13,500
(🏛)(£)

Oakhill College
Wiswell Lane, Whalley,
Clitheroe, Lancashire BB7 9AF
Tel: 01254 823546
Principal:
Michael A Kennedy BSc, MA
Age range: 2–16
No. of pupils: 268
Fees: Day £4,767–£7,389
(£)🖉

Palm Tree School
Oakenhurst Road, Blackburn,
Lancashire BB2 1SN
Tel: 01254 264254
Headteacher: Mrs N Hameed
Age range: 3–11
Fees: Day £1,200

Rossall School
Broadway, Fleetwood,
Lancashire FY7 8JW
Tel: +44 (0)1253 774201
Head: Ms Elaine Purves
Age range: 2–18
No. of pupils: 629 VIth186
Fees: Day £2,550–£4,150
FB £4,400–£11,850
🌐(A)(🏛)(£)(IB)🖉

Scarisbrick Hall School
Southport Road, Scarisbrisk,
Ormskirk, Lancashire L40 9RQ
Tel: 01704 841151
Headmaster: Mr J Shaw
Age range: 0–18
Fees: Day £5,000–£9,500
(A)(£)🖉

St Anne's College Grammar School
293 Clifton Drive South, Lytham
St Annes, Lancashire FY8 1HN
Tel: +44 (0)1253 725815
Principal: Mrs S M Welsby
Age range: 2–18
No. of pupils: VIth16
Fees: Day £4,900–£7,800
WB £5,200 FB £7,500
(A)(🏛)(£)🖉

St Joseph's School, Park Hill
Park Hill, Padiham Road,
Burnley, Lancashire BB12 6TG
Tel: 01282 455622
Headmistress:
Mrs Annette Robinson
Age range: 3–11
Fees: Day £5,600

St Pius X Preparatory School
Oak House, 200 Garstang
Road, Fulwood, Preston,
Lancashire PR2 8RD
Tel: 01772 719937
Headmistress: Miss B M Banks MA
Age range: 2–11
No. of pupils: 260
Fees: Day £6,975–£7,325
(£)🖉

Westholme School
Meins Road, Blackburn,
Lancashire BB2 6QU
Tel: 01254 506070
Principal: Mrs Lynne Horner
BA(Hons), PGCE, DipEd
Age range: 3 months–18 years
No. of pupils: 792 VIth72
Fees: Day £7,200–£10,290
(A)(£)🖉

Merseyside

Avalon Preparatory School
Caldy Road, West Kirby, Wirral,
Merseyside CH48 2HE
Tel: 0151 625 6993
Head of School:
Ms Joanna Callaway
Age range: 2–11
No. of pupils: 178
Fees: Day £1,860–£5,205

Belvedere Preparatory School
23 Belvidere Road, Princes
Park, Aigburth, Liverpool,
Merseyside L8 3TF
Tel: 0151 471 1137
Head of School: Ms Clare Burnham
Age range: 3–11
No. of pupils: 180

Birkenhead School
The Lodge, 58 Beresford Road,
Birkenhead, Merseyside CH43 2JD
Tel: 0151 652 4014
Headmaster:
Mr David John Clark MA
Age range: 3 months–18 years
No. of pupils: VIth103
Fees: Day £6,645–£9,606
(A)(£)🖉

Carleton House Preparatory School
145 Menlove Avenue, Liverpool,
Merseyside L18 3EE
Tel: 0151 722 0756
Head: Mr Peter Andrew
Age range: 4–11
No. of pupils: 145
Fees: Day £5,928
🖉

Christian Fellowship School
Overbury Street, Edge Hill,
Liverpool, Merseyside L7 3HL
Tel: 0151 709 1642
Headteacher: Miss Barbara Lord
Age range: 4–16
No. of pupils: 191
Fees: Day £1,752–£3,528
🖉

Kingsmead School
Bertram Drive, Hoylake, Wirral,
Merseyside CH47 0LL
Tel: 0151 632 3156
Headmaster:
Mr M G Gibbons BComm, MSc, QTS
Age range: 3–16
Fees: Day £2,625–£9,105 WB
£13,050–£15,345 FB £13,755–£16,050
🌐(🏛)(£)🖉

Prenton Preparatory School
Mount Pleasant, Oxton, Wirral,
Merseyside CH43 5SY
Tel: 0151 652 3182
Head: Mr Jones
Age range: 2–11
Fees: Day £4,650
🖉

Redcourt St Anselm's
Redcourt, Devonshire Place,
Birkenhead, Merseyside CH43 1TX
Tel: 0151 652 5228
Head of School: Miss Rachel Jones
Age range: 3–11
No. of pupils: 320
Fees: Day £2,500–£3,000

Runnymede St Edward's School

North Drive, Sandfield Park,
Liverpool, Merseyside L12 1LE
Tel: 0151 281 2300
Headmaster: Mr Bradley Slater
Age range: 3–11
No. of pupils: 270
Fees: Day £6,276–£6,617
£ 🖊

St Mary's College

Everest Road, Crosby, Liverpool,
Merseyside L23 5TW
Tel: 0151 924 3926
Principal: Mr Michael Kennedy
Age range: 0–18
No. of pupils: 880 VIth132
Fees: Day £4,815–£7,533
Ⓐ £ 🖊

Streatham House School

Victoria Road West, Blundellsands,
Liverpool, Merseyside L23 8UQ
Tel: 0151 924 1514
Executive Headteacher:
Mrs Debby Rigby BA(Hons),
PGCE, CertEd(Man)
Age range: B3 months–11
G3 months–16
Fees: Day £1,200
👥 £ 🖊

Tower College

Mill Lane, Rainhill, Prescot,
Merseyside L35 6NE
Tel: 0151 426 4333
Principal: Miss R J Oxley NNEB, RSH
Age range: 3–16
No. of pupils: 486
Fees: Day £5,013–£5,895
🖊

South-East

KEY TO SYMBOLS
(♟) *Boys' school*
(♟) *Girls' school*
(🌐) *International school*
(16+) *Tutorial or sixth form college*
(A) *A levels*
(🏫) *Boarding accommodation*
(£) *Bursaries*
(IB) *International Baccalaureate*
(✐) *Learning support*
(16+) *Entrance at 16+*
(🌐) *Vocational qualifications*
(IAPS) *Independent Association of Prep Schools*
(HMC) *The Headmasters' & Headmistresses' Conference*
(ISA) *Independent Schools Association*
(GSA) *Girls' School Association*
(BSA) *Boarding Schools' Association*
(S) *Society of Heads*
*Unless otherwise indicated, all schools are
coeducational day schools. Single-sex and boarding
schools will be indicated by the relevant icon.*

Berkshire

Alder Bridge School
Bridge House, Mill Lane, Padworth,
Reading, Berkshire RG7 4JU
Tel: 0118 971 4471
Age range: 0–14 years
No. of pupils: 65
Fees: Day £3,354–£8,295

Brigidine School Windsor
Queensmead, King's Road,
Windsor, Berkshire SL4 2AX
Tel: 01753 863779
Headmistress:
Mrs Elizabeth Robinson
Age range: B2–7 G3–18
No. of pupils: 300
Fees: Day £3,945–£11,865

Caversham School
16 Peppard Road, Caversham,
Reading, Berkshire RG4 8JZ
Tel: 0118 948 7684
Head: Mrs Jacqueline Lawson
Age range: 4–11
No. of pupils: 60
Fees: Day £6,750

Claires Court Junior Boys
Maidenhead Thicket,
Maidenhead, Berkshire SL6 3QE
Tel: 01628 411490
Head: J M E Spanswick
Age range: B4–11
No. of pupils: 248
Fees: Day £7,965–£13,860

Claires Court Nursery, Girls and Sixth Form
1 College Avenue, Maidenhead,
Berkshire SL6 6AW
Tel: 01628 411480
Head: Mr Paul Bevis
Age range: B16–18 G3–18
No. of pupils: 495 VIth111
Fees: Day £5,715–£14,580

Crosfields School
Shinfield, Reading,
Berkshire RG2 9BL
Tel: 0118 987 1810
Headmaster: Mr J P Wansey
Age range: 3–13
No. of pupils: 510
Fees: Day £6,600–£10,710

Dolphin School
Waltham Road, Hurst, Reading,
Berkshire RG10 0FR
Tel: 0118 934 1277
Head: Mr Tom Lewis
Age range: 3–13
Fees: Day £8,340–£11,190

Eagle House School
Sandhurst, Berkshire GU47 8PH
Tel: 01344 772134
Headmaster:
Mr A P N Barnard BA(Hons), PGCE
Age range: 3–13
No. of pupils: 395
Fees: Day £10,905–
£17,070 FB £22,920

Elstree School
Woolhampton, Reading,
Berkshire RG7 5TD
Tel: 0118 971 3302
Headmaster: Mr S Inglis
Age range: B3–13 G3–7
No. of pupils: 248
Fees: Day £17,775 FB £22,800

Eton End PNEU School
35 Eton Road, Datchet,
Slough, Berkshire SL3 9AX
Tel: 01753 541075
Headmistress:
Mrs V M Pilgerstorfer BA(Hons), PGCE
Age range: B3–7 G3–11
No. of pupils: 245
Fees: Day £5,850–£6,900

Hemdean House School
Hemdean Road, Caversham,
Reading, Berkshire RG4 7SD
Tel: 0118 947 2590
Headmistress: Mrs J Harris BSc
Age range: B3–11 G3–16
Fees: Day £5,280–£7,200

Herries Preparatory School
Dean Lane, Cookham
Dean, Berkshire SL6 9BD
Tel: 01628 483350
Headmistress: Sophie Green
Age range: 3–11
Fees: Day £6,645–£8,985

Highfield Preparatory School
2 West Road, Maidenhead,
Berkshire SL6 1PD
Tel: 01628 624918
Headteacher: Mrs Joanna Leach
Age range: B3–5 G3–11
Fees: Day £897–£10,110

Holme Grange School
Heathlands Road, Wokingham,
Berkshire RG40 3AL
Tel: 0118 978 1566
Headteacher: Mrs Claire Robinson
Age range: 3–16 years
No. of pupils: 397
Fees: Day £9,690–£13,590

Hurst Lodge
Bagshot Road, Ascot,
Berkshire SL5 9JU
Tel: 01344 622154
Principal: Ms Victoria Smit
Age range: 3–18
No. of pupils: 202 VIth13
Fees: Day £6,420–£25,200
WB £19,905–£34,005

Lambrook School
Winkfield Row, Bracknell,
Berkshire RG42 6LU
Tel: 01344 882717
Headmaster: Mr Jonathan Perry
Age range: 3–13
No. of pupils: 440
Fees: Day £9,078–£15,180 WB
£16,803–£18,009 FB £17,433–£18,639

Long Close School
Upton Court Road, Upton,
Slough, Berkshire SL3 7LU
Tel: 01753 520095
Head: Mr David Brazier
Age range: 2–16
No. of pupils: 283
Fees: Day £5,715–£10,080

LUDGROVE
For further details see p. 70
Wokingham, Berkshire RG40 3AB
Tel: 0118 978 9881
Email:
registrar@ludgroveschool.co.uk
Website: www.ludgrove.net
Head of School: Mr Simon Barber
Age range: B8–13
No. of pupils: 190

LVS Ascot (Licensed Victuallers' School)
London Road, Ascot,
Berkshire SL5 8DR
Tel: 01344 882770
Headmistress: Mrs Christine
Cunniffe BA (Hons), MMus, MBA
Age range: 4–18
No. of pupils: 870
Fees: Day £9,528–£17,079
FB £24,384–£30,006

Meadowbrook Montessori School
Malt Hill Road, Warfield,
Bracknell, Berkshire RG42 6JQ
Tel: 01344 890869
Director of Education: Mrs S Gunn
Age range: 3–11
No. of pupils: 78
Fees: Day £10,200

Newbold School
Popeswood Road, Binfield,
Bracknell, Berkshire RG42 4AH
Tel: 01344 421088
Headteacher: Mrs P Eastwood
Age range: 3–11
Fees: Day £3,000–£4,000

Our Lady's Preparatory School
The Avenue, Crowthorne,
Wokingham, Berkshire RG45 6PB
Tel: 01344 773394
Headmistress: Mrs Helene Robinson
Age range: 3 months–11 years
No. of pupils: 100
Fees: Day £5,328–£10,464

Papplewick School
Windsor Road, Ascot,
Berkshire SL5 7LH
Tel: 01344 621488
Head: Mr T W Bunbury BA, PGCE
Age range: B6–13
No. of pupils: 195

Reddam House Berkshire
Bearwood Road, Wokingham,
Berkshire RG41 5BG
Tel: 0118 974 8300
Headmaster:
Mr Toby Jonathan Mullins MBA, BA
Age range: 3 months–18 years
No. of pupils: 390
Fees: Day £9,945–£16,545 WB
£25,535–£29,445 FB £27,045–£30,945

Redroofs School for the Performing Arts (Redroofs Theatre School)
26 Bath Road, Maidenhead,
Berkshire SL6 4JT
Tel: 01628 674092
Principal: June Rose
Age range: 8–18
No. of pupils: 100
Fees: Day £4,000

St Andrew's School
Buckhold, Pangbourne,
Reading, Berkshire RG8 8QA
Tel: 0118 974 4276
Headmaster:
Dr D Livingstone BSc, PhD, NPQH
Age range: 3–13
Fees: Day £4,050–£14,280
WB £16,950

St Bernard's Preparatory School
Hawtrey Close, Slough,
Berkshire SL1 1TB
Tel: 01753 521821
Head Teacher: Mrs M B
Smith Certtd, NPQH
Age range: 2–11

St Edward's School
64 Tilehurst Road, Reading,
Berkshire RG30 2JH
Tel: 0118 957 4342
Principal: G W Mottram
Age range: B4–13
No. of pupils: 170
Fees: Day £6,660–£8,550

St George's School Windsor Castle
Windsor, Berkshire SL4 1QF
Tel: 01753 865553
Head Master: Mr C F McDade
Age range: 3–13
Fees: Day £8,493–£14,097
WB £18,723 FB £19,203

St John's Beaumont Preparatory School
Priest Hill, Old Windsor,
Berkshire SL4 2JN
Tel: 01784 432428
Headmaster:
Mr G E F Delaney BA(Hons), PGCE
Age range: B3–13
No. of pupils: 310
Fees: Day £7,140–£13,320
WB £17,520 FB £20,250

St Joseph's College
Upper Redlands Road,
Reading, Berkshire RG1 5JT
Tel: 0118 966 1000
Headmaster: Mr Andrew Colpus
Age range: 3–18
No. of pupils: VIth46
Fees: Day £6,084–£10,401

St Piran's Preparatory School
Gringer Hill, Maidenhead,
Berkshire SL6 7LZ
Tel: 01628 594302
Headmaster: Mr J A Carroll
BA(Hons), BPhilEd, PGCE, NPQH
Age range: 3–11
Fees: Day £9,900–£14,550

Sunningdale School
Dry Arch Road, Sunningdale,
Berkshire SL5 9PY
Tel: 01344 620159
Headmaster:
T A C N Dawson MA, PGCE
Age range: B7–13
No. of pupils: 90
Fees: Day £13,950 FB £17,985

The Abbey School
Kendrick Road, Reading,
Berkshire RG1 5DZ
Tel: 0118 987 2256
Head: Mrs Rachel S E Dent
Age range: G3–18
No. of pupils: 1050
Fees: Day £15,720

The Deenway Montessori School
3-5 Sidmouth Street, Reading,
Berkshire RG1 4QX
Tel: 0118 9574737
Headteacher: Mr M Karim
Age range: 3–11

The Marist Preparatory School
King's Road, Sunninghill,
Ascot, Berkshire SL5 7PS
Tel: 01344 626137
Headteacher: J Finlayson
Age range: G2–11
No. of pupils: 225
Fees: Day £8,700–£9,360

The Marist Schools
King's Road, Sunninghill,
Ascot, Berkshire SL5 7PS
Tel: 01344 624291
Head of Secondary School:
Mr K McCloskey
Age range: G2–18
No. of pupils: 550 VIth60
Fees: Day £7,845–£10,695

The Oratory Preparatory School
Great Oaks, Goring Heath,
Reading, Berkshire RG8 7SF
Tel: 0118 984 4511
Headmaster: Mr J J Smith BA, PGCE
Age range: 3–13
No. of pupils: 400
Fees: Day £3,425–£11,475
WB £14,565 FB £15,825

The Vine Christian School
SORCF Christian Centre,
Basingstoke Road, Three Mile
Cross, Reading, Berkshire RG7 1AT
Tel: 0118 988 6464
Head: Mrs Joan Muirhead
Age range: 5–13
No. of pupils: 9

Upton House School
115 St Leonard's Road,
Windsor, Berkshire SL4 3DF
Tel: 01753 862610
Headmistress: Mrs Madeleine
Collins BA(Hons), PGCE(Oxford)
Age range: B2–7 G2–11
No. of pupils: 280

Waverley School
Waverley Way, Finchampstead,
Wokingham, Berkshire RG40 4YD
Tel: 0118 973 1121
Principal: Mrs Jane Sculpher
Age range: 3–11
Fees: Day £3,300–£7,362

Buckinghamshire

Caldicott
Crown Lane, Farnham Royal,
Buckinghamshire SL2 3SL
Tel: 01753 649301
Headmaster:
Mr S J G Doggart BA(Cantab)
Age range: B7–13
No. of pupils: 256
Fees: Day £13,080–
£14,148 FB £19,227

Dair House School
Bishops Blake, Beaconsfield
Road, Farnham Royal,
Buckinghamshire SL2 3BY
Tel: 01753 643964
Headmaster:
Mr Terry Wintle BEd(Hons)
Age range: 3–11
No. of pupils: 125
Fees: Day £3,060–£4,100

Gayhurst School
Bull Lane, Gerrards Cross,
Buckinghamshire SL9 8RJ
Tel: 01753 882690
Headmaster: A J Sims MA(Cantab)
Age range: B3–13 G3–13
Fees: Day £9,882–£12,555

Heatherton House School
Copperkins Lane,
Chesham Bois, Amersham,
Buckinghamshire HP6 5QB
Tel: 01494 726433
Headteacher:
Mrs Debbie Isaachsen
Age range: B3–4 G3–11
Fees: Day £1,068–£12,330

Maltman's Green School
Maltman's Lane, Gerrards Cross,
Buckinghamshire SL9 8RR
Tel: 01753 883022
Headmistress: Mrs Joanna
Pardon MA, BSc(Hons), PGCE
Age range: G2–11
Fees: Day £10,200–£13,500

St Mary's School
94 Packhorse Road, Gerrards
Cross, Buckinghamshire SL9 8JQ
Tel: 01753 883370
Headmistress:
Mrs J A Ross BA(Hons), NPQH
Age range: G3–18
No. of pupils: 320 VIth38
Fees: Day £3,420–£12,155

Thorpe House School
Oval Way, Gerrards Cross,
Buckinghamshire SL9 8QA
Tel: 01753 882474
Headmaster: Mr Terrence Ayres
Age range: B3–16
Fees: Day £9,000–£13,500

East Sussex

Ashdown House School
Forest Row, East Sussex RH18 5JY
Tel: 01342 822574
Headmaster: Haydon Moore
Age range: 7–13
No. of pupils: 125
Fees: FB £23,250

Battle Abbey School
Battle, East Sussex TN33 0AD
Tel: 01424 772385
Headmaster:
Mr R C Clark BA(Hons), MA(Ed)
Age range: 2–18
No. of pupils: 286 VIth48
Fees: Day £6,630–£13,390 FB £23,190

Bricklehurst Manor Preparatory
Bardown Road, Stonegate,
Wadhurst, East Sussex TN5 7EL
Tel: 01580 200448
Headteacher: Mrs C Flowers
Age range: 3–11
No. of pupils: 127
Fees: Day £980–£8,925

Brighton & Hove High School GDST
Montpelier Road, Brighton,
East Sussex BN1 3AT
Tel: 01273 280280
Head: Mrs Lorna Duggleby
Age range: G3–18
No. of pupils: 680 VIth70
Fees: Day £5,028–£8,898

Brighton & Hove Montessori School
67 Stanford Avenue, Brighton,
East Sussex BN1 6FB
Tel: 01273 702485
Headteacher:
Mrs Daisy Cockburn AMI, MontDip
Age range: 2–11
Fees: Day £1,400–£5,900

Brighton College
Eastern Road, Brighton,
East Sussex BN2 0AL
Tel: 01273 704200
Head Master: Richard Cairns MA
Age range: 3–18
No. of pupils: 945 VIth340
Fees: Day £4,890–£18,675 WB
£24,729–£25,884 FB £28,575–£30,141

Brighton Steiner School
John Howard House, Roedean
Road, Brighton, East Sussex BN2 5RA
Tel: 01273 386300
**Chair of the College of
Teachers:** Carrie Rawle
Age range: 3–16
Fees: Day £6,540

Charters Ancaster College
Woodsgate Place, Gunters Lane,
Bexhill-on-Sea, East Sussex TN39 4EB
Tel: 01424 216670
Headmistress: Mrs Miriam Black
Age range: 2–13
No. of pupils: 125
Fees: Day £5,325–£6,750

Claremont Preparatory & Nursery School
Ebdens Hill, Baldslow, St Leonards-
on-Sea, East Sussex TN37 7PW
Tel: 01424 751555
Headmistress: Mrs Diane Durrant
Age range: 1–14
Fees: Day £5,000–£10,000

Darvell School
Darvell Bruderhof, Robertsbridge,
East Sussex TN32 5DR
Tel: 01580 883300
Headteacher: Mr Arnold Meier
Age range: 4–16
No. of pupils: 121

Deepdene School
195 New Church Road, Hove,
East Sussex BN3 4ED
Tel: 01273 418984
Heads: Mrs Nicola Gane
& Miss Elizabeth Brown
Age range: 6 months–11 years
Fees: Day £1,800–£6,870

Dharma School
The White House, Ladies Mile
Road, Patcham, Brighton,
East Sussex BN1 8TB
Tel: 01273 502055
Headmaster: Kevin Fossey BEd
Age range: 3–11
Fees: Day £3,000

Greenfields Independent Day & Boarding School
Priory Road, Forest Row,
East Sussex RH18 5JD
Tel: +44 (0)1342 822189
Executive Head: Mr. Jeff Smith
Age range: 2–19

Lancing College Preparatory School at Hove
The Droveway, Hove,
East Sussex BN3 6LU
Tel: 01273 503452
Headmaster: A P Laurent
Age range: 3–13
No. of pupils: 181
Fees: Day £2,550–£10,155

Lewes New School
Talbot Terrace, Lewes,
East Sussex BN7 1RD
Tel: 01273 477074
Head of School: Linda Morris
Age range: 3–11
No. of pupils: 78
Fees: Day £7,374

Lewes Old Grammar School
High Street, Lewes, East
Sussex BN7 1XS
Tel: 01273 472634
Headmaster: Mr Robert Blewitt
Age range: 3–18
No. of pupils: 463 VIth50
Fees: Day £5,550–£10,815

Michael Hall School
Kidbrooke Park, Priory Road,
Forest Row, East Sussex RH18 5BG
Tel: 01342 822275
Age range: 3–19
Fees: Day £8,840–£12,120
FB £5,400–£7,610

Moira House Girls School
Upper Carlisle Road, Eastbourne,
East Sussex BN20 7TE
Tel: 01323 644144
Headmaster:
Mr James Sheridan MA, BSc
Age range: G0–18
No. of pupils: 289

Sacred Heart School
Mayfield Lane, Durgates,
Wadhurst, East Sussex TN5 6DQ
Tel: 01892 783414
Headteacher:
Mrs H Blake BA(Hons), PGCE
Age range: 3–11
Fees: Day £2,235–£6,225

Skippers Hill Manor Prep School
Five Ashes, Mayfield, East
Sussex TN20 6HR
Tel: 01825 830234
Headmaster: Mr M Hammond
MA, BA, PGCE
Age range: 2–13
Fees: Day £3,852–£12,930

St Andrew's Prep
Meads, Eastbourne, East
Sussex BN20 7RP
Tel: 01323 733203
Headmaster:
Gareth Jones BA(Hons), PGCE
Age range: 9 months–13 years
Fees: Day £9,406–£16,350 FB £23,205

St Bede's Preparatory School
Duke's Drive, Eastbourne,
East Sussex BN20 7XL
Tel: 01323 734222
Head: Mr Nicholas Bevington
Age range: 3 months–13 years
No. of pupils: 395

St Christopher's School
33 New Church Road, Hove,
East Sussex BN3 4AD
Tel: 01273 735404
Headmaster: Mr Julian Withers
Age range: 4–13
Fees: Day £6,570–£8,688

The Drive Prep School
101 The Drive, Hove,
East Sussex BN3 3JE
Tel: 01273 738444
Head Teacher: Mrs S Parkinson
CertEd, CertPerfArts
Age range: 7–16
Fees: Day £3,885–£7,500

Torah Academy
31 New Church Road, Hove,
East Sussex BN3 4AD
Tel: 01273 328675
Principal: P Efune
Age range: 4–11

Vinehall School
Robertsbridge, East Sussex TN32 5JL
Tel: 01580 880413
Headmaster: Richard Follett
Age range: 2–13
No. of pupils: 260
Fees: Day £8,913–£16,620
FB £19,545–£21,675

Windlesham School
190 Dyke Road, Brighton,
East Sussex BN1 5AA
Tel: 01273 553645
Headmistress:
Mrs Aoife Bennett-Odlum
Age range: 3–11
No. of pupils: 233
Fees: Day £5,100–£7,200

Hampshire

Alton Convent School
Anstey Lane, Alton,
Hampshire GU34 2NG
Tel: 01420 82070
Head: Graham Maher
Age range: B0–11 G0–18
No. of pupils: 563 VIth53
Fees: Day £8,655–£12,285

Ballard School
Fernhill Lane, New Milton,
Hampshire BH25 5SU
Tel: 01425 626900
Headmaster: Mr Alastair Reid
Age range: 18 months–16 years
No. of pupils: 500
Fees: Day £2,370–£4,265

Boundary Oak School
Roche Court, Fareham,
Hampshire PO17 5BL
Tel: 01329 280955/820373
Head: Mrs Hazel Kellett
Age range: 2–13
No. of pupils: 120
Fees: Day £7,500–£12,510 WB
£5,370 FB £7,095–£19,605

Brockwood Park & Inwoods School
Brockwood Park, Bramdean,
Hampshire SO24 0LQ
Tel: +44 (0)1962 771744
Co-Principals: Mr Adrian Sydenham
& Dr Gopal Krishnamurthy
Age range: 4–19
No. of pupils: 92
Fees: Day £3,150 FB £17,270

Brookham School
Highfield Lane, Liphook,
Hampshire GU30 7LQ
Tel: 01428 722005
Headteacher: Mrs Sophie Baber
Age range: 3–8
No. of pupils: 141
Fees: Day £10,125–£13,350

Churcher's College
Petersfield, Hampshire GU31 4AS
Tel: 01730 263033
Headmaster:
Mr Simon Williams MA, BSc
Age range: 4–18
No. of pupils: 1067 VIth224
Fees: Day £7,605–£11,955

Daneshill School
Stratfield Turgis, Basingstoke,
Hampshire RG27 0AR
Tel: 01256 882707
Headmaster:
S V Spencer CertEd, DipPhysEd
Age range: 3–13
Fees: Day £3,900–£9,150

Ditcham Park School
Ditcham Park, Petersfield,
Hampshire GU31 5RN
Tel: 01730 825659
Head Teacher:
R J Connolly MEd, BA, PGCE, NPHQ
Age range: 4–16
No. of pupils: 350
Fees: Day £8,025–£13,455

Dunhurst (Bedales Junior School)
Petersfield, Hampshire GU32 2DP
Tel: 01730 300200
Head: Jane Grubb
Age range: 8–13
No. of pupils: 177
Fees: Day £6,107–£6,319
FB £7,047–£7,908

Durlston Court
Becton Lane, Barton-on-Sea, New
Milton, Hampshire BH25 7AQ
Tel: 01425 610010
Head of School: Mr Richard May
Age range: 2–13
No. of pupils: 296
Fees: Day £3,540–£15,390

Farleigh School
Red Rice, Andover,
Hampshire SP11 7PW
Tel: 01264 710766
Headmaster: Father Simon Everson
Age range: 3–13
Fees: Day £3,870–£14,085
FB £16,515–£18,345

Forres Sandle Manor
Fordingbridge, Hampshire SP6 1NS
Tel: 01425 653181
Headmaster:
Mr M N Hartley BSc(Hons)
Age range: 3–13
No. of pupils: 264
Fees: Day £3,150–£14,205
WB £19,380 FB £19,380

Glenhurst School
16 Beechworth Road, Havant,
Hampshire PO9 1AX
Tel: 023 9248 4054
Principal: Mrs E M Haines
Age range: 3 months–8 years
Fees: Day £4,500

Hampshire Collegiate School
Embley Park, Romsey,
Hampshire SO51 6ZE
Tel: 01794 512206
Principal: Mrs Emma-Kate Henry
Age range: 2–18
No. of pupils: 683

Highfield School
Liphook, Hampshire GU30 7LQ
Tel: 01428 728000
Headmaster: Mr Philip Evitt MA
Age range: 8–13
Fees: Day £17,025–£19,575
FB £21,450–£23,550

Kingscourt School
182 Five Heads Road,
Catherington, Hampshire PO8 9NJ
Tel: 023 9259 3251
Head of School: Mrs Jacky Easton
Age range: 3–11
No. of pupils: 210
Fees: Day £2,635

Mayville High School
35/37 St Simon's Road, Southsea,
Portsmouth, Hampshire PO5 2PE
Tel: 023 9273 4847
Headteacher: Mrs L Owens B.Ed
Age range: 6 months–16 years
No. of pupils: 479
Fees: Day £5,481–£8,040

Meoncross School
Burnt House Lane, Stubbington,
Fareham, Hampshire PO14 2EF
Tel: 01329 662182
Headmistress:
Mrs Sarah Ebery BSc (Hons), MEd
Age range: 2–18
No. of pupils: 405
Fees: Day £7,365–£10,485

Moyles Court School
Moyles Court, Ringwood,
Hampshire BH24 3NF
Tel: 01425 472856
Headmaster: Mr Dean
Age range: 3–16
Fees: Day £3,285–£4,650
FB £6,690–£7,740

New Forest Small School
1 Southampton Road, Lyndhurst,
Hampshire SO43 7BU
Tel: 02380 284 415
Headteacher: Mr Nicholas Alp
Age range: 3–16

Norman Court
West Tytherley, Stockbridge,
Hampshire SP5 1NH
Tel: 01980 322 322
Headteacher:
Mr Andrew Hammond

Portsmouth High School GDST
Kent Road, Southsea, Portsmouth,
Hampshire PO5 3EQ
Tel: 023 9282 6714
Headmistress:
Mrs Jane Prescott BSc NPQH
Age range: G3–18
No. of pupils: 500
Fees: Day £2,630–£4,396

Prince's Mead School
Worthy Park House, Kings Worthy,
Winchester, Hampshire SO21 1AN
Tel: 01962 888000
Headmistress: Miss Penelope Kirk
Age range: 4–11
No. of pupils: 270
Fees: Day £9,600–£14,640

Ringwood Waldorf School
Folly Farm Lane, Ashley,
Ringwood, Hampshire BH24 2NN
Tel: 01425 472664
Age range: 3–18
No. of pupils: 235
Fees: Day £3,622–£7,825

Rookwood School
Weyhill Road, Andover,
Hampshire SP10 3AL
Tel: 01264 325900
Headmistress: Mrs L Whetstone MA
Age range: 3–16
Fees: Day £7,770–£12,780
FB £19,545–£22,875

Sherborne House School
Lakewood Road, Chandlers Ford,
Eastleigh, Hampshire SO53 1EU
Tel: 023 8025 2440
Head Teacher:
Mrs Heather Hopson-Hill
Age range: 3–11
No. of pupils: 293
Fees: Day £1,044–£8,730

Sherfield School
Sherfield-on-Loddon, Hook,
Hampshire RG27 0HU
Tel: +44 (0)1256 884 800
Headmaster: Mr Dick Jaine
Age range: 3 months–18 years
No. of pupils: 445 VIth16
Fees: Day £7,350–£13,890 FB £20,946

St John's College
Grove Road South, Southsea,
Portsmouth, Hampshire PO5 3QW
Tel: 023 9281 5118
Headmaster: Mr Timothy Bayley
Age range: 2–18
No. of pupils: 600 VIth86
Fees: Day £8,460–£11,100
FB £23,970–£25,770

ST NEOT'S SCHOOL
For further details see p. 73
St Neot's Road, Eversley,
Hampshire RG27 0PN
Tel: 0118 9739650
Email:
admissions@stneotsprep.co.uk
Website: www.stneotsprep.co.uk
Head of School:
Mrs Deborah Henderson
Age range: Nursery–13 years
No. of pupils: 319
Fees: Day £2,006–£14,994

St Nicholas' School
Redfields House, Redfields
Lane, Church Crookham,
Fleet, Hampshire GU52 0RF
Tel: 01252 850121
Headmistress:
Mrs A V Whatmough BA, CertEd
Age range: B3–7 G3–16
No. of pupils: 370

St Swithun's Junior School
Alresford Road, Winchester,
Hampshire SO21 1HA
Tel: 01962 835750
Headmistress:
Mrs P Grimes BA(Hons)
Age range: B3–7 G3–11
No. of pupils: 183
Fees: Day £1,415–£3,650

St Winifred's School
17-19 Winn Road, Southampton,
Hampshire SO17 1EJ
Tel: 023 8055 7352
Head Teacher:
Mr M Brogan BEd,CertSpNeeds
Age range: 3–11
Fees: Day £6,330

St. Mary's Independent School
57 Midanbury Lane, Bitterne Park,
Southampton, Hampshire SO18 4DJ
Tel: 023 8067 1267
Head of School: Mrs. Owen
Age range: 3–16
No. of pupils: 470
Fees: Day £1,750–£2,350

Stockton House School
Stockton Avenue, Fleet,
Hampshire GU51 4NS
Tel: 01252 616323
Early Years Manager:
Mrs Jenny Bounds BA EYPS
Age range: 2–5
Fees: Day £25.50–£70

The Children's House and Grantham Farm Montessori School
Grantham Farm, Baughurst, Tadley, Hampshire RG26 5JS
Tel: 0118 981 5821
Head Teacher: Ms Emma Wetherley
Age range: 3–8

The Grey House School
Mount Pleasant, Hartley Wintney, Hampshire RG27 8PW
Tel: 01252 842353
Head: Mrs C E Allen BEd(Cantab)
Age range: 4–11+
Fees: Day £7,365–£8,994

The King's School
Lakesmere House, Allington Lane, Fair Oak, Eastleigh, Southampton, Hampshire SO50 7DB
Tel: 023 8060 0986
Head of School:
Mrs H Bowden BA (Hons), PGCE
Age range: 3–16
No. of pupils: 256
Fees: Day £3,900–£6,840

The Pilgrims' School
3 The Close, Winchester, Hampshire SO23 9LT
Tel: 01962 854189
Headmaster: Mr Tom Burden
No. of pupils: 250
Fees: Day £17,685 FB £22,335

The Portsmouth Grammar Junior School
High Street, Portsmouth, Hampshire PO1 2LN
Tel: +44 (0)23 9268 1336
Headmaster: Peter Hopkinson BA, PGCE
Age range: 4–11
No. of pupils: 398
Fees: Day £8,127–£9,012

The Stroud School
Highwood House, Highwood Lane, Romsey, Hampshire SO51 9ZH
Tel: 01794 513231
Headmaster:
Mr Alastair J L Dodds MA(Cantab)
Age range: 3–13
Fees: Day £9,060–£14,775

Twyford School
Twyford, Winchester, Hampshire SO21 1NW
Tel: 01962 712269
Headmaster:
Dr S J Bailey BEd, PhD, FRSA
Age range: 3–13
Fees: Day £6,726–£18,570 WB £4,800

Walhampton
Walhampton, Lymington, Hampshire SO41 5ZG
Tel: 01590 613 300
Headmaster: Mr Titus Mills
Age range: 2–13
No. of pupils: 353
Fees: Day £8,025–£15,555 FB £20,790

West Hill Park Preparatory School
Titchfield, Fareham, Hampshire PO14 4BS
Tel: 01329 842356
Headmaster:
A P Ramsay BEd(Hons), MSc
Age range: 2–13
No. of pupils: 288
Fees: Day £8,985–£14,985 FB £13,785–£19,785

Woodhill School, Botley
Brook Lane, Botley, Southampton, Hampshire SO30 2ER
Tel: 01489 781112
Head Teacher: Mrs M Dacombe
Age range: 3–11
No. of pupils: 100
Fees: Day £2,199–£4,965

Yateley Manor School
51 Reading Road, Yateley, Hampshire GU46 7UQ
Tel: 01252 405500
Headmaster: Mr R J Williams MA(Hons)Edinburgh, PGCE Bedford
Age range: 3–13
No. of pupils: 453
Fees: Day £4,500–£12,150

Isle of Wight

Priory School
Beatrice Avenue, Whippingham, Isle of Wight PO32 6LP
Tel: 01983 861222
Principal: Mr E J Matyjaszek
Age range: 5–18
Fees: Day £3,360–£7,200

Ryde School with Upper Chine
Queen's Road, Ryde, Isle of Wight PO33 3BE
Tel: 01983 617970
Headmaster: Mr M. A. Waldron MA
Age range: 2½–18
No. of pupils: 742
Fees: Day £12,375 WB £24,330 FB £27,255

Kent

Ashford Friars Prep School
Great Chart, Ashford, Kent TN23 3DJ
Tel: 01233 620493
Head: Mr R Yeates BA(Hons)(Exeter)
Age range: 3–11
No. of pupils: 373
Fees: Day £6,414–£11,079

Ashford School
East Hill, Ashford, Kent TN24 8PB
Tel: 01233 739030
Head: Mr M R Buchanan BSc(Hons), CertEd, NPQH, CPhys
Age range: 3 months–18 years
No. of pupils: 835 VIth170
Fees: Day £8,400–£16,200 WB £28,500 FB £32,400

Beech Grove School
Beech Grove Bruderhof, Sandwich Road, Nonington, Dover, Kent CT15 4HH
Tel: 01304 842980
Head: Mr Benjamin Shirky
Age range: 4–14
No. of pupils: 63

Beechwood Sacred Heart
12 Pembury Road, Tunbridge Wells, Kent TN2 3QD
Tel: 01892 532747
Headmaster:
Mr Aaron Lennon BA(Hons)
Age range: 3–18
No. of pupils: 400 VIth70
Fees: Day £9,060–£15,936 WB £23,460 FB £26,460

Bronte School
Mayfield, 7 Pelham Road, Gravesend, Kent DA11 0HN
Tel: 01474 533805
Headmaster: Mr R Dyson
Age range: 4–11
No. of pupils: 120
Fees: Day £7,950

Bryony School
Marshall Road, Rainham, Gillingham, Kent ME8 0AJ
Tel: 01634 231511
Joint Heads:
D E and Mrs M P Edmunds
Age range: 2–11
No. of pupils: 174
Fees: Day £4,551–£5,451

Canterbury Steiner School
Garlinge Green, Chartham, Canterbury, Kent CT4 5RU
Tel: 01227 738285
Age range: 3–18
Fees: Day £3,246–£4,405.50

Chartfield School
45 Minster Road, Westgate on Sea, Kent CT8 8DA
Tel: 01843 831716
Head & Proprietor: Miss L P Shipley
Age range: 4–11
No. of pupils: 50
Fees: Day £2,580–£3,000

Derwent Lodge School for Girls
Somerhill, Tonbridge, Kent TN11 0NJ
Tel: 01732 352124
Headmistress:
Mrs S Michau MA(Oxon), PGCE
Age range: G7–11
No. of pupils: 134
Fees: Day £12,675

Dover College
Effingham Crescent,
Dover, Kent CT17 9RH
Tel: 01304 205969
Headmaster:
Mr Gareth Doodes MA (Hons)
Age range: 3–18
No. of pupils: 301
Fees: Day £7,005 WB
£19,590 FB £21,420

Dulwich Preparatory School
Coursehorn, Cranbrook,
Kent TN17 3NP
Tel: 01580 712179
Headmaster:
Mr Paul David BEd(Hons)
Age range: 3–13
No. of pupils: 535
Fees: Day £4,890–£14,400

Elliott Park School
18-20 Marina Drive, Minster,
Sheerness, Kent ME12 2DP
Tel: 01795 873372
Head: Ms Colleen Hiller
Age range: 3–11
No. of pupils: 65
Fees: Day £5,025

Fosse Bank School
Mountains, Noble Tree
Road, Hildenborough,
Tonbridge, Kent TN11 8ND
Tel: 01732 834212
Headmistress: Mrs Lovatt-Young
Age range: 3–11
No. of pupils: 124
Fees: Day £1,560–£10,671

Gad's Hill School
Higham, Rochester,
Medway, Kent ME3 7PA
Tel: 01474 822366
Headmaster: Mr D G Craggs
BSc, MA, NPQH, FCollP, FRSA
Age range: 3–16
No. of pupils: 370
Fees: Day £6,000–£7,600

Haddon Dene School
57 Gladstone Road,
Broadstairs, Kent CT10 2HY
Tel: 01843 861176
Head: Mrs E Rowe
Age range: 3–11
No. of pupils: 200
Fees: Day £4,950–£6,135

Hilden Grange School
62 Dry Hill Park Road,
Tonbridge, Kent TN10 3BX
Tel: 01732 351169
Headmaster: Mr J Withers BA(Hons)
Age range: 3–13
Fees: Day £9,780–£12,950

Hilden Oaks School & Nursery
38 Dry Hill Park Road,
Tonbridge, Kent TN10 3BU
Tel: 01732 353941
Head of School: Mrs. K J M Joiner
Age range: 0–11 B0–11 G0–11
Fees: Day £8,985–£11,988

Holmewood House School
Langton Green, Tunbridge
Wells, Kent TN3 0EB
Tel: 01892 860006
Headmaster:
Mr J D B Marjoribanks BEd
Age range: 3–13
No. of pupils: 439
Fees: Day £2,160–£17,460
WB £20,640

KENT COLLEGE JUNIOR SCHOOL
For further details see p. 69
Harbledown, Canterbury,
Kent CT2 9AQ
Tel: 01227 762436
Email: prepenquiries@
kentcollege.co.uk
Website:
www.kentcollege.com/junior
Headmaster: Mr Andrew Carter
Age range: 3–11
No. of pupils: 190
Fees: Day £9,939–£15,390
FB £24,375

Kent College Pembury
Old Church Road, Pembury,
Tunbridge Wells, Kent TN2 4AX
Tel: +44 (0)1892 822006
Headmistress: Mrs Sally-Anne
Huang MA(Oxon), MSc, PGCE
Age range: G3–18
No. of pupils: 650 VIth102
Fees: Day £7,887–£17,322
FB £21,471–£27,924

King's Preparatory School, Rochester
King Edward Road, Rochester,
Medway, Kent ME1 1UB
Tel: 01634 888577
Headmaster: Mr R Overend
Age range: 4–13
No. of pupils: 228
Fees: Day £7,125–£10,380 FB £16,005

Linton Park School
3 Eccleston Road, Tovil,
Maidstone, Kent ME17 4HT
Tel: 01622 740820
Headteacher: Mr G Allen
Age range: 7–18
No. of pupils: 134

Lorenden Preparatory School
Painter's Forstal, Faversham,
Kent ME13 0EN
Tel: 01795 590030
Headmistress: Mrs R Simmons
Age range: 3–11
No. of pupils: 100
Fees: Day £7,374–£10,680

Marlborough House School
High Street, Hawkhurst,
Kent TN18 4PY
Tel: 01580 753555
Headmaster: Mr Martyn Ward
Age range: 2–13
No. of pupils: 334
Fees: Day £2,808–£14,700

Meredale Independent Primary School
Solomon Road, Rainham,
Gillingham, Kent ME8 8EB
Tel: 01634 231405
Headteacher:
Miss Michelle Ingledew
Age range: 3–11
No. of pupils: 53
Fees: Day £5,100

Northbourne Park School
Betteshanger, Deal, Kent CT14 0NW
Tel: 01304 611215/218
Headmaster: Mr Sebastian
Rees BA(Hons), PGCE, NPQH
Age range: 3–13
No. of pupils: 148
Fees: Day £8,598–£16,005
WB £19,830 FB £23,040

Radnor House, Sevenoaks
Combe Bank Drive,
Sevenoaks, Kent TN14 6AE
Tel: 01959 563720
Head: Mr David Paton
BComm (Hons) PGCE MA
Age range: 2½–18
No. of pupils: 250

Rose Hill School
Coniston Avenue, Tunbridge
Wells, Kent TN4 9SY
Tel: 01892 525591
Headmaster:
Mr D Westcombe BA, PGCE
Age range: 3–13
Fees: Day £3,040–£4,130

Russell House School
Station Road, Otford,
Sevenoaks, Kent TN14 5QU
Tel: 01959 522352
Headmistress: Mrs Alison Cooke
Age range: 2–11
Fees: Day £4,650–£9,840

Saint Ronan's School
Water Lane, Hawkhurst,
Kent TN18 5DJ
Tel: 01580 752271
Headmaster:
William Trelawny-Vernon BSc(Hons)
Age range: 3–13
No. of pupils: 300
Fees: Day £6,951–£11,892

Sevenoaks Preparatory School
Godden Green, Sevenoaks,
Kent TN15 0JU
Tel: 01732 762336
Headmaster: Mr Luke Harrison
Age range: 2–13
No. of pupils: 388
Fees: Day £3,552–£11,910

Shernold School
Hill Place, Queens Avenue,
Maidstone, Kent ME16 0ER
Tel: 01622 752868
Head Teacher:
Ms. Sandra Dinsmore
Age range: 3–11
No. of pupils: 142
Fees: Day £3,525–£4,200

Solefield School
Solefield Road, Sevenoaks,
Kent TN13 1PH
Tel: 01732 452142
Headmaster:
Mr D A Philps BSc(Hons)
Age range: B4–13
No. of pupils: 180
Fees: Day £9,990–£12,060

Somerhill Pre-Prep
Somerhill, Five Oak Green Road,
Tonbridge, Kent TN11 0NJ
Tel: 01732 352124
Headmistress: Mrs J Ruth
Sorensen BEd(Hons), CertEd
Age range: 3–7
No. of pupils: 245

Spring Grove School
Harville Road, Wye,
Ashford, Kent TN25 5EZ
Tel: 01233 812337
Headmaster: Mr Bill Jones
Age range: 2–11
No. of pupils: 194
Fees: Day £2,050–£3,125

St Andrew's School
24-28 Watts Avenue, Rochester,
Medway, Kent ME1 1SA
Tel: 01634 843479
Principal: Mrs E Steinmann-Gilbert
Age range: 2–11
No. of pupils: 367
Fees: Day £6,672–£7,059

St Christopher's School
New Dover Road,
Canterbury, Kent CT1 3DT
Tel: 01227 462960
The Master: Mr D Evans
Age range: 3–11
Fees: Day £7,600

St Edmund's Junior School
St Thomas Hill, Canterbury,
Kent CT2 8HU
Tel: 01227 475600
Master:
R G Bacon BA(Hons)(Durham)
Age range: 3–13
No. of pupils: 230
Fees: Day £6,969–£14,211
WB £18,969 FB £20,817

St Faith's at Ash School
5 The Street, Ash, Canterbury,
Kent CT3 2HH
Tel: 01304 813409
Headmaster: Mr Lawrence Groves
Age range: 2–11
No. of pupils: 225
Fees: Day £6,435–£8,100

St Joseph's Convent Prep School
46 Old Road East, Gravesend,
Kent DA12 1NR
Tel: 01474 533012
Head Teacher: Mrs Carola Timney
Age range: 3–11
No. of pupils: 146
Fees: Day £6,655

St Lawrence College
Ramsgate, Kent CT11 7AE
Tel: 01843 572931
Principal: Mr Antony Spencer
Age range: 3–18
No. of pupils: 615 VIth140
Fees: Day £7,047–£17,436
FB £23,640–£31,452

St Michael's Preparatory School
Otford Court, Otford,
Sevenoaks, Kent TN14 5SA
Tel: 01959 522137
Headteacher: Mrs Jill Aisher
Age range: 2–13
No. of pupils: 472
Fees: Day £2,064–£12,555

Steephill School
Off Castle Hill, Fawkham,
Longfield, Kent DA3 7BG
Tel: 01474 702107
Head:
Mrs C Birtwell BSc, MBA, PGCE
Age range: 3–11
No. of pupils: 131
Fees: Day £6,860

Sutton Valence Preparatory School
Chart Sutton, Maidstone,
Kent ME17 3RF
Tel: 01622 842117
Head: Miss C Corkran
Age range: 3–11
No. of pupils: 320
Fees: Day £8,490–£13,035

The Granville School
2 Bradbourne Park Road,
Sevenoaks, Kent TN13 3LJ
Tel: 01732 453039
Headmistress:
Mrs J Scott BEd(Cantab)
Age range: B3–4 G3–11
No. of pupils: 195
Fees: Day £5,184–£13,371

The Junior King's School, Canterbury
Milner Court, Sturry,
Canterbury, Kent CT2 0AY
Tel: 01227 714000
Headmaster:
Mr Peter Wells BEd(Hons)
Age range: 3–13
Fees: Day £8,610–£14,610 FB £19,830

The Mead School
16 Frant Road, Tunbridge
Wells, Kent TN2 5SN
Tel: 01892 525837
Headmistress: Mrs A
Culley CertEd(Oxon)
Age range: 3–11
No. of pupils: 188
Fees: Day £3,900–£9,945

The New Beacon School
Brittains Lane, Sevenoaks,
Kent TN13 2PB
Tel: 01732 452131
Headmaster: Mr M Piercy BA(Hons)
Age range: B4–13
No. of pupils: 400
Fees: Day £9,405–£12,135

Walthamstow Hall Pre-Prep and Junior School
Sevenoaks, Kent TN13 3LD
Tel: 01732 451334
Headmistress:
Mrs Jill Milner MA(Oxford)
Age range: G2–11
No. of pupils: 218
Fees: Day £1,230–£9,990

Wellesley House
114 Ramsgate Road,
Broadstairs, Kent CT10 2DG
Tel: 01843 862991
Headmaster:
Mr S T P O'Malley MA(Hons), PGCE
Age range: 7–13
No. of pupils: 133
Fees: Day £14,985–
£17,850 FB £22,575

Yardley Court
Somerhill, Five Oak Green Road,
Tonbridge, Kent TN11 0NJ
Tel: 01732 352124
Headmaster: J T Coakley
MA, BA(Hons), PGCE
Age range: B7–13
No. of pupils: 260
Fees: Day £13,150

Surrey

Aberdour School
Brighton Road, Burgh Heath,
Tadworth, Surrey KT20 6AJ
Tel: 01737 354119
Headmaster: Mr Simon Collins
Age range: 2–13
No. of pupils: 255
Fees: Day £3,990–£10,605

ACS Cobham International School
Heywood, Portsmouth Road,
Cobham, Surrey KT11 1BL
Tel: +44 (0) 1932 867251
Head of School: Mr A Eysele
Age range: 2–18
No. of pupils: 1460
Fees: Day £10,690–£25,050
FB £36,810–£39,310

ACS Egham International School
Woodlee, London Road,
Egham, Surrey TW20 0HS
Tel: +44 (0) 1784 430 800
Head of School: Jeremy Lewis
Age range: 3–18
Fees: Day £7,080–£24,020

Aldro School
Shackleford, Godalming,
Surrey GU8 6AS
Tel: 01483 810266
Headmaster:
Mr D W N Aston BA(Hons), PGCE
Age range: B7–13
No. of pupils: 220
Fees: Day £14,610 FB £18,795

Amesbury
Hazel Grove, Hindhead,
Surrey GU26 6BL
Tel: 01428 604322
Headmaster: Mr Nigel Taylor MA
Age range: 2–13
No. of pupils: 325
Fees: Day £9,060–£13,875

Barfield School
Guildford Road, Runfold,
Farnham, Surrey GU10 1PB
Tel: 01252 782271
Head of School: James Reid
Age range: 2–13 years
No. of pupils: 170
Fees: Day £3,168–£13,620

BARROW HILLS SCHOOL
For further details see p. 68
Roke Lane, Witley, Godalming,
Surrey GU8 5NY
Tel: +44 (0)1428 683639
Email: info@barrowhills.org
Website: www.barrowhills.org
Headmaster: Mr Sean Skehan
Age range: 2–13
No. of pupils: 230
Fees: Day £14,985

Belmont Preparatory School
Feldemore, Holmbury St Mary,
Dorking, Surrey RH5 6LQ
Tel: 01306 730852
Headmistress: Mrs Helen Skrine
BA, PGCE, NPQH, FRSA
Age range: 2–13
No. of pupils: 227
Fees: Day £6,120–£10,428
WB £15,345

Bishopsgate School
Bishopsgate Road, Englefield
Green, Egham, Surrey TW20 0YJ
Tel: 01784 432109
Headmaster:
Mr Andrew Cowell BEd, CPSE
Age range: 3–13
Fees: Day £4,500–£12,726

Bloo House School
The Lodge (Moore Place),
Portsmouth Road, Esher,
Surrey KT10 9LN
Tel: 01372 477113
Head of School: Ms Melissa Carter
Age range: 5–11
No. of pupils: 32
Fees: Day £5,200

Bramley School
Chequers Lane, Walton-on-the-
Hill, Tadworth, Surrey KT20 7ST
Tel: 01737 812004
Head of School: Ms Paula Burgess
Age range: G3–11
No. of pupils: 78
Fees: Day £5,355–£12,285

Caterham School
Harestone Valley, Caterham,
Surrey CR3 6YA
Tel: 01883 343028
Head: Mr C. W. Jones MA(Cantab)
Age range: 11–18
No. of pupils: Vlth321

Chinthurst School
Tadworth Street, Tadworth,
Surrey KT20 5QZ
Tel: 01737 812011
Headmaster:
Mr David Williams BA (Hons), PGCE
Age range: B3–13
No. of pupils: 120
Fees: Day £3,800–£10,650

City of London Freemen's School
Ashtead Park, Ashtead,
Surrey KT21 1ET
Tel: 01372 277933
Headmaster:
Mr Philip MacDonald MA(Oxon)
Age range: 7–18
No. of pupils: 877 Vlth213
Fees: Day £10,872–
£14,598 FB £23,238

Claremont Fan Court School
Claremont Drive, Esher,
Surrey KT10 9LY
Tel: 01372 467841
Head of Senior School:
Mr Jonathan Insall-Reid
Age range: 21/2–18
No. of pupils: 780
Fees: Day £4,995–£16,530

Coworth Flexlands School
Chertsey Road, Chobham,
Woking, Surrey GU24 8TE
Tel: 01276 855707
Headmistress: Mrs Anne Sweeney
Age range: B21/2–7 G21/2–11
No. of pupils: 150
Fees: Day £8,250–£12,825

Cranleigh Preparatory School
Horseshoe Lane, Cranleigh,
Surrey GU6 8QH
Tel: 01483 274199
Headmaster: Mr M T Wilson BSc
Age range: 7–13
No. of pupils: 290
Fees: Day £11,385 FB £14,025

Cranmore School
Epsom Road, West Horsley,
Surrey KT24 6AT
Tel: 01483 280340
Headmaster: Mr Michael
Connolly BSc, BA, MA, MEd
Age range: 21/2–13
No. of pupils: 479
Fees: Day £11,850

Danes Hill School
Leatherhead Road, Oxshott,
Surrey KT22 0JG
Tel: 01372 842509
Headmaster: Mr W Murdock BA
Age range: 3–13
No. of pupils: 872
Fees: Day £6,405–£17,745

Danesfield Manor School
Rydens Avenue, Walton-on-
Thames, Surrey KT12 3JB
Tel: 01932 220930
Principal: Mrs Helen Chalmers
Age range: 2–11
No. of pupils: 170
Fees: Day £8,400

Date Valley School
Mitcham Court, Cricket Green,
Mitcham, Surrey CR4 4LB
Tel: +44 (0)20 8648 4647
Headteacher: Mrs Razina Karim
Age range: 3–11
No. of pupils: 110
Fees: Day £1,869–£3,150

Downsend School
1 Leatherhead Road,
Leatherhead, Surrey KT22 8TJ
Tel: 01372 372197
Headmaster: Mr Ian Thorpe
Age range: 2–13
No. of pupils: 740
Fees: Day £13,455

Downsend School
Ashtead Lodge, 22 Oakfield
Road, Ashtead, Surrey KT21 2RE
Tel: 01372 385439
Head Teacher: Mrs K Barrett
Age range: 2–6
No. of pupils: 66
Fees: Day £2,190–£8,250

Downsend School
Epsom Lodge, 6 Norman Avenue,
Epsom, Surrey KT17 3AB
Tel: 01372 385438
Head Teacher: Miss J Birchall
Age range: 2–6
No. of pupils: 110
Fees: Day £2,325–£11,640

Downsend School
Leatherhead Lodge, Epsom Road,
Leatherhead, Surrey KT22 8ST
Tel: 01372 372123
Headteacher: Mrs Gill Brooks
Age range: 2–6
Fees: Day £6,780–£8,250

Drayton House School
35 Austen Road, Guildford,
Surrey GU1 3NP
Tel: 01483 504707
Headmistress: Mrs J Tyson-Jones
Froebel Cert.Ed. London University
Age range: 3 months–7 years
Fees: Day £4,420–£12,500

Duke of Kent School
Peaslake Road, Ewhurst,
Surrey GU6 7NS
Tel: 01483 277313
Head: Mrs Judith Fremont-Barnes
Age range: 3–16
No. of pupils: 234
Fees: Day £4,860–£14,130 WB
£13,350–£16,770 FB £15,735–£18,855

Dunottar School
High Trees Road, Reigate,
Surrey RH2 7EL
Tel: 01737 761945
Head: Mrs Rowena Cole
Age range: 11–18
No. of pupils: 200 Vlth40
Fees: Day £14,700

Edgeborough
Frensham, Farnham,
Surrey GU10 3AH
Tel: 01252 792495
Headmaster: Mr C J Davies BA
Age range: 2–13
No. of pupils: 285
Fees: Day £9,105–£14,850
WB £16,752–£18,282

Emberhurst School
94 Ember Lane, Esher,
Surrey KT10 8EN
Tel: 020 8398 2933
Headmistress: Mrs P Chadwick BEd
Age range: 2 +–7+
No. of pupils: 70
Fees: Day £2,265–£6,495

Essendene Lodge School
Essendene Road, Caterham,
Surrey CR3 5PB
Tel: 01883 348349
Head Teacher: Mrs J Wermig
Age range: 2–11
No. of pupils: 153
Fees: Day £2,775–£5,550

Ewell Castle School
Church Street, Ewell, Epsom,
Surrey KT17 2AW
Tel: 020 8393 1413
Principal: Peter Harris
Age range: B3–18 G3-11–16-18
No. of pupils: 531
Fees: Day £6,750–£13,020

Feltonfleet School
Cobham, Surrey KT11 1DR
Tel: 01932 862264
Headmaster: P C Ward
Age range: 3–13
No. of pupils: 356
Fees: Day £7,680–£11,250
WB £15,750

Focus School – Hindhead Campus
Tilford Road, Hindhead,
Surrey GU26 6SJ
Tel: 01428 601800
Head: Mr S Hardy
Age range: 8–18
No. of pupils: 90

Frensham Heights
Rowledge, Farnham,
Surrey GU10 4EA
Tel: 01252 792561
Headmaster:
Mr Andrew Fisher BA, MEd, FRSA
Age range: 3–18
No. of pupils: 497 Vlth105
Fees: Day £5,205–£15,300
FB £19,485–£22,680

Glenesk School
Ockham Road North, East
Horsley, Surrey KT24 6NS
Tel: 01483 282329
Headmistress: Mrs S Christie-Hall
Age range: 2–7
Fees: Day £1,350–£8,112

Greenfield
Brooklyn Road, Woking,
Surrey GU22 7PP
Tel: 01483 772525
Headmistress: Mrs Tania Botting BEd
Age range: 3–11
No. of pupils: 179
Fees: Day £4,284–£9,450

Guildford High School
London Road, Guildford,
Surrey GU1 1SJ
Tel: 01483 561440
Headmistress:
Mrs F J Boulton BSc, MA
Age range: G4–18
No. of pupils: 980 Vlth160
Fees: Day £9,879–£16,032

Hall Grove School
London Road, Bagshot,
Surrey GU19 5HZ
Tel: 01276 473059
Headmaster:
Mr A R Graham BSc, PGCE
Age range: 3–13
Fees: Day £8,880–£12,480

Halstead Preparatory School
Woodham Rise, Woking,
Surrey GU21 4EE
Tel: 01483 772682
Headmistress: Mrs P Austin
Age range: G3–11
No. of pupils: 220
Fees: Day £2,673–£12,162

Hampton Court House
Hampton Court Road, East
Molesey, Surrey KT8 9BS
Tel: 020 8943 0889
Headmaster: Mr Guy Holloway
Age range: 3–16
No. of pupils: Vlth20
Fees: Day £7,842–£10,017

Hawley Place School
Fernhill Road, Blackwater,
Camberley, Surrey GU17 9HU
Tel: 01276 32028
Head of School: Mr Michael Stone
Age range: B2–11 G2–16
No. of pupils: 370
Fees: Day £4,446–£11,400
(£)(⌀)

Hazelwood School
Wolf's Hill, Limpsfield,
Oxted, Surrey RH8 0QU
Tel: 01883 712194
Head: Mrs Maxine Shaw
Age range: 2–13
No. of pupils: 399
Fees: Day £3,585–£11,100
(£)(⌀)

Hoe Bridge School
Hoe Place, Old Woking Road,
Woking, Surrey GU22 8JE
Tel: 01483 760018 & 01483
772194
Head: Mr N Arkell BSc
Age range: 2–14
Fees: Day £5,355–£14,080
(£)(⌀)

International School of London (ISL) Surrey
Old Woking Road, Woking,
Surrey GU22 8HY
Tel: +44 (0)1483 750409
**Campus Principal & Head of
Secondary:** Richard Parker
Age range: 2–18 years
No. of pupils: 252
Fees: Day £17,700–£21,900
(⌀)(£)(IB)(⌀)

Kingswood House School
56 West Hill, Epsom, Surrey KT19 8LG
Tel: 01372 723590
Headmaster:
Mr Peter Brooks MA, BEd(Hons)
Age range: B3–16 G3–7
No. of pupils: 202
(⌀)(£)(⌀)

Lanesborough
Maori Road, Guildford,
Surrey GU1 2EL
Tel: 01483 880650
Head: Mrs Clare Turnbull
BA(Hons) MEd
Age range: B3–13
No. of pupils: 350
Fees: Day £10,047–£14,082
(⌀)(£)(⌀)

Lingfield Notre Dame School
Lingfield, Surrey RH7 6PH
Tel: 01342 833176
Headmaster: Mr R Bool
Age range: 2–18
No. of pupils: 886 VIth120
Fees: Day £8,900–£12,000
(A)(£)(⌀)

Longacre School
Hullbrook Lane, Shamley Green,
Guildford, Surrey GU5 0NQ
Tel: 01483 893225
Head of School: Mrs Alexia Bolton
Age range: 21/2–11
No. of pupils: 250
Fees: Day £3,075–£4,535
(£)(⌀)

Lyndhurst School
36 The Avenue, Camberley,
Surrey GU15 3NE
Tel: 01276 22895
Head: Mr A Rudkin BEd(Hons)
Age range: 2–11
Fees: Day £9,690–£11,655
(£)(⌀)

Manor House School
Manor House Lane, Little Bookham,
Leatherhead, Surrey KT23 4EN
Tel: 01372 458538
Headmistress: Miss Zara Axton
Age range: G2–16
No. of pupils: 360
Fees: Day £750–£4,070
(⌀)(£)(⌀)

Maple House School
23 Parchmore Road, Thornton
Heath, Surrey CR7 8LY
Tel: 020 8653 1827
Headteacher: Mrs Pauline Khoo
Age range: 5–10
No. of pupils: 97
(⌀)

Micklefield School
10/12 Somers Road, Reigate,
Surrey RH2 9DU
Tel: 01737 242615
Headmistress: Mrs L Rose
BEd(Hons), CertEd, Dip PC
Age range: 3–11
No. of pupils: 272
Fees: Day £2,565–£9,030
(⌀)

**MILBOURNE LODGE
SCHOOL**
For further details see p. 71
Arbrook Lane, Esher,
Surrey KT10 9EG
Tel: 01372 462737
Email:
registrar@milbournelodge.co.uk
Website:
www.milbournelodge.co.uk
Head: Mrs Judy Waite
Age range: 4–13
No. of pupils: 255
Fees: Day £11,325–£14,085
(£)

NOTRE DAME SCHOOL
For further details see p. 72
Cobham, Surrey KT11 1HA
Tel: 01932 869990
Email:
admissions@notredame.co.uk
Website: www.notredame.co.uk
Head of Seniors: Mrs Anna King
MEd, MA (Cantab), PGCE
Age range: 2–18
No. of pupils: 600
(⌀)(A)(£)(⌀)

Oakhyrst Grange School
160 Stanstead Road,
Caterham, Surrey CR3 6AF
Tel: 01883 343344
Headmaster: Mr A Gear
Age range: 4–11
No. of pupils: 142
Fees: Day £1,107–£2,450

Parkside School
The Manor, Stoke d'Abernon,
Cobham, Surrey KT11 3PX
Tel: 01932 862749
Headmaster:
Mr David Aylward BEd(Hons), MA
Age range: B2–13 G2–4
No. of pupils: 382
Fees: Day £1,089–£13,350
(⌀)

Priory Preparatory School
Bolters Lane, Banstead,
Surrey SM7 2AJ
Tel: 01737 366920
Headmaster:
Graham D Malcom MA, BEd, FRSA
Age range: B2–13
No. of pupils: 200
Fees: Day £4,650–£10,350
(⌀)(⌀)

Reigate St Mary's Prep & Choir School
Chart Lane, Reigate,
Surrey RH2 7RN
Tel: 01737 244880
Headmaster:
Mr Marcus Culverwell MA
Age range: 3–11
No. of pupils: 280
(£)(⌀)

Ripley Court School
Rose Lane, Ripley, Surrey GU23 6NE
Tel: 01483 225217
Headmaster: Mr A J Gough
Age range: 3–13
No. of pupils: 281
Fees: Day £8,745–£12,960
(£)(⌀)

Rowan Preparatory School
6 Fitzalan Road, Claygate,
Surrey KT10 0LX
Tel: 01372 462627
Headteacher: Mrs Susan Clarke
Age range: G2–11
No. of pupils: 330
Fees: Day £3,366–£4,465
(⌀)(£)(⌀)

Rydes Hill Preparatory School
Rydes Hill House, Aldershot Road,
Guildford, Surrey GU2 8BP
Tel: 01483 563160
Headmistress:
Mrs Stephanie Bell MA(Oxon)
Age range: B3–7 G3–11
No. of pupils: 200
Fees: Day £897–£3,771
(£)(⌀)

Shrewsbury Lodge School
22 Milbourne Lane, Esher,
Surrey KT10 9EA
Tel: 01372 462781
Head: Mrs Gill Hope
Age range: 3–7
Fees: Day £2,475–£3,945

St Catherine's School
Bramley, Guildford, Surrey GU5 0DF
Tel: 01483 893363
Headmistress:
Mrs A M Phillips MA(Cantab)
Age range: G4–18
No. of pupils: 900
Fees: Day £7,695–£15,660 FB £25,770
(⌀)(⌀)(A)(⌀)(⌀)

St Christopher's School
6 Downs Road, Epsom,
Surrey KT18 5HE
Tel: 01372 721807
Headteacher:
Mrs A C Thackray MA, BA(Hons)
Age range: 3–7
No. of pupils: 137
Fees: Day £1,250–£2,450
(£)(⌀)

St Edmund's School
Portsmouth Road, Hindhead,
Surrey GU26 6BH
Tel: 01428 604808
Headmaster: Mr A J Walliker
MA(Cantab), MBA, PGCE
Age range: 2–13
Fees: Day £2,160–£13,842
(⌀)(£)(⌀)

St George's Junior School
Thames Street, Weybridge,
Surrey KT13 8NL
Tel: 01932 839400
Head Master: Mr Antony Hudson
Age range: 3–11 years
No. of pupils: 652
Fees: Day £4,980–£12,915
(£)(⌀)

St Hilary's School
Holloway Hill, Godalming,
Surrey GU7 1RZ
Tel: 01483 416551
Headmistress:
Mrs Jane Whittingham
BEdCert, ProfPracSpLD
Age range: B2–7 G2–11
No. of pupils: 250
Fees: Day £9,705–£14,280
(£)(⌀)

St Ives School
Three Gates Lane, Haslemere,
Surrey GU27 2ES
Tel: 01428 643734
Headteacher:
Mrs S E Cattaneo CertEd
Age range: B3–4 G3–11
No. of pupils: 149
Fees: Day £6,600–£9,225
(⌀)(£)(⌀)

St Teresa's Effingham (Preparatory School)
Effingham, Surrey RH5 6ST
Tel: 01372 453456
Headmaster: Mr. Mike Farmer
Age range: B2–4 G2–11
No. of pupils: 100
Fees: Day £735–£11,235
WB £19,845 FB £21,780
(⌀)(⌀)(⌀)

St. Andrew's School
Church Hill House, Horsell,
Woking, Surrey GU21 4QW
Tel: 01483 760943
Headmaster: Mr A Perks
Age range: 3–13
No. of pupils: 314
Fees: Day £3,591–£14,130
(£)(⌀)

Surbiton Preparatory School
3 Avenue Elmers, Surbiton,
Surrey KT6 4SP
Tel: 020 8390 6640
Head of Surbiton High, Junior Girls' & Bo: Ms C Bufton BA(Hons)
Age range: B4–11
No. of pupils: 135
Fees: Day £6,783–£9,246

Sutton High School GDST
55 Cheam Road, Sutton,
Surrey SM1 2AX
Tel: 020 8642 0594
Headmistress:
Mrs Katharine Crouch
Age range: G3–18
No. of pupils: 600 VIth60
Fees: Day £9,153–£15,450

TASIS The American School in England
Coldharbour Lane, Thorpe,
Surrey TW20 8TE
Tel: +44 (0)1932 582316
Head: Dr Mindy Hong
Age range: 3–18
No. of pupils: 740
Fees: Day £6,810–£22,510
FB £39,500

The Hawthorns School
Pendell Court, Bletchingley,
Redhill, Surrey RH1 4QJ
Tel: 01883 743048
Headmaster:
Mr A E Floyd BSc(Hons), PGCE
Age range: 2–13
No. of pupils: 535
Fees: Day £1,920–£12,600

The Royal School, Haslemere
Farnham Lane, Haslemere,
Surrey GU27 1BE
Tel: 01428 603052
Principal:
Mrs Anne Lynch BEd, PGCE, FRSA
Age range: B6 weeks–16 years G6 weeks–18 years
No. of pupils: 500
Fees: Day £3,026–£5,619 WB £7,741–£8,290 FB £8,893–£9,442

Tormead School
27 Cranley Road, Guildford,
Surrey GU1 2JD
Tel: 01483 575101
Headmistress: Mrs Christina Foord
Age range: G4–18
No. of pupils: 760 VIth120
Fees: Day £5,520–£11,565

Warlingham Park School
Chelsham Common,
Warlingham, Surrey CR6 9PB
Tel: 01883 626844
Headmaster: Mr M R Donald BSc
Age range: 3–11
No. of pupils: 110
Fees: Day £3,660–£7,410

Weston Green School
Weston Green Road, Thames Ditton, Surrey KT7 0JN
Tel: 020 8398 2778
Head: Mrs Lucia Harvey CertEd
Age range: 4–8
Fees: Day £4,574–£7,800

Westward Preparatory School
47 Hersham Road, Walton-on-Thames, Surrey KT12 1LE
Tel: 01932 220911
Headmistress:
Mrs P Robertson CertEd
Age range: 3–12
No. of pupils: 140
Fees: Day £4,560–£5,655

Woodcote House School
Snows Ride, Windlesham,
Surrey GU20 6PF
Tel: 01276 472115
Headmaster: Mr Henry Knight
Age range: B7–13
No. of pupils: 100
Fees: Day £14,025 FB £18,900

Yehudi Menuhin School
Stoke Road, Stoke d'Abernon,
Cobham, Surrey KT11 3QQ
Tel: 01932 864739
Headmaster: Dr. Richard J Hillier MA(Cantab), PhD
Age range: 7–19
No. of pupils: 80 VIth36
Fees: FB £41,928

West Sussex

Ardingly College Preparatory School
Haywards Heath, West Sussex RH17 6SQ
Tel: 01444 893200
Headmaster: Mr Chris Calvey BEd
Age range: 2–13
Fees: Day £5,925–£13,950

Brambletye
Brambletye, East Grinstead,
West Sussex RH19 3PD
Tel: 01342 321004
Headmaster: Will Brooks
Age range: 2–13
No. of pupils: 280
Fees: Day £16,500 FB £22,800

Burgess Hill Girls
Keymer Road, Burgess Hill,
West Sussex RH15 0EG
Tel: 01444 241050
Head: Mrs Kathryn Bell BSc (Hons), PGCE
Age range: B21/2–4 G21/2–18
No. of pupils: 550 VIth87
Fees: Day £7,350–£16,950 FB £27,300–£30,450

Conifers School
Egmont Road, Midhurst,
West Sussex GU29 9BG
Tel: 01730 813243
Headmistress: Mrs Emma Smyth
Age range: 2–13
No. of pupils: 104
Fees: Day £6,030–£8,400

Copthorne Prep School
Effingham Lane, Copthorne,
West Sussex RH10 3HR
Tel: 01342 712311
Headmaster: Mr Chris Jones
Age range: 2–13
No. of pupils: 340
Fees: Day £2,860–£4,980 WB £5,650

Cottesmore School
Buchan Hill, Pease Pottage,
West Sussex RH11 9AU
Tel: 01293 520648
Head: T F Rogerson
Age range: 4–13
No. of pupils: 150
Fees: Day £4,800–£12,600 WB £16,875 FB £18,750

Cumnor House School
London Road, Danehill, Haywards Heath, West Sussex RH17 7HT
Tel: 01825 792 006
Headmaster: Christian Heinrich
Age range: 2–13
No. of pupils: 385
Fees: Day £8,025–£18,795 FB £22,365

Dorset House School
The Manor, Church Lane, Bury, Pulborough, West Sussex RH20 1PB
Tel: 01798 831456
Headmaster:
R C M Brown MA, PGCE
Age range: 3–13
No. of pupils: 135
Fees: Day £7,290–£14,595 WB £15,810–£17,685

Farlington Preparatory School
Strood Park, Horsham,
West Sussex RH12 3PN
Tel: 01403 282566
Prep Headmistress:
Ms Frances Mwale
Age range: G3–11
No. of pupils: 150
Fees: Day £6,975–£12,915 WB £21,780 FB £22,770

Great Ballard School
Eartham, Chichester,
West Sussex PO18 0LR
Tel: 01243 814236
Head: Mr Richard Evans
Age range: 2–13
No. of pupils: 125
Fees: Day £7,800–£13,650 WB £15,000 FB £21,000

Great Walstead School
East Mascalls Lane,
Lindfield, Haywards Heath,
West Sussex RH16 2QL
Tel: 01444 483528
Headmaster:
Mr C Baty NPQH, BEd(Waikato NZ)
Age range: 21/2–13
No. of pupils: 465
Fees: Day £7,695–£14,835

Handcross Park School
Handcross, Haywards Heath,
West Sussex RH17 6HF
Tel: 01444 400526
Headmaster: Mr Richard Brown
Age range: 2–13
No. of pupils: 339
Fees: Day £3,060–£6,040 FB £5,090–£7,720

Hurstpierpoint College Prep School
Hurstpierpoint, West Sussex BN6 9JS
Tel: 01273 834975
Head: Mr I D Pullison BSc
Age range: 4–13
No. of pupils: 360

Lancing College Preparatory School at Worthing
Broadwater Road, Worthing,
West Sussex BN14 8HU
Tel: 01903 201123
Head of School: Mrs Heather Beeby
Age range: 2–13
No. of pupils: 177
Fees: Day £540–£8,400

Oakwood Preparatory School
Chichester, West Sussex PO18 9AN
Tel: 01243 575209
Headteacher: Mrs Clare Bradbury
Age range: 2½–11
No. of pupils: 260
Fees: Day £1,600–£4,565

Our Lady of Sion School
Gratwicke Road, Worthing,
West Sussex BN11 4BL
Tel: 01903 204063
Headmaster: Mr M Scullion MA, BEd
Age range: 2–18
No. of pupils: 528 VIth55
Fees: Day £5,715–£9,150

Pennthorpe School
Church Street, Horsham,
West Sussex RH12 3HJ
Tel: 01403 822391
Headmaster:
Mr Matthew King BA(Hons)
Age range: 2–13
No. of pupils: 362
Fees: Day £1,392–£12,690

Seaford College
Lavington Park, Petworth,
West Sussex GU28 0NB
Tel: 01798 867392
Headmaster: J P Green MA BA
Age range: 7–18
No. of pupils: 695 VIth190
Fees: Day £9,660–£20,160 WB
£20,100–£27,180 FB £22,530–£31,185

Shoreham College
St Julians Lane, Shoreham-by-
Sea, West Sussex BN43 6YW
Tel: 01273 592681
Headmaster: Mr R Taylor-West
Age range: 3–16 years
No. of pupils: 375
Fees: Day £8,550–£13,350

Sompting Abbotts Preparatory School for Boys and Girls
Church Lane, Sompting,
West Sussex BN15 0AZ
Tel: 01903 235960
Principal: Mrs P M Sinclair
Age range: 2–13
No. of pupils: 185
Fees: Day £7,860–£10,095

The Prebendal School
54 West Street, Chichester,
West Sussex PO19 1RT
Tel: 01243 772220
Head Master: Mr T R Cannell
Age range: 3–13
No. of pupils: 200
Fees: Day £7,500–£14,250
WB £18,450 FB £19,350

The Towers Convent School
Convent of the Blessed Sacrement,
Henfield Road, Upper Beeding,
Steyning, West Sussex BN44 3TF
Tel: 01903 812185
Headmistress: Mrs Clare Trelfa
Age range: B2–8 G2–16
No. of pupils: 320
Fees: Day £7,320–£10,200

Westbourne House School
Shopwyke, Chichester,
West Sussex PO20 2BH
Tel: 01243 782739
Headmaster: Mr Martin Barker
Age range: 2½–13 years
No. of pupils: 458
Fees: Day £9,360–£15,840 FB £19,410

Willow Tree Montessori School
Charlwood House, Charlwood
Road, Lowfield Heath, Crawley,
West Sussex RH11 0QA
Tel: 01293 820721
Headmistress:
Mrs G Kerfante MontDip
Age range: 1–8
Fees: Day £2,310–£2,700

Windlesham House School
Washington, Pulborough,
West Sussex RH20 4AY
Tel: 01903 874700
Headmaster:
Mr Richard Foster BEd(Hons)
Age range: 4–13
No. of pupils: 350

South-West

KEY TO SYMBOLS

- (♷) Boys' school
- (♀) Girls' school
- (🌐) International school
- (16·) Tutorial or sixth form college
- (A) A levels
- (♨) Boarding accommodation
- (£) Bursaries
- (IB) International Baccalaureate
- (✐) Learning support
- (16·) Entrance at 16+
- (🎓) Vocational qualifications
- (IAPS) Independent Association of Prep Schools
- (HMC) The Headmasters' & Headmistresses' Conference
- (ISA) Independent Schools Association
- (GSA) Girls' School Association
- (BSA) Boarding Schools' Association
- (⑤) Society of Heads

Unless otherwise indicated, all schools are
coeducational day schools. Single-sex and boarding
schools will be indicated by the relevant icon.

Cornwall

Polwhele House School
Truro, Cornwall TR4 9AE
Tel: 01872 273011
Headmaster: Mr Alex McCullough
Age range: 3–13
No. of pupils: 100
Fees: Day £1,350–£10,845
WB £10,929–£14,865
ⓘ Ⓔ🖉

Roselyon School
St Blazey Road, Par,
Cornwall PL24 2HZ
Tel: 01726 812110
Head Teacher: Hilary Mann
Age range: 2–11
No. of pupils: 103
Fees: Day £628–£8,625
Ⓔ🖉

St Joseph's School
15 St Stephen's Hill, Launceston,
Cornwall PL15 8HN
Tel: 01566 772580
Head Teacher: Mrs Sue Rowe
Age range: 3–16
No. of pupils: 226
Fees: Day £4,566–£8,475
Ⓔ🖉

St Petroc's School
Ocean View Road, Bude,
Cornwall EX23 8NJ
Tel: 01288 352876
Headmaster: D. J. W. Thornburn
Age range: 0–11
Fees: Day £4,950–£7,335
Ⓔ🖉

St Piran's School
Trelissick Road, Hayle,
Cornwall TR27 4HY
Tel: 01736 752612
Headteacher: Mrs Carol de
Labat BEd(Hons), CertEd
Age range: 3–16
Fees: Day £2,823–£12,480
Ⓔ🖉

The Valley Nursery
Trevowah Road, Crantock,
Newquay, Cornwall TR8 5RU
Tel: 01637 830680
Principal: Mrs Gail P Wilson
Age range: 3 months–5 years
Fees: Day £1,098–£2,700
Ⓔ🖉

Truro High School for Girls
Falmouth Road, Truro,
Cornwall TR1 2HU
Tel: 01872 272830
Head: Caroline Pascoe
Age range: B3–5 G3–18
No. of pupils: 432 VIth60
Fees: Day £7,254–£10,890 WB
£19,755–£20,460 FB £19,998–£20,703
🚣 Ⓐ ⓘ Ⓔ 🖉

Truro School
Trennick Lane, Truro, Cornwall TR1 1TH
Tel: 01872 272763
Headmaster: Mr A S Gordon-
Brown BCom, MSc, CA (SA)
Age range: 3–18
No. of pupils: 751 VIth200
🚣 Ⓐ ⓘ Ⓔ 🖉

Devon

Abbey School
Hampton Court, St Marychurch,
Torquay, Devon TQ1 4PR
Tel: 01803 327868
Principal: Mrs S J Greinig
Age range: 0–11
Fees: Day £673.20–£7,200
🖉

Blundell's Preparatory School
Milestones House, Blundell's
Road, Tiverton, Devon EX16 4NA
Tel: 01884 252393
Head Master:
Mr Andrew Southgate BA Ed (Hons)
Age range: 2½–11
No. of pupils: 220
Fees: Day £1,658–£11,100

Bramdean School
Richmond Lodge, Homefield Road,
Heavitree, Exeter, Devon EX1 2QR
Tel: 01392 273387
Head: D Stoneman NAHT
Age range: 3–18
No. of pupils: 180 VIth12
Fees: Day £4,740–£7,875
🚣 Ⓐ Ⓔ

EXETER CATHEDRAL SCHOOL
For further details see p. 74
The Chantry, Palace Gate,
Exeter, Devon EX1 1HX
Tel: 01392 255298
Email: admissions@exetercs.org
Website: www.exetercs.org
Headmaster:
James Featherstone
Age range: 3–13
No. of pupils: 275
Fees: Day £6,519–£10,872
FB £16,683–£17,658
ⓘ Ⓔ Ⓒ 🖉

Exeter School
Victoria Park Road, Exeter,
Devon EX2 4NS
Tel: 01392 273679
Headmaster: Mr R Griffin
Age range: 7–18
No. of pupils: 923 VIth218
Fees: Day £10,695–£11,865
Ⓐ Ⓔ 🖉

Fletewood School
88 North Road East,
Plymouth, Devon PL4 6AN
Tel: 01752 663782
Headmaster: J Martin
Age range: 3–11
Fees: Day £4,275

King's School
Hartley Road, Mannamead,
Plymouth, Devon PL3 5LW
Tel: 01752 771789
Headteacher: Mrs Jane Lee
Age range: 3–11
No. of pupils: 142
Fees: Day £5,625–£7,095
🖉

Kingsley School
Northdown Road, Bideford,
Devon EX39 3LY
Tel: 01237 426200
Headmaster: Mr Pete Last
Age range: 0–18
No. of pupils: 395
Fees: Day £1,895 WB
£5,495 FB £7,070
🚣 Ⓐ ⓘ Ⓔ 🖉

Magdalen Court School
Mulberry House, Victoria Park
Road, Exeter, Devon EX2 4NU
Tel: 01392 494919
Head: Mr Jeremy Bushrod
Age range: 0–18+
No. of pupils: 150 VIth20
Fees: Day £1,800–£8,250
Ⓐ Ⓔ 🖉

Park School
Park Road, Dartington,
Totnes, Devon TQ9 6EQ
Tel: 01803 864588
Teacher-in-charge:
Amanda Bellamy
Age range: 3–12
Fees: Day £4,518–£6,738
Ⓔ 🖉

Plantings School
33 Old Park Road, Peverell,
Plymouth, Devon PL3 4PY
Tel: 01752 265171
Headmistress:
Miss D J Webber CertEd
Age range: 3–16
No. of pupils: 6
Fees: Day £1,200–£1,440
🖉

Plymouth College Preparatory School
St Dunstan's Abbey, The Millfields,
Plymouth, Devon PL1 3JL
Tel: 01752 201352
Headmaster: Chris Gatherer
Age range: 3–11
No. of pupils: 310
Fees: Day £1,867–£6,000
🖉

Rudolf Steiner School
Hood Manor, Buckfastleigh Road,
Dartington, Totnes, Devon TQ9 6AB
Tel: 01803 762528
Education Manager: Ms Gillian Mills
Age range: 3–16
No. of pupils: 307
Fees: Day £2,397–£3,978
Ⓔ 🖉

Shebbear College
Shebbear, Beaworthy,
Devon EX21 5HJ
Tel: 01409 282000
Headmaster: Mr S. D.
Weale MA (Oxon)
Age range: 3–18
No. of pupils: 350 VIth54
Fees: Day £7,185–£11,400 WB
£12,390–£17,190 FB £15,990–£22,245
🚣 Ⓐ ⓘ Ⓔ 🖉

St Christopher's Preparatory School
Mount Barton, Staverton,
Devon TQ9 6PF
Tel: 01803 762202
Headmistress: Victoria Kennington
Age range: 3–11
No. of pupils: 100
Fees: Day £3,600–£5,565
Ⓔ 🖉

St John's International School
Broadway, Sidmouth,
Devon EX10 8RG
Tel: 01395 513984
Headmaster: Mr Mike Burgess
Age range: 2–18
No. of pupils: 197 VIth5
Fees: Day £6,495–£10,215
WB £12,141 FB £15,570–£19,200
🚣 ⓘ Ⓘ🅑 🖉

St Peter's School
Harefield, Lympstone,
Exmouth, Devon EX8 5AU
Tel: 01395 272148
Headmaster:
N Neeson NPQH, BEd(Hons)
Age range: 3–13
No. of pupils: 275
Fees: Day £6,042–£10,350
WB £15,580
ⓘ Ⓔ Ⓒ 🖉

St Wilfrid's School
25-29 St David's Hill, Exeter,
Devon EX4 4DA
Tel: 01392 276171
Headmistress: Mrs Alexandra E
M MacDonald-Dent DPhyEd
Age range: 5–16
Fees: Day £2,085–£3,060
Ⓔ

Stover School
Newton Abbot, Devon TQ12 6QG
Tel: 01626 354505
Principal:
Mrs Sue Bradley BSc, CBiol, MSB
Age range: 3–18
No. of pupils: 423 VIth67
Fees: Day £6,879–£10,695 WB
£15,183–£21,894 FB £16,575–£20,850
🚣 Ⓐ ⓘ Ⓔ 🖉

The Maynard School
Denmark Road, Exeter,
Devon EX1 1SJ
Tel: 01392 273417
Headmistress: Ms B Hughes
Age range: G7–18
No. of pupils: VIth80
Fees: Day £8,790–£10,992

The New School
The Avenue, Exminster,
Exeter, Devon EX6 8AT
Tel: 01392 496122
Headmistress:
Miss M Taylor BA(Hons), PGCE
Age range: 3–7
No. of pupils: 61
Fees: Day £690–£5,430

Tower House School
Fisher Street, Paignton,
Devon TQ4 5EW
Tel: 01803 557077
Headteacher:
Mrs A Jordan BA, HDE
Age range: 2–16
Fees: Day £6,552–£9,576

Trinity School
Buckeridge Road, Teignmouth,
Devon TQ14 8LY
Tel: 01626 774138
Headmaster: Mr Lawrence Coen
Age range: 4–11
No. of pupils: 110

West Buckland School
Barnstaple, Devon EX32 0SX
Tel: 01598 760281
Headmaster: J Vick MA(Cantab)
Age range: 3–18
No. of pupils: VIth135
Fees: Day £2,280–£4,250 WB
£6,760–£7,880 FB £6,760–£7,880

Dorset

Bournemouth Collegiate School
St Osmunds Road, Parkstone,
Poole, Dorset BH14 9JY
Tel: 01202 436 550
Head Teacher: Mrs Mercer
Age range: 2–16
No. of pupils: 301
Fees: Day £2,925–£9,225

Buckholme Towers School & Nursery
18 Commercial Road, Lower
Parkstone, Poole, Dorset BH14 0JW
Tel: 01202 742871
Headteacher: Mr Iain Robertson
Age range: 3–11
No. of pupils: 106
Fees: Day £6,030–£8,100

Castle Court School
Knoll Lane, Corfe Mullen,
Wimborne, Dorset BH21 3RF
Tel: 01202 694438
Headmaster: Mr Richard Stevenson
Age range: 2–13
No. of pupils: 307
Fees: Day £1,350–£12,945

Claysmore Preparatory School
Iwerne Minster, Blandford
Forum, Dorset DT11 8PH
Tel: 01747 813155
Head of School: Mr William Dunlop
Age range: 3–13
No. of pupils: 230
Fees: Day £12,630–£17,910
FB £16,860–£23,970

Dumpton School
Deans Grove House, Deans Grove,
Wimborne, Dorset BH21 7AF
Tel: 01202 883818
Headmaster:
Mr A W Browning BSc (Hons),
PGCE, MA(Ed), CChem MRSC
Age range: 2–13
No. of pupils: 340
Fees: Day £8,265–£14,808

Hanford School
Child Okeford, Blandford,
Dorset DT11 8HN
Tel: 01258 860219
Headmaster: Mr Rory Johnston
Age range: G7–13
No. of pupils: 100
Fees: Day £5,800 FB £7,050

Knighton House School and The Orchard Pre-prep
Durweston, Blandford
Forum, Dorset DT11 0PY
Tel: 01258 452065
Head of School:
Mrs Sarah Wicks BEd
Age range: B3–7 G3–13
No. of pupils: 140
Fees: Day £2,325–£4,260 FB £7,200

Leweston Preparatory School
Leweston, Sherborne,
Dorset DT9 6EN
Tel: 01963 210790
Headteacher: Mrs M Allen
Age range: 2–11
No. of pupils: 84
Fees: Day £7,485–£10,695
WB £13,695 FB £15,855

Park School
45-49 Queens Park, South Drive,
Bournemouth, Dorset BH8 9BJ
Tel: 01202 396640
Headmaster:
Mr Andrew D. Edwards
Age range: 2–11
No. of pupils: 387
Fees: Day £6,045–£8,400

Port Regis
Motcombe Park, Shaftesbury,
Dorset SP7 9QA
Tel: 01747 857800
Headmaster: B H Dunhill BA(Hons)
(London), PGCE(Sussex)
Age range: 3–13
No. of pupils: 324
Fees: Day £6,300–£15,105
WB £19,395 FB £19,395

Sherborne Preparatory School
Acreman Street, Sherborne,
Dorset DT9 3NY
Tel: 01935 812097
Headmaster: Mr Nick Folland
Bsc (Hons), MIAPS, MISI
Age range: 2–13
No. of pupils: 258
Fees: Day £7,305–£13,515 WB
£18,495–£19,350 FB £18,495–£19,350

St Martin's School
15 Stokewood Road,
Bournemouth, Dorset BH3 7NA
Tel: 01202 292011
Headteacher: Laura Richards
Age range: 4–11 years
No. of pupils: 100
Fees: Day £4,485–£6,996

St Mary's School
Shaftesbury, Dorset SP7 9LP
Tel: 01747 852416
Headmaster: Mr Richard James
BMus(Hons)(London), ARCM
Age range: G11–18
No. of pupils: 275 VIth91
Fees: Day £17,220–£19,335
FB £24,960–£28,050

St Thomas Garnet's School
Parkwood Road, Boscombe,
Bournemouth, Dorset BH5 2BH
Tel: 01202 420172
Headteacher: Mrs Sarah Breeze
Age range: 3–11
Fees: Day £5,580–£7,800

Sunninghill Preparatory School
South Court, South Walks,
Dorchester, Dorset DT1 1EB
Tel: 01305 262306
Headmaster: Mr Andrew Roberts-
Wray BA(Hons) Dunelm, PGCE
Age range: 3–13

Talbot Heath
Rothesay Road, Bournemouth,
Dorset BH4 9NJ
Tel: 01202 761881
Head: Mrs A Holloway MA, PGCE
Age range: G3–18
No. of pupils: 535 VIth80
Fees: Day £5,658–£12,539
WB £21,032 FB £21,950

Talbot House Preparatory School
8 Firs Glen Road, Bournemouth,
Dorset BH9 2LR
Tel: 01202 510348
Headteacher: Mrs Emma Haworth
Age range: 3–11
Fees: Day £1,182–£2,279

Yarrells Preparatory School
Yarrells House, Upton,
Poole, Dorset BH16 5EU
Tel: 01202 622229
Headmistress:
Mrs Charlotte Oosthizen
Age range: 2–13
No. of pupils: 212
Fees: Day £1,642–£3,365

Somerset

All Hallows Preparatory School
Cranmore Hall, Shepton Mallet, Somerset BA4 4SF
Tel: 01749 881600
Head:
Ms A M Lee MA,BA,LTCL,PGCE
Age range: 3–13
No. of pupils: 300

Chard School
Fore Street, Chard, Somerset TA20 1QA
Tel: 01460 63234
Head of School: Mrs Sarah Graham
Age range: 0–11
No. of pupils: 100
Fees: Day £6,258–£7,359

Hazlegrove Prep School
Hazlegrove House, Sparkford, Somerset BA22 7JA
Tel: 01963 440314
Headmaster: Mr R B Fenwick MA
Age range: 2–13
No. of pupils: 375
Fees: Day £2,760–£5,596
FB £6,429–£8,203

King's Hall School
Kingston Road, Taunton, Somerset TA2 8AA
Tel: 01823 285920
Headmaster:
Mr Justin Chippendale
Age range: 3–13
Fees: Day £4,350–£11,520
FB £13,110–£17,040

Millfield Preparatory School
Edgarley Hall, Glastonbury, Somerset BA6 8LD
Tel: 01458 832446
Headmistress: Mrs S Shayler
Age range: 2–13
No. of pupils: 435
Fees: Day £2,665–£5,850
WB £8,600 FB £8,600

Perrott Hill
North Perrott, Crewkerne, Somerset TA18 7SL
Tel: 01460 72051
Headteacher: Mr R Morse BEd
Age range: 3–13
No. of pupils: 204
Fees: Day £5,265–£13,755
WB £14,835 FB £18,345

Queen's College
Trull Road, Taunton, Somerset TA1 4QS
Tel: 01823 272559
Headmaster: Mr Christopher J Alcock BSc, FRSG, FRSA
Age range: 3–18
No. of pupils: 784 VIth150
Fees: Day £5,250–£14,700
FB £10,605–£23,400

Springmead Preparatory School & Nursery
Castle Corner, Beckington, Frome, Somerset BA11 6TA
Tel: 01373 831555
Principal: Ms Madeleine Taylor
Age range: 2–11
No. of pupils: 105
Fees: Day £5,445–£6,051

Sunny Hill Prep School
Sunny Hill, Bruton, Somerset BA10 0NT
Tel: 01749 814 427
Head: Mrs Helen Snow BEd
Age range: B2–7 G2–11
No. of pupils: 68
Fees: Day £4,650–£9,600 WB £15,750–£16,050 FB £16,905–£17,205

Taunton Preparatory School
Staplegrove Road, Taunton, Somerset TA2 6AE
Tel: 01823 703305
Headmaster: Duncan Sinclair
Age range: 0–13
No. of pupils: 418
Fees: Day £7,920–£14,925 WB £11,010–£19,170 FB £13,770–£23,955

The Park School
The Park, Yeovil, Somerset BA20 1DH
Tel: 01935 423514
Head: Mrs J Huntington ARAM GRSM LRAM CPSEd
Age range: 3–18+
No. of pupils: VIth30
Fees: Day £4,350–£8,640 WB £14,385–£15,405 FB £15,750–£17,550

Wellington Prep School
South Street, Wellington, Somerset TA21 8NT
Tel: 01823 668700
Headmaster: Adam Gibson
Age range: 3–11
Fees: Day £5,685–£10,350
WB £16,521 FB £21,036

Wellington School
South Street, Wellington, Somerset TA21 8NT
Tel: 01823 668800
Headmaster:
Henry Price MA (Oxon)
Age range: 3–18
No. of pupils: VIth165
Fees: Day £12,459–£13,659
FB £25,668–£28,185

Wells Cathedral Junior School
8 New Street, Wells, Somerset BA5 2LQ
Tel: 01749 834400
Headteacher:
Mr N M Wilson BA, PGCE
Age range: 3–11
No. of pupils: 150
Fees: Day £6,054–£11,265
WB £15,951 FB £19,545

Wells Cathedral School
The Liberty, Wells, Somerset BA5 2ST
Tel: 01749 834200
Head: Mrs Elizabeth Cairncross
Age range: 3–18
No. of pupils: 752
Fees: Day £6,999–£17,223
FB £23,196–£28,824

West Midlands

KEY TO SYMBOLS

- ♂ *Boys' school*
- ♀ *Girls' school*
- 🌐 *International school*
- 16 *Tutorial or sixth form college*
- Ⓐ *A levels*
- ⚓ *Boarding accommodation*
- £ *Bursaries*
- ⒾⒷ *International Baccalaureate*
- ✎ *Learning support*
- 16 *Entrance at 16+*
- 🎭 *Vocational qualifications*
- (IAPS) *Independent Association of Prep Schools*
- (HMC) *The Headmasters' & Headmistresses' Conference*
- (ISA) *Independent Schools Association*
- (GSA) *Girls' School Association*
- (BSA) *Boarding Schools' Association*
- Ⓢ *Society of Heads*

Unless otherwise indicated, all schools are coeducational day schools. Single-sex and boarding schools will be indicated by the relevant icon.

Herefordshire

Hereford Cathedral Junior School
28 Castle Street, Hereford,
Herefordshire HR1 2NW
Tel: 01432 363511
Headmaster:
Mr T C Wheeler MA, BA, PGCE
Age range: 3–11
Fees: Day £7,200–£8,937
£ ✎

Lucton School
Lucton, Leominster,
Herefordshire HR6 9PN
Tel: 01568 782000
Headmistress: Mrs Gill Thorne MA
Age range: 7–19
No. of pupils: 348 VIth53
Fees: Day £6,285–£12,330 WB
£19,845–£23,430 FB £27,180
⊕ Ⓐ 🏠 £ ✎

Shropshire

Adcote School for Girls
Little Ness, Shrewsbury,
Shropshire SY4 2JY
Tel: 01939 260202
Headmaster: Mr Gary Wright
Age range: G4–18
No. of pupils: 280
Fees: Day £4,635–£13,320 WB
£15,495–£18,645 FB £17,160–£24,325
⊕ ⚥ Ⓐ 🏠 £ ✎

Bedstone College
Bedstone, Bucknell,
Shropshire SY7 0BG
Tel: 01547 530303
Headmaster:
Mr David Gajadharsingh
Age range: 4–18
No. of pupils: 230
Fees: Day £10,500–£14,505 WB
£13,600–£20,650 FB £17,295–£26,265
⊕ Ⓐ 🏠 £ ✎

Birchfield School
Albrighton, Wolverhampton,
Shropshire WV7 3AF
Tel: 01902 372534
Headmaster: Mr H Myott
Age range: B4–13 G4–12
No. of pupils: 145
Fees: Day £5,995–£12,420
WB £17,565
🏠 £ ✎

Castle House School
Chetwynd End, Newport,
Shropshire TF10 7JE
Tel: 01952 811035
Headmaster:
Mr M Crewe-Read BSc Econ, PGCE
Age range: 2–11
No. of pupils: 91
Fees: Day £6,330–£7,275
£ ✎

Ellesmere College
Ellesmere, Shropshire SY12 9AB
Tel: 01691 622321
Head:
Mr B J Wignall MA, FRSA, MCMI
Age range: 7–18
No. of pupils: VIth161
Fees: Day £9,756–£15,975 WB
£20,079–£20,646 FB £21,564–£26,955
⊕ Ⓐ 🏠 £ ⒤ ✎

MOOR PARK
For further details see p. 76
Ludlow, Shropshire SY8 4DZ
Tel: 01584 872342
Email: head@moorpark.org.uk
Website: www.moorpark.org.uk
Headmaster: Mr Charles
G O'B Minogue
Age range: 3–13 years
No. of pupils: 227
Fees: Day £7,140–£15,930
FB £19,560–£23,475
🏠 £ ✎

MORETON FIRST
For further details see p. 77
Weston Rhyn, Oswestry,
Shropshire SY11 3EW
Tel: 01691 776028
Email:
moretonfirst@moretonhall.com
Website: www.moretonhall.org/
moreton-first
Head: Mrs Catherine
Ford M.A., B.Sc.
Age range: 6 months–11 years
No. of pupils: 119
Fees: Day £9,225–
£13,020 FB £21,270
⊕ ⚥ Ⓐ 🏠 £ ✎

OSWESTRY SCHOOL
For further details see p. 78
Upper Brook Street, Oswestry,
Shropshire SY11 2TL
Tel: 01691 655711
Email: admissions@
oswestryschool.org.uk
Website:
www.oswestryschool.org.uk
Headmaster: Mr Julian
Noad BEng
Age range: 4–19
No. of pupils: VIth92
Fees: Day £8,160–£14,700
WB £21,390–£25,920 FB
£24,570–£30,750
⚥ Ⓐ 🏠 £ ✎

Packwood Haugh School
Ruyton XI Towns, Shrewsbury,
Shropshire SY4 1HX
Tel: 01939 260217
Headmaster: Clive Smith-
Langridge BA (Hons), PGCE
Age range: 4–13
No. of pupils: 210
Fees: Day £8,100–£17,250 FB £21,750
🏠 £ ✎

Prestfelde Preparatory School
London Road, Shrewsbury,
Shropshire SY2 6NZ
Tel: 01743 245400
Headmaster: Mr M C Groome
Age range: 3–13
No. of pupils: 275
Fees: Day £4,020–£12,825
WB £16,500
🏠 £ ✎

Shrewsbury High School GDST
32 Town Walls, Shrewsbury,
Shropshire SY1 1TN
Tel: 01743 494000
Headmaster:
Mr M Getty BA(Hons), NPQH
Age range: B3–13 G3–18
No. of pupils: VIth120
Fees: Day £8,049–£11,082
⊕ ⚥ Ⓐ £ ✎

ST WINEFRIDE'S CONVENT SCHOOL
For further details see p. 79
Belmont, Shrewsbury,
Shropshire SY1 1TE
Tel: 01743 369883
Email: st.winefrides@
btconnect.com
Website:
www.stwinefrides.weebly.com
Headmistress: Sister M
Felicity CertEd, BA(Hons)
Age range: 3–11
No. of pupils: 179
Fees: Day £4,335–£4,380
✎

The Old Hall School
Stanley Road, Wellington,
Shropshire TF1 3LB
Tel: 01952 223117
Headmaster: Martin Stott
Age range: 4–11
No. of pupils: 239
Fees: Day £7,605–£11,775
£ ✎

White House School
Heath Road, Whitchurch,
Shropshire SY13 2AA
Tel: 01948 662730
Headmistress: Mrs H M Clarke
Age range: 3–11
Fees: Day £3,900
✎

Staffordshire

Abbots Bromley School
High Street, Abbots Bromley,
Rugeley, Staffordshire WS15 3BW
Tel: 01283 840232
Executive Head:
Mrs Victoria Musgrave BA M Ed
Age range: B3-11 & 15-18 G3-18
No. of pupils: 198
Fees: Day £4,518–£15,357 WB
£17,040–£21,552 FB £20,904–£25,725
(symbols)

Abbotsholme School
Rocester, Uttoxeter,
Staffordshire ST14 5BS
Tel: 01889 590217
Headmaster: Mr Steve Fairclough
Age range: 2-18
No. of pupils: 310 VIth55
Fees: Day £8,490–£20,715 WB
£16,545–£25,470 FB £22,625–£30,420
(symbols)

Chase Grammar School
Lyncroft House, St John's Road,
Cannock, Staffordshire WS11 0UR
Tel: 01543 501800
Principal: Mr Mark Ellse
Age range: 11-18
No. of pupils: 219 VIth9
Fees: Day £2,940–£10,092 FB £13,320
(symbols)

Copsewood Primary School
Verulam Road, Stafford,
Staffordshire ST16 3EA
Tel: 01785 258482
Head: Mr J Spicer
Age range: 7-11
No. of pupils: 20

Denstone College Preparatory School
Smallwood Manor, Uttoxeter,
Staffordshire ST14 8NS
Tel: 01889 562083
Headmaster: Mr Jerry Gear
Age range: 2-11
No. of pupils: 155
Fees: Day £3,115–£3,995
(symbols)

Edenhurst Preparatory School
Westlands Avenue, Newcastle-
under-Lyme, Staffordshire ST5 2PU
Tel: 01782 619348
Headmaster:
N H F Copestick BSc, CertEd
Age range: 3 months–11 years
Fees: Day £7,780–£9,335
(symbols)

Lichfield Cathedral School
The Palace, The Close, Lichfield,
Staffordshire WS13 7LH
Tel: 01543 306170
Head: Mrs Susan E l lannam
BA (Hons) MA PGCE
Age range: 3-18 years
No. of pupils: 426
Fees: Day £1,795–£5,960
(symbols)

Newcastle-under-Lyme School
Mount Pleasant, Newcastle-
under-Lyme, Staffordshire ST5 1DB
Tel: 01782 631197
Headmaster: D M Williamson BA MA
Age range: 3-18
No. of pupils: 879 VIth152
Fees: Day £8,382–£11,514
(symbols)

St Bede's School
Bishton Hall, Wolseley Bridge,
Stafford, Staffordshire ST17 0XN
Tel: 01889 881277
Headmaster: Mr Charlie Northcote
Age range: 3-13
No. of pupils: 75
Fees: Day £6,000–£9,900
WB £12,000 FB £12,000
(symbols)

St Dominic's Priory School Stone
21 Station Road, Stone,
Staffordshire ST15 8EN
Tel: +44 (0)1785 814181
Headteacher:
Mrs Patricia Adamson
Age range: B3 months–11
G3 months–18
No. of pupils: 320 VIth40
Fees: Day £6,522–£10,242
(symbols)

St Joseph's Preparatory School
London Road, Trent Vale, Stoke-
on-Trent, Staffordshire ST4 5NT
Tel: 01782 417533
Head: Mrs S D Hutchinson
Age range: 3-11
Fees: Day £1,460–£1,930
(symbols)

St. Dominic's Brewood
32 Bargate Street, Brewood,
Staffordshire ST19 9BA
Tel: 01902 850248
Headteacher:
Mr Harvey R J Trump MA, NPQH
Age range: B3-11 years G3-18 years
No. of pupils: 198 VIth31
Fees: Day £6,015–£11,625
FB £21,500–£21,500
(symbols)

Yarlet School
Yarlet, Stafford,
Staffordshire ST18 9SU
Tel: 01785 286568
Headmaster:
Mr I Raybould BEd(Hons)
Age range: 2-13
No. of pupils: 169
Fees: Day £2,305–£3,865
(symbols)

Warwickshire

Arnold Lodge School
15-17 Kenilworth Road, Leamington
Spa, Warwickshire CV32 5TW
Tel: 01926 778050
Headmaster: David Williams
Age range: 3-16
No. of pupils: 252
Fees: Day £6,960–£9,540
(symbols)

Bilton Grange
Dunchurch, Rugby,
Warwickshire CV22 6QU
Tel: 01788 810217
Headmaster:
Mr Alex Osiatynski MA Oxon PGCE
Age range: 4-13
No. of pupils: 321
(symbols)

Crackley Hall School
St Joseph's Park, Kenilworth,
Warwickshire CV8 2FT
Tel: 01926 514444
Headmaster: Mr R Duigan
Age range: 2-11
No. of pupils: 233
Fees: Day £7,836–£8,274
(symbols)

Emscote House School
46 Warwick Place, Leamington
Spa, Warwickshire CV32 5DE
Tel: 01926 425067
Headmistress:
Mrs G J Andrews CertEd, BEd
Age range: 2-8
No. of pupils: 47
Fees: Day £6,450

Milverton House School
Holman Way, Park
Street, Attleborough,
Warwickshire CV11 4EL
Tel: 024 7664 1722
Head Teacher: Mr O Pipe
Age range: 0-11
No. of pupils: 275
Fees: Day £3,400 £3,800
(symbols)

Stratford Preparatory School
Church House, Old Town,
Stratford-upon-Avon,
Warwickshire CV37 6BG
Tel: 01789 297993
Headmaster: Mr N Musk
MA, BA(Jt Hons), PGCE
Age range: 2-11
Fees: Day £6,600–£10,650
(symbols)

The Crescent School
Bawnmore Road, Bilton, Rugby,
Warwickshire CV22 7QH
Tel: 01788 521595
Headteacher: Mr Huw Marshall
Age range: 3-11
No. of pupils: 171
Fees: Day £6,990–£7,560
(symbols)

The Croft Preparatory School
Alveston Hill, Loxley Road, Stratford-
upon-Avon, Warwickshirc CV37 7RL
Tel: 01789 293795
Headmaster: Mr Marcus Cook
Age range: 2-11
No. of pupils: 425
Fees: Day £1,560–£10,800

The Kingsley School
Beauchamp Avenue, Leamington
Spa, Warwickshire CV32 5RD
Tel: 01926 425127
Headteacher: Ms Heather Owens
Age range: B3-11 G3-18
No. of pupils: 333 VIth61
Fees: Day £10,035–£12,555
(symbols)

Twycross House Pre-Preparatory School
The Hollies, The Green, Atherstone,
Warwickshire CV9 3PQ
Tel: 01827 880725
Joint Heads: Mr S D Assinder
BA & Mrs R T Assinder BEd
Age range: 4-8
Fees: Day £6,000

Twycross House School
Main Road, Twycross, Atherstone,
Warwickshire CV9 3QA
Tel: 01827 880651
Headmaster: Mr S D Assinder
Age range: 8-18
Fees: Day £5,775–£6,750
(symbols)

Warwick Preparatory School
Bridge Field, Banbury Road,
Warwick, Warwickshire CV34 6PL
Tel: 01926 491545
Headmaster: Mr M Turner
BA(Hons), PCGE, NPQH
Age range: B3-7 G3-11
No. of pupils: 438
Fees: Day £3,393–£8,670
(symbols)

Warwick School
Myton Road, Warwick,
Warwickshire CV34 6PP
Tel: 01926 776400
Head Master:
Mr A R Lock MA (Oxon)
Age range: B7–18
No. of pupils: 1214 VIth249
Fees: Day £8,505–£10,935
WB £21,870 FB £23,337

West Midlands

Al-Ameen Primary School
Stanfield House, 447 Warwick Way,
Birmingham, West Midlands B11 2JR
Tel: 0121 706 3322
Officer in Charge: Mrs Shefa Malik
Age range: 3–11
No. of pupils: 22

Al-Hijrah School
Cherrywood Centre, Burbidge
Road, Bordesley Green,
Birmingham, West Midlands B9 4US
Tel: 0121 7737979
Headteacher:
Mohammad Abdul Karim Saqib
Age range: 5–10
No. of pupils: 306

Bablake Junior School
Coundon Road, Coventry,
West Midlands CV1 4AU
Tel: 024 7627 1260
Headmaster: Mr N Price
Age range: 3–11
Fees: Day £8,334

Bablake PrePrep
8 Park Road, Coventry,
West Midlands CV1 2LH
Tel: 024 7622 1677
Head of Pre Prep: Mrs T Horton
Age range: 3–8
Fees: Day £6,654

Birmingham Muslim School
Bisley Works, Golden Hillock
Road, Sparkbrook, Birmingham,
West Midlands B11 2PY
Tel: 0121 7668129
Principal: Ms A Abdrabba
Age range: 4–10
No. of pupils: 90

**Childfirst Day
Nursery Solihull**
Cooks Lane, Kingshurst, Solihull,
West Midlands B37 6NZ
Tel: 0121 788 8148

Coventry Muslim School
643 Foleshill Road, Coventry,
West Midlands CV6 5JQ
Tel: 024 7626 1803
Head: Mrs Ashique
Age range: G5–16
No. of pupils: 97
Fees: Day £1,300

**Edgbaston High
School for Girls**
Westbourne Road, Edgbaston,
Birmingham, West Midlands B15 3TS
Tel: 0121 454 5831
Head: Dr Ruth A Weeks BSc, PhD
Age range: G2–18
No. of pupils: 950 VIth104
Fees: Day £6,501–£10,005

**Elmfield Rudolf
Steiner School**
14 Love Lane, Stourbridge,
West Midlands DY8 2EA
Tel: 01384 394633
College of Teachers:
Education Admin
Age range: 3–17
No. of pupils: VIth100
Fees: Day £3,240–£6,290

**Emmanuel School
(Walsall)**
36 Wolverhampton Road, Walsall,
West Midlands WS2 8PR
Tel: 01922 635810
Head Teacher:
Mr Jonathan Swain BA PGCE
Age range: 3–16
No. of pupils: 82
Fees: Day £558–£7,200

**Eversfield Preparatory
School**
Warwick Road, Solihull,
West Midlands B91 1AT
Tel: 0121 705 0354
Headmaster:
Mr R A Yates BA, PGCE, LPSH
Age range: 2–11
Fees: Day £4,337–£9,066

Hallfield School
Church Road, Edgbaston,
Birmingham, West Midlands B15 3SJ
Tel: 0121 454 1496
Head of School:
Headmaster Roger Outwin-Flinders
Age range: 3 months–11
No. of pupils: 570

**Hamd House
Preparatory School**
730 Bordesley Green, Birmingham,
West Midlands B9 5PQ
Tel: +44 (0) 121 771 3030
Headteacher: Mr S Ali
Age range: 3–11
No. of pupils: 206

Highclare School
10 Sutton Road, Erdington,
Birmingham, West
Midlands B23 6QL
Tel: 0121 373 7400
Head: Dr Richard Luker
Age range: B1–12 G1–18
No. of pupils: 638 VIth28
Fees: Day £3,990–£9,330

Hydesville Tower School
25 Broadway North, Walsall,
West Midlands WS1 2QG
Tel: 01922 624374
Acting Headteachers: Mrs Gill
Whitehouse & Miss Kam Nijjar
Age range: 3–16
No. of pupils: 286
Fees: Day £2,895

**KING HENRY VIII
PREPARATORY SCHOOL**
For further details see p. 75
Kenilworth Road, Coventry,
West Midlands CV3 6PT
Tel: 024 7627 1307
Email: admissions@khps.co.uk
Website: www.khps.co.uk
Headteacher: Mrs Gillian Bowser
Age range: 3–11
Fees: Day £8,334–£8,880

Kingswood School
St James Place, Shirley, Solihull,
West Midlands B90 2BA
Tel: 0121 744 7883
Headmaster:
Mr Rob Luckham BSc(Hons), PGCE
Age range: 2–11
No. of pupils: 66
Fees: Day £5,586–£6,264

Lambs Christian School
113 Soho Hill, Hockley, Birmingham,
West Midlands B19 1AY
Tel: 0121 5543790
Headteacher:
Mrs Patricia Ekhuenelo
Age range: 3–11
No. of pupils: 43

**Mayfield Preparatory
School**
Sutton Road, Walsall, West
Midlands WS1 2PD
Tel: 01922 624107
Headmaster: Mr Matthew Draper
Age range: 2–11
No. of pupils: 209
Fees: Day £4,680–£7,800

**Newbridge
Preparatory School**
51 Newbridge Crescent,
Tettenhall, Wolverhampton,
West Midlands WV6 0LH
Tel: 01902 751088
Headmistress: Mrs Sarah Fisher
Age range: B3–4 G3–11
No. of pupils: 148
Fees: Day £4,215–£6,408

Norfolk House School
4 Norfolk Road, Edgbaston,
Birmingham, West Midlands B15 3PS
Tel: 0121 454 7021
Headmistress: Mrs Sarah
Morris BA (Hons), PGCE
Age range: 3–11
No. of pupils: 146
Fees: Day £6,420–£8,391

Pattison College
86–90 Binley Road, Coventry,
West Midlands CV3 1FQ
Tel: 024 7645 5031
Principal:
Mrs E.A.P. McConnell B.Ed. (Hons)
Age range: 3–16
No. of pupils: 110 VIth16
Fees: Day £5,964–£7,878

Priory School
39 Sir Harry's Road, Edgbaston,
Birmingham, West Midlands B15 2UR
Tel: 0121 440 4103
Headmaster: Mr J Cramb
Age range: 6 months–18 years
No. of pupils: 438 VIth23
Fees: Day £2,705–£4,085

Rosslyn School
1597 Stratford Road, Hall Green,
Birmingham, West Midlands B28 9JB
Tel: 0121 744 2743
Principal: Mrs Jane Scott
Age range: 2–11
Fees: Day £2,000–£3,900

Ruckleigh School
17 Lode Lane, Solihull, West
Midlands B91 2AB
Tel: 0121 705 2773
Headmistress: Mrs Barbara Forster
Age range: 3–11
Fees: Day £2,549–£7,404

Saint Martin's School
Malvern Hall, Brueton Avenue,
Solihull, West Midlands B91 3EN
Tel: 0121 705 1265
Headmistress:
Mrs J Carwithen BSc, MA, PGCE
Age range: G3–18
No. of pupils: 430 VIth40
Fees: Day £7,335–£10,095

Salafi Independent School
472 Coventry Road, Birmingham,
West Midlands B10 0UG
Tel: 0121 7724567
Headteacher: Abdul Moxin
Age range: 5–11
No. of pupils: 159

Solihull School
Warwick Road, Solihull,
West Midlands B91 3DJ
Tel: 0121 705 0958
Headmaster: Mr David E J J Lloyd
Age range: 7–18
No. of pupils: 1013 VIth279
Fees: Day £8,673–£10,590

**St George's School,
Edgbaston**
31 Calthorpe Road, Birmingham,
West Midlands B15 1RX
Tel: 0121 625 0398
Head of School:
Mr Gary Neal BEd (Hons)
Age range: 2–18
No. of pupils: 368 VIth48
Fees: Day £4,965–£9,765

Tettenhall College
Wood Road, Tettenhall,
Wolverhampton, West
Midlands WV6 8QX
Tel: 01902 751119
Head: Mr D C Williams
Age range: 2–18
No. of pupils: VIth66
Fees: Day £7,002–£13,284 WB
£15,156–£20,541 FB £19,044–£25,518

The Blue Coat School
Somerset Road, Edgbaston,
Birmingham, West Midlands B17 0HR
Tel: 0121 410 6800
Headmaster: Mr N G Neeson
Age range: 2–11
Fees: Day £3,798–£11,898

The Shrubbery School
Walmley Ash Road, Walmley, Sutton
Coldfield, West Midlands B76 1HY
Tel: 0121 351 1582
Head Teacher: Hilary Atkins
Age range: 3–11
Fees: Day £1,542–£3,093

WEST HOUSE SCHOOL
For further details see p. 80
24 St James Road,
Edgbaston, Birmingham,
West Midlands B15 2NX
Tel: 0121 440 4097
Email:
secretary@westhouseprep.com
Website:
www.westhouseprep.com
Headmaster: Mr Alistair M J
Lyttle BA(Hons), PGCE, NPQH
Age range: B1–11 G1–4
No. of pupils: 320
Fees: Day £1,466–£3,695

Worcestershire

Abberley Hall
Abberley Hall, Worcester,
Worcestershire WR6 6DD
Tel: 01299 896275
Headmaster: Mr Will Lockett
Age range: 2–13
Fees: Day £7,200–£15,495 FB £19,440

Bowbrook House School
Peopleton, Pershore,
Worcestershire WR10 2EE
Tel: 01905 841242
Headteacher: Mr C D
Allen BSc(Hons)
Age range: 3–16
Fees: Day £3,480–£6,450

**Bromsgrove
Preparatory School**
Old Station Road, Bromsgrove,
Worcestershire B60 2BU
Tel: 01527 579600
Headmaster: P Lee-Smith
Age range: 7–13
Fees: Day £7,860–£10,245 WB
£10,260–£13,245 FB £15,600–£19,350

**Bromsgrove Pre-
preparatory &
Nursery School**
Avoncroft House, Hanbury Road,
Bromsgrove, Worcestershire B60 4JS
Tel: 01527 873007
Headmistress: Mrs Susan
Pickering BPhil(Ed), CertEd
Age range: 2–7
Fees: Day £2,490–£4,800

**Cambian New
Elizabethan School**
Quarry Bank, Hartlebury,
Kidderminster,
Worcestershire DY11 7TE
Tel: 0800 138 1184
Headteacher: Craig Moreton
BA (Hons), PGCE, NPQH
Age range: 7–19
No. of pupils: 21
Fees: Day £3,000–£7,500

Dodderhill School
Crutch Lane, Droitwich,
Worcestershire WR9 0BE
Tel: 01905 778290
Headmistress: Mrs C H M Awston
Age range: B3–9 G3–16
No. of pupils: 220
Fees: Day £7,500–£9,750

Heathfield School
Wolverley Road, Wolverley,
Nr. Kidderminster,
Worcestershire DY10 3QE
Tel: 01562 850204
Head of School: Mr. L. G. Collins
B.Sc.(Hons), M.A.,P.G.C.E.
Age range: 3 months–16 years
No. of pupils: 200
Fees: Day £6,540–£10,830

King's Hawford
Hawford Lock Lane, Claines,
Worcester, Worcestershire WR3 7SE
Tel: 01905 451292
Headmaster: Mr J Turner
Age range: 2–11
No. of pupils: 357
Fees: Day £5,150–£9,585

King's St Alban's School
Mill Street, Worcester,
Worcestershire WR1 2NJ
Tel: 01905 354906
Headmaster: Mr I R Griffin BA (Hons) QTS
Age range: 4–11
No. of pupils: 216
Fees: Day £5,904–£10,305

**Madresfield Early
Years Centre**
Hayswood Farm, Madresfield,
Malvern, Worcestershire WR13 5AA
Tel: 01684 574378
Head: Mrs A Bennett M.B.E.
Age range: 1–5
No. of pupils: 216
Fees: Day £5,800–£6,500

Moffats School
Kinlet Hall, Kinlet, Bewdley,
Worcestershire DY12 3AY
Tel: 01299 841230
Head: Mrs R McCarthy MA (Oxon)
Age range: 3–13
No. of pupils: 60
Fees: Day £6,825–£10,560 FB £18,600

RGS Springfield
Springfield, Britannia Square,
Worcester, Worcestershire WR1 3DL
Tel: 01905 24999
Headmistress: Laura Brown
Age range: 2–11
Fees: Day £2,484–£3,822

RGS The Grange
The Grange, Grange Lane, Claines
Worcester, Worcestershire WR3 7RR
Tel: 01905 451205
Headmaster: Mr Gareth Hughes
Age range: 2–11
No. of pupils: 367
Fees: Day £2,484–£3,822

River School
Oakfield House, Droitwich Road,
Worcester, Worcestershire WR3 7ST
Tel: 01905 457047
Principal: Mr Richard Wood
Age range: 5–16
Fees: Day £4,140

The Downs Malvern
Colwall, Malvern,
Worcestershire WR13 6EY
Tel: 01684 544100
Headmaster: Mr Alastair Cook
Age range: 3–13
Fees: Day £5,793–£13,908
FB £13,968–£18,408

The Elms
Colwall, Malvern,
Worcestershire WR13 6EF
Tel: 01684 540344
Headmaster: Mr A J L Thomas
Age range: 3–13
No. of pupils: 200
Fees: Day £6,720–£17,052
FB £17,880–£18,870

The Knoll School
33 Manor Avenue, Kidderminster,
Worcestershire DY11 6EA
Tel: 01562 822622
Head of School:
Mr N J Humphreys BEd(Hons)
Age range: 3 months–11 years
No. of pupils: 125
Fees: Day £1,796–£2,731

Winterfold House
Chaddesley Corbett, Kidderminster,
Worcestershire DY10 4PL
Tel: 01562 777234
Headmaster: Mr W Ibbetson-
Price BA, MA, NPQH
Age range: 6 weeks–13 years
Fees: Day £6,360–£10,680

Yorkshire & Humberside

KEY TO SYMBOLS

- ⚲ *Boys' school*
- ⚲ *Girls' school*
- 🌐 *International school*
- (16) *Tutorial or sixth form college*
- (A) *A levels*
- 🏫 *Boarding accommodation*
- (£) *Bursaries*
- (IB) *International Baccalaureate*
- ✎ *Learning support*
- (16) *Entrance at 16+*
- ✸ *Vocational qualifications*
- (IAPS) *Independent Association of Prep Schools*
- (HMC) *The Headmasters' & Headmistresses' Conference*
- (ISA) *Independent Schools Association*
- (GSA) *Girls' School Association*
- (BSA) *Boarding Schools' Association*
- (S) *Society of Heads*

Unless otherwise indicated, all schools are coeducational day schools. Single-sex and boarding schools will be indicated by the relevant icon.

East Riding of Yorkshire

Froebel House School
5 Marlborough Avenue,
Kingston upon Hull, East
Riding of Yorkshire HU5 3JP
Tel: 01482 342272
Headmistress:
Mrs L A Roberts CertEd, BA(Ed)
Age range: 4–11
No. of pupils: 131
Fees: Day £4,473

Hessle Mount School
Jenny Brough Lane, Hessle, East
Riding of Yorkshire HU13 0JZ
Tel: 01482 643371
Headmistress: Mrs C Cutting
Age range: 3–8
No. of pupils: 155
Fees: Day £3,300–£3,525

Hull Collegiate School
Tranby Croft, Anlaby, Kingston
upon Hull, East Riding of
Yorkshire HU10 7EH
Tel: 01482 657016
Headteacher: Mrs Rebecca Glover
Age range: 3–18
No. of pupils: 650
Fees: Day £4,890–£11,229
Ⓐ Ⓔ 🖉

Hymers College
Hymers Avenue, Kingston upon Hull,
East Riding of Yorkshire HU3 1LW
Tel: 01482 343555
Headmaster: Mr D Elstone
Age range: 8–18
No. of pupils: 977 VIth215
Fees: Day £7,443–£8,946
Ⓐ Ⓔ

North Yorkshire

Ashville College
Green Lane, Harrogate,
North Yorkshire HG2 9JP
Tel: 01423 566358
Headmaster: D M Lauder
Age range: 3–18
No. of pupils: VIth152
Fees: Day £7,650–£13,225
FB £16,400–£26,575
🏫 Ⓐ 🏛 Ⓔ 🖉

Aysgarth School
Newton le Willows, Bedale,
North Yorkshire DL8 1TF
Tel: 01677 450240
Head of School: Rob Morse
No. of pupils: 200
Fees: Day £5,865 WB
£880–£1,165 FB £7,635
🏃 🏫 🏛 Ⓔ 🖉

Bootham Junior School
Rawcliffe Lane, York, North
Yorkshire YO30 6NP
Tel: 01904 655021
Head: Mrs Helen Todd
Age range: 3–11
Fees: Day £6,390–£9,285
🖉

Botton Village School
Danby, Whitby, North
Yorkshire YO21 2NJ
Tel: 01287 661 206
Age range: 4–14

Brackenfield School
128 Duchy Road, Harrogate,
North Yorkshire HG1 2HE
Tel: 01423 508558
Headteacher: Ms Patricia Sowa
Age range: 2–11
No. of pupils: 179
Fees: Day £2,065–£2,230
🖉

Chapter House Preparatory School
Thorpe Underwood Hall, Ouseburn,
York, North Yorkshire YO26 9SZ
Tel: 01423 333330
Head Teacher:
Mrs Karen Kilkenny BSc
Age range: 3–10
No. of pupils: 122
Fees: Day £4,518–£6,144
FB £20,250–£20,904
🏛 Ⓔ 🖉

Clifton School and Nursery
York, North Yorkshire YO30 6AB
Tel: 01904 527361
Head: Philip Hardy BA (Hons) PGCE
Age range: 3–8
No. of pupils: 199
Fees: Day £7,200–£7,620

Cundall Manor School
Helperby, York, North
Yorkshire YO61 2RW
Tel: 01423 360200
Joint Heads: Mrs Amanda Kirby
BA (Hons) PGCE, NPQH & Mr
John Sample BSc (Hons) PGCE
Age range: 2–16
No. of pupils: 350
Fees: Day £8,985–£14,415
WB £18,975
🏛 Ⓔ 🖉

Fyling Hall School
Robin Hood's Bay, Whitby,
North Yorkshire YO22 4QD
Tel: 01947 880353
Headmaster: Mr. Steven Allen
Age range: 4–18
No. of pupils: VIth54
Fees: Day £6,552–£8,736 WB
£15,288–£17,784 FB £15,912–£19,032
🏫 Ⓐ 🏛 Ⓔ 🖉

Giggleswick Junior School
Mill Lane, Giggleswick, Settle,
North Yorkshire BD24 0DG
Tel: 01729 893100
Headmaster: Mr. James Mundell
Age range: 3–11 (boarding from 9)
No. of pupils: 75
Fees: Day £3,912 FB £6,515
🏛 Ⓔ 🖉

Highfield Prep School
Clarence Drive, Harrogate,
North Yorkshire HG1 2QG
Tel: 01423 504 543
Headmistress: Rachel Colbourn
Age range: 4–10
No. of pupils: 216
Fees: Day £6,090–£6,600

POCKLINGTON PREP SCHOOL
For further details see p. 81
West Green, Pocklington, York,
North Yorkshire YO42 2NH
Tel: 01759 321228
Email:
prep@pocklingtonschool.com
Website:
www.pocklingtonschool.com
Headmaster: Mr I D Wright
BSc(Hons), PGCE, NPQH
Age range: 3–11
No. of pupils: 225
Fees: Day £7,275–£11,412
WB £19,923 FB £21,462
🏛 Ⓔ 🖉

Queen Ethelburga's Collegiate Foundation
Thorpe Underwood Hall, Ouseburn,
York, North Yorkshire YO26 9SS
Tel: 01423 33 33 30
Principal: Steven Jandrell BA
Age range: 3–19
No. of pupils: 1550 VIth595
🏫 Ⓐ 🏛 Ⓔ 🖉

Queen Mary's School
Baldersby Park, Topcliffe, Thirsk,
North Yorkshire YO7 3BZ
Tel: 01845 575000
Head:
Mr Robert McKenzie Johnston
Age range: B3–8 G3–16
No. of pupils: 235
Fees: Day £5,445–£13,050
FB £14,400–£16,995
🏃 🏫 🏛 Ⓔ 🖉

Read School
Drax, Selby, North Yorkshire YO8 8NL
Tel: 01757 618248
Headmaster:
J A Sweetman BSc, PhD
Age range: 3–18
No. of pupils: VIth36
Fees: Day £6,480–£9,180 WB
£15,447–£17,748 FB £17,295–£19,800
🏫 Ⓐ 🏛 Ⓔ 🖉

Scarborough College
Filey Road, Scarborough,
North Yorkshire YO11 3BA
Tel: +44 (0)1723 360620
Headmaster: Charles Ellison
Age range: 3–18
No. of pupils: 339
Fees: Day £6,819–£13,883
FB £19,785–£25,548
🏫 Ⓐ 🏛 Ⓔ ⒷⒷ 🖉

St Martins Ampleforth
Gilling Castle, Gilling East, York,
North Yorkshire YO62 4HP
Tel: 01439 766600
Headmaster: Mr M O'Donnell
Age range: 3–13 years
No. of pupils: 164
Fees: Day £7,578–£14,046 FB £21,132
🏛 Ⓔ 🖉

St Olave's School
Clifton, York, North
Yorkshire YO30 6AB
Tel: 01904 527416
The Master: Mr A Falconer
Age range: 8–13
No. of pupils: 355
Fees: Day £11,325–£13,695
FB £21,120–£23,295
🏛 Ⓔ 🖉

Terrington Hall
Terrington, York, North
Yorkshire YO60 6PR
Tel: 01653 648227
Headmaster: Mr. Stephen
Mulryne B.Ed (Hons) Liverpool
Age range: 3–13
No. of pupils: 150
🏛 Ⓔ 🖉

The Minster School
Deangate, York, North
Yorkshire YO1 7JA
Tel: 0844 939 0000
Headmaster: Mr A Donaldson
Age range: 3–13
Fees: Day £4,674–£7,188
🖉

Tregelles
Junior Department, The Mount
School, Dalton Terrace, York,
North Yorkshire YO24 4DD
Tel: 01904 667513
Head: Mr Martyn Andrews
BSc(Hons), PGCE
Age range: 3–11
Fees: Day £1,710–£2,280
🖉

Wharfedale Montessori School
Bolton Abbey, Skipton, North Yorkshire BD23 6AN
Tel: 01756 710452
Headmistress/Principal: Mrs Jane Lord
Age range: 2–12
Fees: Day £6,225

York Steiner School
Danesmead, Fulford Cross, York, North Yorkshire YO10 4PB
Tel: 01904 654983
Administrator: Maurice Dobie
Age range: 3–14
No. of pupils: 197
Fees: Day £728–£4,800

North-East Lincolnshire

Montessori School
Station Road, Stallingborough, North-East Lincolnshire DN41 8AJ
Tel: 01472 886000
Headteacher: Ms Theresa Ellerby
Age range: 4–11
No. of pupils: 21

St James' School
22 Bargate, Grimsby, North-East Lincolnshire DN34 4SY
Tel: 01472 503260
Headmaster: Dr J Price
Age range: 2–18
No. of pupils: 238 VIth25
Fees: Day £4,605–£11,067 WB £11,775–£17,367 FB £13,125–£18,717

St Martin's Preparatory School
63 Bargate, Grimsby, North-East Lincolnshire DN34 5AA
Tel: 01472 878907
Headmaster: Mr S Thompson BEd
Age range: 2–11
Fees: Day £4,620–£5,790

South Yorkshire

Ashdell Preparatory School
266 Fulwood Road, Sheffield, South Yorkshire S10 3BL
Tel: 0114 266 3835
Headteacher: Mrs Anne Camm
Age range: B3–4 G3–11
No. of pupils: 130
Fees: Day £8,985–£9,600

Bethany School
Finlay Street, Sheffield, South Yorkshire S3 7PS
Tel: 0114 272 6994
Headteacher: K Walze
Age range: 4–16
No. of pupils: 76

Birkdale School
Oakholme Road, Sheffield, South Yorkshire S10 3DH
Tel: 0114 2668409
Head Master: Dr Paul Owen
Age range: B4–18 G16–18
No. of pupils: VIth200
Fees: Day £7,716–£11,052

Handsworth Christian School
231 Handsworth Road, Handsworth, Sheffield, South Yorkshire S13 9BJ
Tel: 0114 2430276
Headteacher: Mrs Pauline Elizabeth Arnott
Age range: 4–16
No. of pupils: 148
Fees: Day £2,340

Hill House School
6th Avenue, Auckley, Doncaster, South Yorkshire DN9 3GG
Tel: +44 (0)1302 776300
Principal: David Holland
Age range: 2 3–16
Fees: Day £6,150–£879

Hope House School Barnsley
Hope House, Blucher Street, Barnsley, South Yorkshire S70 1AP
Tel: 01226 211011
Headteacher: Mr G J Barnes
Age range: 4–16
No. of pupils: 79
Fees: Day £3,300–£4,980

Mylnhurst Preparatory School & Nursery
Button Hill, Woodholm Road, Ecclesall, Sheffield, South Yorkshire S11 9HJ
Tel: 0114 2361411
Headmaster: Christopher Emmott BSc(Hons), PGCE
Age range: 3–11
No. of pupils: 185
Fees: Day £7,575

Sheffield High School GDST
10 Rutland Park, Sheffield, South Yorkshire S10 2PE
Tel: 0114 266 0324
Headmistress: Mrs Dunsford BA
Age range: G4–18
No. of pupils: 1020
Fees: Day £6,912–£9,531

Sycamore Hall Preparatory School
1 Hall Flat Lane, Balby, Doncaster, South Yorkshire DN4 8PT
Tel: 01302 856800
Headmistress: Miss J Spencer
Age range: 3–11
Fees: Day £1,650

Westbourne School
Westbourne Road, Sheffield, South Yorkshire S10 2QT
Tel: 0114 2660374
Headmaster: Mr John B Hicks MEd
Age range: 4–16
No. of pupils: 338
Fees: Day £2,550–£3,590

West Yorkshire

Ackworth School
Pontefract Road, Ackworth, nr. Pontefract, West Yorkshire WF7 7LT
Tel: 01977 611401
Head: Mr. Anton Maree BA Rhodes (HDE)
Age range: 3–18
No. of pupils: 490
Fees: Day £7,800–£13,185 FB £25,005

Al Mu'min Primary School
Clifton St, Bradford, West Yorkshire BD8 7DA
Tel: 01274 488593
Headteacher: Mr M M Azam
Age range: 3–10
No. of pupils: 102

Al-Furqan Preparatory School
Drill Hall House, Bath Street, Dewsbury, West Yorkshire WF13 2JR
Tel: 01924 453 661
Headteacher: Mr Ahmad Farook Raja
Age range: 5–11
No. of pupils: 139

Bradford Christian School
Livingstone Road, Bolton Woods, Bradford, West Yorkshire BD2 1BT
Tel: 01274 532649
Headmaster: P J Moon BEd(Hons)
Age range: 4–16
Fees: Day £1,236–£2,532

Bradford Grammar School
Keighley Road, Bradford, West Yorkshire BD9 4JP
Tel: 01274 553702
Headmaster: Mr Kevin Riley BA, MEd
Age range: 6–18
No. of pupils: VIth266

Bronte House School
Apperley Bridge, Bradford, West Yorkshire BD10 0NR
Tel: 0113 2502811
Headmaster: Simon W Dunn
Age range: 2–11
No. of pupils: 300
Fees: Day £7,500–£900 WB £17,000 FB £18,000

Crystal Gardens
38-40 Greaves Street, Bradford,
West Yorkshire BD5 7PE
Tel: 01274 575400
Headteacher:
Muhammad Abdur Raqeeb
Age range: 5–11
No. of pupils: 20

Dale House Independent School
Ruby Street, Carlinghow, Batley,
West Yorkshire WF17 8HL
Tel: 01924 422215
Headmistress:
Mrs S M G Fletcher BA, CertEd
Age range: 2–11
No. of pupils: 100
(£)(✎)

Darul Uloom Dawatul Imaan
Harry Street, Off Wakefield Road,
Bradford, West Yorkshire BD4 9PH
Tel: 01274 402233
Principal: Mr Mohamed Bilal Lorgat
Age range: B11–13
No. of pupils: 112
(✝)

Fulneck Junior School
Fulneck, Pudsey, Leeds,
West Yorkshire LS28 8DS
Tel: 0113 257 0235
Head of Junior School:
Mr Chris Bouckley
Age range: 3–11 (boarding
from age 9)
No. of pupils: 128

Gateways School
Harewood, Leeds, West
Yorkshire LS17 9LE
Tel: 0113 2886345
Headmistress: Dr Tracy Johnson
Age range: B2–11 G2–18
No. of pupils: 394 VIth48
Fees: Day £7,620–£12,720
(✝)(A)(£)(✎)

Ghyll Royd School and Pre-School
Greystone Manor, Ilkley
Road, Burley in Wharfedale,
West Yorkshire LS29 7HW
Tel: 01943 865575
Headteacher:
Mr David Martin BA MA PGCE
Age range: 2–11
No. of pupils: 110
Fees: Day £2,850–£3,100
(£)(✎)

Hipperholme Grammar Junior School
45 Wakefield Road, Lightcliffe,
Halifax, West Yorkshire HX3 8AQ
Tel: 01422 201330
Headteacher: Mrs Louise Reynolds
Age range: 3–11
No. of pupils: 131
Fees: Day £3,250–£7,845
(£)(✎)

Hipperholme Grammar School
Bramley Lane, Hipperholme,
Halifax, West Yorkshire HX3 8JE
Tel: 01422 202256
Headmaster:
Mr Jack D Williams BSc
Age range: 3–18
No. of pupils: VIth30
Fees: Day £8,799–£10,995
(A)(£)(✎)

Huddersfield Grammar School
Royds Mount, Luck Lane,
Marsh, Huddersfield, West
Yorkshire HD1 4QX
Tel: 01484 424549
Headmaster: Mr Tim Hoyle
Age range: 3–16
No. of pupils: 510
Fees: Day £7,878–£9,664
(£)(✎)

Islamic Tarbiyah Preparatory School
Ambler Street, Bradford,
West Yorkshire BD8 8AW
Tel: 01274 490462
Headteacher: Mr S A Nawaz
Age range: 5–10
No. of pupils: 123

Lady Lane Park School & Nursery
Lady Lane, Bingley, West
Yorkshire BD16 4AP
Tel: 01274 551168
Headmistress: Mrs Gill Wilson
Age range: 2–11
No. of pupils: 150
Fees: Day £7,554
(✎)

Leeds Menorah School
393 Street Lane, Leeds,
West Yorkshire LS17 6HQ
Tel: 0113 268 3390
Headteacher: Rabbi J Refson
Age range: 5–16
No. of pupils: 55

Madni Muslim Girls High School
Thornie Bank, Off Scarborough
St, Savile Town, Dewsbury,
West Yorkshire WF12 9AX
Tel: 01924 520720
Headmistress: Mrs S A Mirza
Age range: G3–18
No. of pupils: 250
(✝)(A)

Mill Cottage Montessori School
Wakefield Road, Brighouse,
West Yorkshire HD6 4HA
Tel: 01484 400500
Principal: Ailsa Nevile
Age range: 0–11

Moorfield School
Wharfedale Lodge, 11
Ben Rhydding Road, Ilkley,
West Yorkshire LS29 8RL
Tel: 01943 607285
Headmistress: Mrs Jessica Crossley
Age range: 2–11
Fees: Day £8,139
(£)(✎)

Moorlands School
Foxhill, Weetwood Lane, Leeds,
West Yorkshire LS16 5PF
Tel: 0113 2785286
Headmaster: Mr J Davies
Age range: 2.2–13
No. of pupils: 197
Fees: Day £7,491–£8,379
(£)(✎)

Mount School
3 Binham Road, Edgerton,
Huddersfield, West
Yorkshire HD2 2AP
Tel: 01484 426432
Headteacher: Janet Brook
Age range: 3–11
Fees: Day £6,075
(✎)

Netherleigh & Rossefield School
Parsons Road, Heaton, Bradford,
West Yorkshire BD9 4AY
Tel: 01274 543162
Headteacher: Richard McIntosh
Age range: 2–11
No. of pupils: 141
Fees: Day £6,495
(£)(✎)

Paradise Primary School
1 Bretton Street, Dewsbury,
West Yorkshire WF12 9BB
Tel: 01924 439803
Headteacher: Mr Rashid Kola
Age range: 5–11
No. of pupils: 121

Queen Elizabeth Grammar School (Junior School)
158 Northgate, Wakefield,
West Yorkshire WF1 3QY
Tel: 01924 373821
Head: Mrs L A Gray
Age range: B7–11
No. of pupils: 261
Fees: Day £6,207–£6,558
(✝)(£)

Queenswood School
Queen Street, Morley, Leeds,
West Yorkshire LS27 9EB
Tel: 0113 2534033
Headteacher: Mrs J A Tanner
MMus, BA, FTCL, ARCO
Age range: 4–11
Fees: Day £3,885–£4,275

Rastrick Independent School
Ogden Lane, Rastrick, Brighouse,
West Yorkshire HD6 3HF
Tel: 01484 400344
Headmistress: Mrs S A Vaughey
Age range: 0–16
No. of pupils: 200
Fees: Day £5,985–£8,760
(A)(£)(✎)

Richmond House School
170 Otley Road, Leeds,
West Yorkshire LS16 5LG
Tel: 0113 2752670
Headmistress: Mrs J E Disley
Age range: 3–12
No. of pupils: 211
Fees: Day £1,980–£7,725
(£)(✎)

Rishworth School
Rishworth, Halifax, West
Yorkshire HX6 4QA
Tel: 01422 822217
Headmaster: Mr. A S Gloag
Age range: 3–18
No. of pupils: 600 VIth90
Fees: Day £4,905–£9,585 WB
£15,285–£16,725 FB £16,830–£18,360
(🌐)(A)(♿)(£)(✎)

Silcoates School
Wrenthorpe, Wakefield,
West Yorkshire WF2 0PD
Tel: 01924 291614
Headmaster: Darryl S Wideman
Age range: 7–18
No. of pupils: 768
Fees: Day £6,618–£11,181
(A)(£)

St Hilda's School
Dovecote Lane, Horbury,
Wakefield, West Yorkshire WF4 6BB
Tel: 01924 260706
Headmistress: Mrs J L Sharpe
Age range: B0–7 G0–11
No. of pupils: 127
Fees: Day £4,722–£4,944

Sunny Hill House School
Wrenthorpe Lane, Wrenthorpe,
Wakefield, West Yorkshire WF2 0QB
Tel: 01924 291717
Headmistress:
Mrs H K Cushing CertEd, MA
Age range: 2–7
No. of pupils: 116
Fees: Day £5,256
(✎)

The Branch Christian School
Dewsbury Revival Centre,
West Park Street, Dewsbury,
West Yorkshire WF13 4LA
Tel: +44 (0)1924 452511
Headteacher: R Ward
Age range: 3–16
No. of pupils: 26
(✎)

The Gleddings School
Birdcage Lane, Savile Park,
Halifax, West Yorkshire HX3 0JB
Tel: 01422 354605
School Director: Mrs P J Wilson CBE
Age range: 3–11
No. of pupils: 191
Fees: Day £3,555–£5,910
(✎)

The Grammar School at Leeds

Alwoodley Gates, Harrogate Road, Leeds, West Yorkshire LS17 8GS
Tel: 0113 2291552
Principal and CEO:
Mr Michael Gibbons
Age range: 3–18
No. of pupils: 2120 VIth418
Fees: Day £7,723–£11,282
Ⓐ Ⓔ ✐

Wakefield Girls' High School (Junior School)

2 St John's Square, Wakefield, West Yorkshire WF1 2QX
Tel: 01924 374577
Headmistress:
Daphne Cawthorne BEd
Age range: B3–7 G3–11
No. of pupils: 493
Fees: Day £6,609–£7,212
⚤ Ⓔ ✐

Wakefield Independent School

The Nostell Centre, Doncaster Road, Nostell, Wakefield, West Yorkshire WF4 1QG
Tel: 01924 865757
Headmistress: Mrs K E Caryl
Age range: 2½–16
No. of pupils: 190
Fees: Day £4,590–£6,375
Ⓔ ✐

West Cliffe Montessori School & Nursery

33, Barlow Road, access Belgrave Road, Keighley, West Yorkshire BD21 2TA
Tel: 01535 609797
Principal: Mrs T Bisby
Age range: 0–8
No. of pupils: 42
✐

Westville House Preparatory School

Carter's Lane, Middleton, Ilkley, West Yorkshire LS29 0DQ
Tel: 01943 608053
Headteacher:
Mrs R James BSc(Hons), PGCE
Age range: 3–11
Fees: Day £4,545–£7,875
✐

Northern Ireland

KEY TO SYMBOLS

- Boys' school
- Girls' school
- International school
- Tutorial or sixth form college
- A levels
- Boarding accommodation
- Bursaries
- International Baccalaureate
- Learning support
- Entrance at 16+
- Vocational qualifications
- Independent Association of Prep Schools
- The Headmasters' & Headmistresses' Conference
- Independent Schools Association
- Girls' School Association
- Boarding Schools' Association
- Society of Heads

Unless otherwise indicated, all schools are coeducational day schools. Single-sex and boarding schools will be indicated by the relevant icon.

County Antrim

Campbell College Junior School
Belmont Road, Belfast,
County Antrim BT4 2ND
Tel: 028 9076 3076
Head: Mrs H M Rowan
Age range: B3–11 G3–4
Fees: Day £3,484–£3,740

Inchmarlo
Cranmore Park, Belfast,
County Antrim BT9 6JR
Tel: 028 9038 1454
Head of School: Mr A Smyth

Methodist College
1 Malone Road, Belfast,
County Antrim BT9 6BY
Tel: 028 9020 5205
Principal: J Scott W Naismith
Age range: 4–19
No. of pupils: 2307 VIth548
Fees: Day £130–£3,425

Victoria College Belfast
Cranmore Park, Belfast,
County Antrim BT9 6JA
Tel: 028 9066 1506
Principal: Ms Patricia Slevin
Age range: G5–18
No. of pupils: 1070 VIth224
Fees: Day £432 WB £10,500
FB £10,500–£17,100

County Down

Holywood Steiner School
34 Croft Road, Holywood,
County Down BT18 0PR
Tel: 028 9042 8029
**Chairperson of the School
Management Team:** Julie Higgins
Age range: 2 years 10
months–17 years
No. of pupils: 110
Fees: Day £4,008–£4,512

Rockport School
Craigavad, Holywood,
County Down BT18 0DD
Tel: 028 9042 8372
Headmaster: Mr George Vance
Age range: 3–18
No. of pupils: 200
Fees: Day £5,640–£12,360 WB
£12,720–£16,470 FB £16,770–£20,460

Scotland

KEY TO SYMBOLS
- (♂) *Boys' school*
- (♀) *Girls' school*
- (🌐) *International school*
- (16·) *Tutorial or sixth form college*
- (A) *A levels*
- (🏫) *Boarding accommodation*
- (£) *Bursaries*
- (IB) *International Baccalaureate*
- (✎) *Learning support*
- (16·) *Entrance at 16+*
- (⚙) *Vocational qualifications*
- (IAPS) *Independent Association of Prep Schools*
- (HMC) *The Headmasters' & Headmistresses' Conference*
- (ISA) *Independent Schools Association*
- (GSA) *Girls' School Association*
- (BSA) *Boarding Schools' Association*
- (S) *Society of Heads*

Unless otherwise indicated, all schools are coeducational day schools. Single-sex and boarding schools will be indicated by the relevant icon.

Aberdeen

Albyn School
17-23 Queen's Road,
Aberdeen AB15 4PB
Tel: 01224 322408
Headmaster:
Ian E Long AKC, PhD, FRGS, FRSA
Age range: B2–14 G2–18
No. of pupils: 675 VIth57
Fees: Day £3,500–£9,785
£ ✎

Robert Gordon's College
Schoolhill, Aberdeen AB10 1FE
Tel: 01224 646346
Head of College:
Mr Hugh Ouston MA, DipEd
Age range: 4–18
No. of pupils: 1573 VIth350
Fees: Day £5,949–£9,264
£ ✎

St Margaret's
School for Girls
17 Albyn Place, Aberdeen AB10 1RU
Tel: 01224 584466
Headmistress: Miss A Tomlinson
MTheol (Hons), PGCE
Age range: B3–5 years G3–18 years
No. of pupils: 400
Fees: Day £7,071–£11,202
🧍 £ ✎

Aberdeenshire

The International
School of Aberdeen
Pitfodels House, North Deeside
Road, Pitfodels, Cults, Aberdeen,
Aberdeenshire AB15 9PN
Tel: 01224 730300
Director: Dr D A Hovde
Age range: 3–18
No. of pupils: VIth64
Fees: Day £18,235–£20,420
🌐 £ IB ✎

Angus

Lathallan School
Brotherton Castle, Johnshaven,
Montrose, Angus DD10 0HN
Tel: 01561 362220
Headmaster: Mr R Toley
Age range: 0–18
No. of pupils: 220
Fees: Day £9,000–£14,500
🏫 £ ✎

Argyll & Bute

Lomond School
10 Stafford Street, Helensburgh,
Argyll & Bute G84 9JX
Tel: +44 (0)1436 672476
Principal: Mrs Johanna Urquhart
Age range: 3–18
No. of pupils: 400
Fees: Day £7,890–£11,100 FB £25,230
🌐 🏫 £ ✎

Borders

St Mary's Prep School
Abbey Park, Melrose,
Borders TD6 9LN
Tel: 01896 822517
Headmaster: Mr Liam Harvey
Age range: 2–13
Fees: Day £8,700–£11,550
WB £14,250
🏫 £ ✎

Clackmannanshire

Dollar Academy
Dollar, Clackmannanshire FK14 7DU
Tel: 01259 742511
Rector: Mr David Knapman Mphil
Age range: 5–18
No. of pupils: 1200 VIth142
Fees: Day £7,974–£10,665 WB
£20,637–£23,328 FB £21,978–£24,669

Dundee

High School of Dundee
Euclid Crescent, Dundee DD1 1HU
Tel: 01382 202921
Rector: Dr John Halliday
Age range: 3–18
No. of pupils: 1053
Fees: Day £8,499–£12,063

East Lothian

Belhaven Hill
Dunbar, East Lothian EH42 1NN
Tel: 01368 862785
Headmaster: Mr. Henry Knight
Age range: 8–13
No. of pupils: 122
Fees: Day £14,325 FB £20,655

Loretto Junior School
North Esk Lodge, 1 North
High Street, Musselburgh,
East Lothian EH21 6JA
Tel: 0131 653 4570
Headmaster: Richard Selley BEd
Age range: 3–12
No. of pupils: 200
Fees: Day £6,210–£11,550
FB £13,500–£15,000

The Compass School
West Road, Haddington,
East Lothian EH41 3RD
Tel: 01620 822642
Headmaster:
Mr Mark Becher MA(Hons), PGCE
Age range: 4–12
No. of pupils: 120
Fees: Day £6,685–£7,755

Edinburgh

Cargilfield School
45 Gamekeeper's Road,
Edinburgh EH4 1PU
Tel: 0131 336 2207
Headmaster: Mr. Robert Taylor
Age range: 3–13
No. of pupils: 325
Fees: Day £4,080–£11,850
WB £14,400 FB £15,000

Clifton Hall
Newbridge, Edinburgh EH28 8LQ
Tel: 0131 333 1359
Headmaster: Mr R Grant
Age range: 3–18
No. of pupils: 299 VIth8
Fees: Day £1,500–£9,500

Edinburgh Steiner School
60 Spylaw Road,
Edinburgh EH10 5BR
Tel: 0131 337 3410
Age range: 3–18
Fees: Day £3,756–£7,860

**Fettes College
Preparatory School**
East Fettes Avenue,
Edinburgh EH4 1QZ
Tel: 0131 332 2976
Headmaster: Mr A A Edwards
Age range: 7–13
No. of pupils: 169
Fees: Day £11,331 FB £17,739

George Heriot's School
Lauriston Place, Edinburgh EH3 9EQ
Tel: 0131 229 7263
Principal: Mr Gareth E Doodes MA
Age range: 4–18
No. of pupils: 1641 VIth352
Fees: Day £6,867–£10,299

George Watson's College
Colinton Road, Edinburgh EH10 5EG
Tel: 0131 446 6000
Principal: Mr Melvyn Roffe
Age range: 3–18
No. of pupils: 2362
Fees: Day £4,491–£11,577

**MERCHISTON
CASTLE SCHOOL**
For further details see p. 84
294 Colinton Road,
Edinburgh EH13 0PU
Tel: 0131 312 2201
Email:
admissions@merchiston.co.uk
Website: www.merchiston.co.uk
Headmaster: Mr A R Hunter BA
Age range: B7–18
No. of pupils: 460
Fees: Day £14,100–£22,710
FB £19,650–£30,660

St George's School for Girls
Garscube Terrace,
Edinburgh EH12 6BG
Tel: 0131 311 8000
Head: Ms Anne Everest BA(Hons)
Age range: B2–5 years G2–18 years
Fees: Day £7,785–£12,645 FB £26,630

St Mary's Music School
Coates Hall, 25 Grosvenor
Crescent, Edinburgh EH12 5EL
Tel: 0131 538 7766
Headteacher:
Mrs Jennifer Rimer BMus(Hons),
LRAM, DipEd, Hon ARAM
Age range: 9–19
No. of pupils: VIth17

The Edinburgh Academy
42 Henderson Row,
Edinburgh EH3 5BL
Tel: 0131 556 4603
Rector: Marco Longmore
Age range: 2–18
No. of pupils: 992 VIth93
Fees: Day £8,860–£14,960

**The Mary Erskine &
Stewart's Melville
Junior School**
Queensferry Road,
Edinburgh EH4 3EZ
Tel: 0131 311 1111
Headmaster: Mr Bryan Lewis
Age range: 3–11
No. of pupils: 1218
Fees: Day £5,574–£7,218 WB
£14,628–£14,814 FB £15,051–£15,237

Fife

St Leonards School
St Andrews, Fife KY16 9QJ
Tel: 01334 472126
Head of School:
Dr Michael Carslaw
Age range: 5–18
No. of pupils: 510
Fees: Day £13,137 FB £32,040

Glasgow

Belmont House School
Sandringham Avenue, Newton
Mearns, Glasgow G77 5DU
Tel: 0141 639 2922
Principal: Mr Melvyn D Shanks
BSc, DipEd, MInstP, CPhys, SQH
Age range: 3–18
No. of pupils: 300
Fees: Day £5,976–£11,316

Craigholme School
72 St Andrews Drive, Pollokshields,
Glasgow G41 4HS
Tel: 0141 427 0375
Principal: Ms Gillian C K
Stobo BSc, MSc, DipEd
Age range: B3–5 G3–18
No. of pupils: 442 VIth30
Fees: Day £4,137–£9,735

Fernhill School
Fernbrae Avenue, Burnside,
Rutherglen, Glasgow G73 4SG
Tel: 0141 634 2674
Headteacher: Mrs Jacqueline
Sexton BSc, PGCE
Age range: B4–11 G4–18
No. of pupils: 300 VIth16
Fees: Day £7,470–£8,976

Hutchesons'
Grammar School
21 Beaton Road, Glasgow G41 4NW
Tel: 0141 423 2933
Rector: Mr Colin Gambles
BSc (Hons) PGCE
Age range: 5–18
No. of pupils: 1242 VIth139
Fees: Day £9,098–£11,304

St Aloysius' College
45 Hill Street, Glasgow G3 6RJ
Tel: 0141 332 3190
Headmaster: Mr J E Stoer BA
Age range: 3–18
No. of pupils: 1289 VIth81
Fees: Day £6,804–£9,009

The Glasgow Academy
Colebrooke Street, Kelvinbridge,
Glasgow G12 8HE
Tel: 0141 334 8558
Rector: Mr Peter Brodie MA, MA(Ed)
Age range: 3–18
No. of pupils: 1148 VIth221
Fees: Day £3,255–£9,645

The Glasgow
Academy Dairsie
54 Newlands Road, Newlands,
Glasgow G43 2JG
Tel: 0141 632 0736
Headmistress: Mrs Shona McKnight
Age range: 3–9
No. of pupils: 74
Fees: Day £2,730–£5,505

The Glasgow Academy,
Milngavie
Mugdock Road, Milngavie,
Glasgow G62 8NP
Tel: +44 (0)1419 563758
Head of School: Miss JA McMorran
Fees: Day £3,540–£8,025

The High School
of Glasgow
637 Crow Road, Glasgow G13 1PL
Tel: 0141 954 9628
Rector: John O'Neill
Age range: 3–18
No. of pupils: 1022 VIth93
Fees: Day £4,125–£11,919

The Kelvinside Academy
33 Kirklee Road, Glasgow G12 0SW
Tel: 0141 357 3376
Rector: Mrs Lesley Douglas
Age range: 3–18
No. of pupils: 640 VIth73
Fees: Day £2,313–£8,895

Moray

GORDONSTOUN
For further details see p. 83
Elgin, Moray IV30 5RF
Tel: 01343 837829
Email:
admissions@gordonstoun.org.uk
Website:
www.gordonstoun.org.uk
Principal: Mr Simon Reid BA
Age range: 7–18
No. of pupils: 570
Fees: Day £13,473 WB
£21,912 FB £21,912

Moray Steiner School
Drumduan, Clovenside Road,
Forres, Moray IV36 2RD
Tel: 01309 676300
Age range: 3–16

Perth & Kinross

Ardvreck School
Gwydyr Road, Crieff, Perth
& Kinross PH7 4EX
Tel: 01764 653112
Headmaster: Mr Dan Davey
Age range: 4–13
Fees: Day £13,484 FB £20,280

Craigclowan
Preparatory School
Edinburgh Road, Perth,
Perth & Kinross PH2 8PS
Tel: 01738 626310
Head of School: John Gilmour
Age range: 3–13
No. of pupils: 245
Fees: Day £11,820

KILGRASTON SCHOOL
For further details see p. 86
Bridge of Earn, Perth, Perth
& Kinross PH2 9BQ
Tel: 01738 812257
Email: headspa@kilgraston.com
Website: www.kilgraston.com
Head: Mrs Dorothy MacGinty
Age range: G5–18
No. of pupils: 260
Fees: Day £3,385–£5,490
FB £7,165–£9,380

Morrison's Academy
Crieff, Perth & Kinross PH7 3AN
Tel: 01764 653885
Principal: Simon Pengelley BA(Hons)
Age range: 3–18
No. of pupils: VIth51
Fees: Day £7,161–£10,839

Renfrewshire

Cedars School of
Excellence
31 Ardgowan Square, Greenock,
Renfrewshire PA16 8NJ
Tel: 01475 723905
Headteacher: Mrs Alison Speirs
Age range: 5–16
No. of pupils: 95
Fees: Day £3,400–£5,000

St Columba's School
Duchal Road, Kilmacolm,
Renfrewshire PA13 4AU
Tel: 01505 872238
Rector:
Mr D Girdwood DL, BSc, MEd, SQH
Age range: 3–18
No. of pupils: 701 VIth125
Fees: Day £2,800–£10,860

South Ayrshire

Wellington School
Carleton Turrets, Ayr, South
Ayrshire KA7 2XH
Tel: 01292 269321
Head: Mr R M Parlour BSc(Hons), BA,
PGCE(Oxon), MMBA, FIAP, FRSA
Age range: 3–18
No. of pupils: VIth45
Fees: Day £5,304–£10,407

South Lanarkshire

Hamilton College
Bothwell Road, Hamilton,
South Lanarkshire ML3 0AY
Tel: 01698 282700
Principal: Ms Margaret Clarke
Age range: 3–18
No. of pupils: VIth49
Fees: Day £6,450–£8,574

Stirling

Beaconhurst School
52 Kenilworth Road, Bridge
of Allan, Stirling FK9 4RR
Tel: 01786 832146
Headmaster:
Mr Iain Kilpatrick BA, MEd, FRSA
Age range: 3–18
No. of pupils: 403
Fees: Day £6,474–£8,706

Wales

KEY TO SYMBOLS

- 🧍 Boys' school
- 🧍 Girls' school
- 🌐 International school
- 16· Tutorial or sixth form college
- Ⓐ A levels
- 🏛 Boarding accommodation
- £ Bursaries
- IB International Baccalaureate
- ✎ Learning support
- 16· Entrance at 16+
- ✿ Vocational qualifications
- (APS) Independent Association of Prep Schools
- (HMC) The Headmasters' & Headmistresses' Conference
- (ISA) Independent Schools Association
- (GSA) Girls' School Association
- (BSA) Boarding Schools' Association
- Ⓢ Society of Heads

Unless otherwise indicated, all schools are coeducational day schools. Single-sex and boarding schools will be indicated by the relevant icon.

Wales

Carmarthenshire

St Michael's School
Bryn, Llanelli, Carmarthenshire
SA14 9TU
Tel: 01554 820325
Head of School: Mr Alun Millington
Age range: 3–18
No. of pupils: 420 VIth80
Fees: Day £4,179–£7,968 FB £18,250
(symbols)

Clwyd

**Rydal Penrhos
Preparatory School**
Pwllycrochan Avenue, Colwyn
Bay, Clwyd LL29 7BP
Tel: 01492 530381
Headmaster: Mr Roger McDuff
Age range: 2½–11
No. of pupils: 167
Fees: Day £7,020–£9,345
(symbols)

Denbighshire

Fairholme School
The Mount, Mount Road, St
Asaph, Denbighshire LL17 0DH
Tel: 01745 583505
Principal: Mrs E Perkins MA(Oxon)
Age range: 3–11
No. of pupils: 110
Fees: Day £6,000–£6,600

Ruthin School
Ruthin, Denbighshire LL15 1EE
Tel: 01824 702543
Headmaster: Mr T J Belfield
Age range: 3–18
No. of pupils: 240 VIth41
Fees: Day £5,550–£10,320
WB £13,965 FB £16,755
(symbols)

Glamorgan

**Howell's School,
Llandaff GDST**
Cardiff Road, Llandaff, Cardiff,
Glamorgan CF5 2YD
Tel: 029 2056 2019
Principal: Mrs Sally Davis BSc
Age range: 16–18 G3–18
No. of pupils: 780
Fees: Day £7,829–£13,317
(symbols)

Kings Monkton School
6 West Grove, Cardiff,
Glamorgan CF24 3XL
Tel: 02920 482854
Principal: Mr Paul Norton
Age range: 3–18
No. of pupils: 250
Fees: Day £2,650–£4,600
(symbols)

Oakleigh House School
38 Penlan Crescent, Uplands,
Swansea, Glamorgan SA2 0RL
Tel: 01792 298537
Headmistress:
Mrs R Ferriman BA(Hons)Ed, MEd
Age range: 2–11
Fees: Day £5,550–£6,570
(symbols)

St Clare's School
Newton, Porthcawl,
Glamorgan CF36 5NR
Tel: 01656 782509
Head of School: Mr S Antwis
Age range: 3–18
No. of pupils: 298 VIth45
Fees: Day £5,685–£9,885
(symbols)

St John's College, Cardiff
College Green, Old St Mellons,
Cardiff, Glamorgan CF3 5YX
Tel: 029 2077 8936
Acting Headteacher: Rosemary
Hart BA (Hons) London, PGCE
Age range: 3–18
No. of pupils: 515
Fees: Day £7,155–£13,314
(symbols)

**The Cathedral
School, Llandaff**
Llandaff, Cardiff,
Glamorgan CF5 2YH
Tel: 029 2056 3179
Headmaster: Mr P L Gray
MA(Cantab), ARCO, PGCE
Age range: 3–16
Fees: Day £5,625–£8,175
(symbols)

Westbourne School
Hickman Road, Penarth,
Glamorgan CF64 2AJ
Tel: 029 2070 5705
Head of School:
Mr K W Underhill MA(Ed)
Age range: 3–18
No. of pupils: 162
Fees: Day £6,450–£11,700
FB £23,350–£25,850
(symbols)

Gwynedd

Hillgrove School
5 Ffriddoedd Road, Bangor,
Gwynedd LL57 2TW
Tel: 01248 353568
Heads: Mr J G Porter & Mrs S Porter
Age range: 3–16
No. of pupils: 155
Fees: Day £2,475–£4,200

St Gerard's School
Ffriddoedd Road, Bangor,
Gwynedd LL57 2EL
Tel: 01248 351656
Headteacher:
Miss Anne Parkinson BA(Hons)
Age range: 3–18
No. of pupils: VIth25
Fees: Day £5,790–£8,760
Ⓐ Ⓔ

Monmouthshire

Haberdashers' Agincourt School
Dixton Lane, Monmouth,
Monmouthshire NP25 3SY
Tel: 01600 713970
Head: Mrs E Thomas
Age range: 3–7
No. of pupils: 124
Fees: Day £2,574–£4,134
🖊

Haberdashers' Monmouth School for Girls
Hereford Road, Monmouth,
Monmouthshire NP25 5XT
Tel: 01600 711104
Head: Mrs H Davy MA(Oxon)
Age range: G7–18
No. of pupils: 582 VIth156
Fees: Day £9,537–£12,141
FB £18,171–£23,112
🧍 🌐 Ⓐ 🏛 Ⓔ 🖊

Monmouth School
Almshouse Street, Monmouth,
Monmouthshire NP25 3XP
Tel: 01600 710433
Headmaster:
Dr. Andrew J Daniel BSc, MEd, PhD
Age range: B7–18
No. of pupils: 649 VIth183
Fees: Day £10,149–£14,427
FB £18,999–£27,801
🧍 🌐 Ⓐ 🏛 Ⓔ 🖊

Rougemont School
Llantarnam Hall,
Malpas Road, Newport,
Monmouthshire NP20 6QB
Tel: 01633 820800
Headmaster: Mr Robert Carnevale
Age range: 3–18
No. of pupils: 700 VIth111
Fees: Day £5,880–£9,240
Ⓐ Ⓔ 🖊

St John's-on-the-Hill
Tutshill, Chepstow,
Monmouthshire NP16 7LE
Tel: 01291 622045
Headmaster: Mr N Folland BSc
Age range: 3 months–13 years
No. of pupils: 362
Fees: Day £7,005–£11,565
WB £16,275 FB £16,275
🏛 Ⓔ 🖊

Pembrokeshire

Nant-y-Cwm Steiner School
Llanycefn, Clunderwen,
Pembrokeshire SA66 7QJ
Tel: 01437 563 640
Age range: 0–14

Redhill Preparatory School
The Garth, St David's
Road, Haverfordwest,
Pembrokeshire SA61 2UR
Tel: 01437 762472
Principal: Mrs Lovegrove
Age range: 0–11
Fees: Day £4,950–£5,100
Ⓔ 🖊

Appendix

Glossary of abbreviations

AEB	Associated Examining Board for the General Certificate of Education
AGBIS	Association of Governing Bodies of Independent Schools
ASCL	Association of School & College Leaders
BA	Bachelor of Arts
BAC	British Accreditation Council for Independent Further and Higher Education
BEd	Bachelor of Education
BSA	Boarding Schools' Association
BSc	Bachelor of Science
BTEC	Range of work-related, practical programmes leading to qualifications equivalent to GCSEs and A levels awarded by Edexcel
Cantab	Cambridge University
CertEd	Certificate of Education
DipEd	Diploma of Education
Edexcel	GCSE Examining group, incorporating Business and Technology Education Council (BTEC) and University of London Examinations and Assessment Council (ULEAC)
EFL	English as a Foreign Language
ESL	English as a Second Language
FRSA	Fellow of the Royal Society of Arts
GCSE	General Certificate of Secondary Education
GDST	Girls' Day School Trust
GNVQ	General National Vocational Qualifications
GSVQ	General Scottish Vocational Qualifications
GSA	Girls' Schools Association
HMC	Headmasters' and Headmistresses' Conference
HMCJ	Headmasters' and Headmistresses' Conference Junior Schools
IAPS	Independent Association of Prep Schools
IB	International Baccalaureate
ISA	Independent Schools Association
ISBA	Independent Schools' Bursars' Association
ISC	Independent Schools Council
ISEB	Independent Schools Examination Board
ITEC	International Examination Council
LA	Local Authority (formerly LEA - Local Educational Authority)
MA	Master of Arts
MEd	Master of Education
MLitt	Master of Letters
MMI	Maria Montessori Institute
MSc	Master of Science
NAGC	National Association for Gifted Children
NAHT	National Association of Head Teachers
NAIS	National Association of Independent Schools
NVQ	National Vocational Qualifications
OCR	Oxford, Cambridge and RSA Examinations
Oxon	Oxford University
PGCE	Post Graduate Certificate in Education
PhD	Doctor of Philosophy
QCA	Qualifications and Curriculum Authority
RSIS	The Round Square Schools
SATIPS	Support & Training in Prep Schools
SCIS	Scottish Council of Independent Schools
SEN	Special Educational Needs
SoH	Society of Heads
SQA	Scottish Qualifications Authority

Index

Index

Index

Index

Index

Index

Index